Theodor Plievier was born in Berlin in 1892, the son of a 'prolaterianized' workman. At the age of seventeen he ran away from home – years of sea travel and wandering ensued. During the First World War he served as a sailor in the German Navy. In 1918 he took part in the sailors' mutiny, and afterwards was a committed anarchist – a political speaker and writer, and the publisher of leftwing writings. In 1925 he turned towards literature and from 1929 his first books were published. In 1933 he emigrated from Germany; from 1934 to 1945 he was an exile in the USSR; in 1945 he returned to Soviet-occupied Germany; and in 1947 he escaped to the American-occupied .
Theodor Plievier died in 1955 in Switzerl

By the same author

Stalingrad
Berlin

THEODOR PLIEVIER

Moscow

PANTHER
Granada Publishing

Panther Books
Granada Publishing Ltd
8 Grafton Street, London W1X 3LA

Published by Panther Books 1976
Reprinted 1985

First published in Great Britain by
Frederick Muller Ltd 1953
Translated from the German by Stuart Hood

ISBN 0-586-02795-5

Printed and bound in Great Britain by
Collins, Glasgow

Set in Linotype Times

PART I

"The first man to sight the spires of Moscow from the forward positions will earn the victor's crown."
From an Order of the Day of XII German Army Corps.

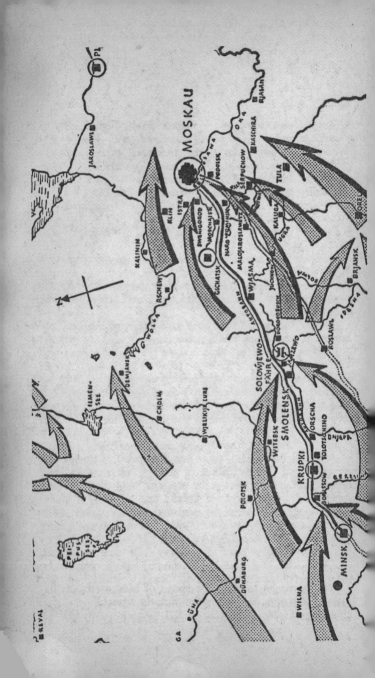

Firstly, we have two regiments from High Germany —their captains, Eck von Romschach and Kunrat von Bomelbuerg—more than nine thousand men-at-arms:

Secondly, we have eight thousand German horse, well-equipped, from the Low Countries:

Thirdly, we have seven thousand Dutch foot:

Further, we have two troops of foreign mercenaries and Spaniards:

Further, we have two companies of sappers with mattock and spade:

Further, we have three companies of musketeers with all ammunition and equipment:

Further, we have taken the town of St. Paul by the sword and killed three thousand men, both horse and foot, and burned the town:

Further, taken a town they call Muntrol, sacked and burned it, and other small towns lying within its territory:

Further, we have come to a town they call Terbona and are minded with the help of God to sack and burn it too. There is as now no further intelligence. Such as there is, I shall have sent to Your Grace. I would Your Grace had seen the sport. Done before Terbona in the field this 17th day of June, in the year of Our Lord, 1537.

* * *

Firstly, secondly, thirdly—we have, we have. . .

Well, we have them, too—men-at-arms and horses and muskets and some troops of foreign mercenaries and Spaniards and sappers with mattock and hoe as well (evacuated Jews, most of them, and it's my opinion they're not much use at digging) and we have taken more than one town by the sword with the villages and places round them and we have plundered, too, although they call it something else nowadays—"all raw materials, manufactured and semi-manufactured goods are to be requisitioned" and so on. And there is something else which is the same—we, too, have come to a town, but it isn't called Terbona, it is a whole great land and with God's help we are minded to sack that, too. . .

7

"What's the meaning of this joke? What has it come to me for?"

Lieutenant-General von Bomelbuerg laid the facsimile of the old document back on the table along with the orders for the day and the Top Secret Document, both of which had just come in; he laid his glasses beside them, too, together with the magnifying glass he had been using. He turned to the door and called for his aide.

It was in the living-room of a Polish peasant house. The General's desk took up practically all the space. There were chairs, too, but they were piled with papers and files.

"Sit down, will you?"

Major Butz had first to clear away a pile of papers. He sat down near the General, with his face near the other's left ear.

"What's the meaning of this?" asked the General.

"Colonel Schadow came across it, sir, among some documents at Lodz—it dates from the year 1537, from one of Charles the Fifth's campaigns. He thought it might interest you, sir."

"Ah, because of this Kunrat Bomelbuerg! Well, I suppose there have been a few Bomelbuergs like that. I know nothing about them. I know about my father and my grandfather and they knew the same and that's that. But thank Schadow, in any case, for me. And now let's get on with secondly and thirdly—the balloon is going up, then, tomorrow morning. Is that quite clear?"

"Yes, sir. Would you like to speak to the regimental liaison officers, sir? They are just leaving."

"Where are they?"

"In the Ops room."

"Well, I'll go and see them right away."

The conversation between the General and his aide had been conducted as follows—the aide had said into the General's ear anything the General wasn't familiar with, such as the bit about Colonel Schadow and the facsimile; the rest—about the LO's, which was something you could guess right away—the General had learned by lip-reading, leaning forward a little to see more closely the play of the aide's features and his face, which otherwise he distinguished only as a pale patch. Now he stood up and, followed by his aide, entered the office of Lieutenant-Colonel Neudeck, the senior staff officer in charge of operations, who was giving final instructions to the liaison officers.

"Well, gentlemen," said the General, turning to the liaison officers, "things start moving tomorrow morning. You know what that means. Ah, there you are, Langhoff," he said, recognising the commander of the horsed troop, who was standing near him. "See that the fire-plan works. Above all, I want that long strip of village at the crossroads properly knocked about so that the infantry can push right on. It's all a question of surprise—tell everyone that. Well, boys, I know you'll do it. Everything went like clockwork in the past. It'll go like clockwork this time, too. Have you got the Fuehrer's Order of the Day?"

"Yes, sir," they answered in chorus.

"Well, I want that order to be read out before the attack. And so, gentlemen, good-bye."

"Good-bye, sir." The liaison officers clicked their heels and remained at attention until the General had left the room.

"Now the divisional IO has something to say to you."

In his hand the divisional intelligence officer had the order containing the "Special instructions concerning commissars."

"Gentlemen, I have something short but important to tell you. Please take notes. The Fuehrer has decided that the Soviet commissars are to be treated as noncombatants. They are therefore to be shot on the spot where they are actually captured—that is to say, naturally, forward of regimental HQ."

"Forward of regimental HQ—so it's supposed to look as if they had been killed in action," Lieutenant Holmers, the LO from the artillery regiment, was heard to say.

"Do you wish to add anything to the Fuehrer's order, Lieutenant Holmers?"

"No—merely to get it quite clear. I naturally have my own ideas about it."

Langhoff, too, had his own ideas, and Holmers's intervention confirmed them. Presumably Holmers was thinking that this was an order contrary to international

9

law—one which could give rise to international complications.

"All you need to know is that we don't want to be bothered with it," said the IO in conclusion. The LOs closed their notebooks, drew on their overcoats and made ready to go forward to their HQs. Holmers and Langhoff went the same way together.

* * *

"All right—now, give me Deisendorf," said Bomelbuerg to a young lieutenant, who was there in his room along with the aide.

Lieutenant Hasse got through to Colonel Deisendorf, commanding officer of the artillery regiment, and handed the receiver to Bomelbuerg.

"Well, Deisendorf, everything all right? Good, good, fine. Well, I only wanted to remind you that Langhoff's troop naturally comes under you only for the first barrage, and that I want it back quickly. Remember, it's only on loan. Otherwise all the best, Deisendorf."

Bomelbuerg felt among the papers spread out on the table. His hand pointed to a green file-cover. "My dear man, all this stuff here," he blustered. "Don't have any of it lying about on my table. There's nothing about preventive warfare or anything of that sort in it—only stuff about agrarian policy and minerals and what we have to take from people. Tell the administrative branch to bury the stuff as far down as possible. Nobody need look at it. And that's all for today."

Lieutenant Hasse and Major Butz were dismissed. When they had both gone Bomelbuerg leant back in his chair. Everything had been done. The division: three infantry regiments, an artillery regiment, signals, transport and supply columns—altogether 17,000 men—stood ready. All you had to do was to press the button and everything would get under way. The orders were there. D-day was 22 June 1941; H-hour—0305 hours.

* * *

It was a warm night. Soft clouds lay over the wet gurgling earth, over marshes and fields and the low cottages of the village. Holmers and Langhoff strode along the only road; it was wide enough for a parade ground.

10

"As far as war is concerned, the whole world lies between the two fronts," Langhoff philosophised, "and what happens in that world is decided by the parallelogram of forces—and I mean the moral forces—of the two sides. I'm not asking who is right and who is wrong—whether the east is to blame or whether we are. But a front which runs between Germans and Englishmen, between Germans and Russians, will be different in each case. And a Russo-German front or a Russo-Chinese front will be different again, because no one can detach himself from the other fellow, and what one decides to do affects not only the other fellow but comes back on one's own head, and then one can't disentangle things any more. And in the end no one has any idea what is happening or why or who started it—isn't that so, Holmers?"

"I suppose you are talking about the special instruction on commissars, Langhoff. Do you think that Bomelbuerg agrees with it? I shouldn't think so—he believes in fighting a war according to the rules, after all."

"This war certainly won't be according to the rules, or an easy one either. Just think of it—you have a military organisation with people in it who have no other choice but death—don't you think they'll fight to the bitter end? It's a filthy business, I tell you, and it's stupid besides. Maybe you can say the same about war in general, about every war. And so nobody believes there will be one till it comes to the point. At least that's what happened this time. Up till yesterday no two people could agree about it."

"It was like that at home, too—you should see the sort of thing they wrote. All that's going on in your part of the world, they said, is just a bluff to make the Russians deliver more stuff. It's a feint—England is next on the list and then Iraq. War with Russia, when we have the concession over the Ukraine as good as in the bag? That's sheer madness. That's how they wrote, and it's what they hoped. But then we trained in France for the Russian offensive, and when we moved here three days ago and took up position it looked damned like the final preparations for a big offensive after all."

Holmers and Langhoff drew near the end of the village. An officer in a long greatcoat came towards them—

Colonel Zecke, commanding 101 Infantry Regiment.

"Ah, it's you—evening, Holmers; good evening, Langhoff. You're coming from up there? All sorts of orders being handed out, I suppose."

"Not too bad, sir, we've got quite a packet of them."

"I suppose the old man is sleeping already? No—of course not, just stretching himself out for a bit. So things are going to start up. We're enjoying wonderful peaceful relations with these folks; we've got a friendship pact and all that and then somebody starts a war."

"Yes, sir, it's starting all right. There's no doubt about that."

"Quite right. I only meant to say Russia is a bloody great country and I've been there and I've seen that they have their Prussians, too—that I *can* tell you."

Zecke had been a long time in Russia with Seeckt, when the Reichswehr was, so to speak, a guest there. He had attended the Military Academy with Zhukov, one of their leading marshals—or so people said. Zecke had made the same remark over the bridge-table the day before. Schadow, the commander of 100 Infantry Regiment, had looked up from his cards and said casually: "I think we'll be able to have a decent breakfast in Smolensk with caviare and vodka in about four weeks or so." Zecke, who wanted to take Schadow down a peg, had then produced his remark about having come across Prussians there, too, and had been laughed out of court. "The Bolsheviks don't know anything about soldiering," they had told him. And the Chief of Staff—so the Chief's son-in-law reported—had said that the Russians were so hopelessly deployed that it would be difficult even for the German General Staff, faced with a muck-up like that, to carry out any task, whether offensive or defensive.

"When you get back to your command posts, have a look at your maps," said Zecke to the two young artillery officers. "Just think about all the people who foundered there—beginning with Genghis Khan, that's what I'd like you to note. Good evening, gentlemen." Zecke went on his way; in his long coat he was like a guilty conscience stalking along in front of the houses. Langhoff and Holmers watched him in astonishment.

"That leaves you flat—it almost takes your breath

12

away. According to him we've lost the war before we've even begun it. Yet he's from the General Staff. We've only had him here a few weeks. A man like that shouldn't be surprised at what's going on."

"But he isn't. They've had everything ready for ages, and now that the business is due to pass from the planning stage to the real thing they're getting nervous."

"Nobody wants to admit to it—nobody wants to be the man who did it."

"Yet they're all shaking with excitement. If you look at Bomelbuerg, he's just the same as he was before the French campaign."

Holmers and Langhoff halted and listened to the chorus of frogs swelling up from beyond the village. Below them spread a billowing white mist, and that twisting milky streak—the northern arm of the Bug—was the frontier between two empires.

"Yes, like before the campaign in France, like a racehorse at the starting-post. And when you look at him you seem to see flecks of foam falling from him."

"My CO isn't much better and he's just as restless as Zecke. I'd better get back to my HQ."

Holmers turned down stream. Langhoff had taken the footpath in the opposite direction. He had not gone far when he saw some men sitting together at a place where you could look straight down to the river: three infantrymen—a sergeant, corporal and lance-corporal.

"You'd better turn in and sleep."

"Yes, sir, but it won't be long now."

Langhoff went on and reached his observation post. He had eight men, including wireless operators, signallers and runners; some were still awake. "Turn in now, you won't get a proper sleep for a long time. Tomorrow morning—that's to say in an hour—we're off."

Langhoff lay stretched out on his camp-bed and did not know whether he had really slept. The hum of a midge made him open his eyes again. It was a moment of absolute stillness; his wrist-watch said ten past two. Exactly fifty minutes yet.

*   *   *

Under the trees it was still night, but down there beyond the river the new day was beginning to take

13

shape. The three infantrymen still sat in the same place. Across the river they saw open country. A strip of standing rye rose out of the billowing mist. The peasant huts, touched with pale colour, seemed to have come that very moment out of the hands of the Creator. The tips of an island of trees swam on the flat sea of mist. Farther away, where grey cliffs seemed to rim the sky, lay the town of Brest-Litovsk.

The crow of a cock came from the village.

"So this is it again. I said right away that it was all rot about a walk-over and all that stuff."

"Moscow."

"Yes, Moscow."

"That other time—in Poland—we finished things off in seventeen days. Russia will take a bit longer, of course, six weeks or maybe eight. Damned lucky that we're all together."

"Yes, that's a bit of luck—we all know each other."

"We came out on top in Berlin in '33, and now we're coming out on top in other places, too. Isn't that right, August?"

"Never mind the past. Tomorrow looks after itself."

But it was not unintentionally that Sergeant Riederheim had stressed their common past. He wanted to see how Corporal Gnotke reacted; he had lost sight of him for a long time and wanted to know, to find out what he thought about things. "Of course, we had a hell of a time sometimes, August, but it's nice to look back on."

"Now they are letting the cows out," said Gnotke.

From the village they could hear the creaking of byre doors, the crack of a whip, the angry low of a cow. The mist bore the noises with it, so that it seemed as if the village street was not across the river but began here under their very noses.

"Yes, they are letting the cows out," said Feierfeil.

Riederheim confined himself to a nod of the head.

These three men were not only comrades from the Brownshirts. They had grown up together in the same village. There isn't so much difference between a village in Pomerania and one in Russia. So they did not need to see, to know what was going on over there, in the village street, during this quarter of an hour.

"Do you know that the Driborg boys are still at home? In the SS, but on home duties, and now that all the men are away you can just imagine what they're like. . ."

"I can." As son of the local factor, Riederheim knew the Driborgs even better than Gnotke and Feierfeil.

"They're after Pauline," said Gnotke.

"Pauline will make them keep their distance. Let's write her a card—now. We'll send it with the first mail from over there."

Riederheim had a piece of paper in his hand already.

"Dear Pauline—The balloon goes up in an hour. Another sixty minutes and the real war begins. I'm sitting here beside the river with Emil and we're thinking about you—August, too. I didn't stop until I was transferred to the same company. This is quite a moment—you can hear the wings of history. There are twenty of us in company HQ, will there still be twenty of us tomorrow? I am suddenly conscious of being no longer Hans Riederheim, but one of the seeds of corn broadcast by history. Best wishes and Heil Hitler from Hans Riederheim."

"Greetings from August," Gnotke added.

"Your brother, Emil," wrote Feierfeil.

Down among the vegetable gardens things came to life. Sappers brought collapsible boats and laid them near a hedge. Back in the wood tents were struck. The infantry festooned themselves with groundsheets, blankets, cooking utensils and entrenching tools.

"It's time," said Gnotke, and stood up.

"There's a chap called Heydebreck in your section," Riederheim added. "It's the same name. You remember —the Roehm Putsch, the one with only one arm."

"Don't let's go into that—yes, the same name, the same name. The old man was an uncle I think."

A terrible memory—a night heavy with clouds; blood was spilt, their own blood, half of their company, half their own platoon. A cloud veiled the moon and sheep bleated, for it took place in a cattleyard.

It had been like that in Berlin, too, and in Munich. Gruppenfuehrer Heydebreck from Pomerania had been shot in Munich.

"So he's the nephew?"

15

"I don't know. Don't ask me. I don't want anything to do with it."

Gnotke turned away at last and sought out his platoon. Riederheim looked after him.

"A man who has seen his own blood being spilt can spill other people's, too," he said. "Without that night where would we have got the material for what came after and what is still to come?"

Feierfeil and Riederheim belonged to company HQ. They, too, went to their rendezvous. Everyone was ready to take up position in the low brushwood and among the bushes. But before that the whole rifle company paraded once more and the company commander, Captain Boblink, read out the Feuhrer's Order of the Day.

* * *

Lieutenant-Colonel Vilshofen sat next to the driver. Even when he shut his eyes he still had the strip of road before him, lit by the headlights; then the grey strip of concrete seemed to run right through him, they had been driving so long.

At two in the afternoon they had left Berlin. Now it was nearly two again—two in the morning. It wasn't only the grey strip of road—it was something else, just as endless, like a film, a bad film, that kept running through his head. It was the fact that, because he was head of a department under the Deputy Chief of Staff at GHQ, he had to bear-lead foreign visitors and often important German industrialists and businessmen as well. To be more precise, it was the stuff he had to repeat and explain which was so annoying, with all its simplifications and distortions of complicated problems.

The latest visitor was a distinguished Finn; the one the day before had been a Slovak.

No, I won't play any more.

We have, we have, we have. . .

Firstly, secondly and thirdly. . . Firstly, we have Army Group Centre; secondly, Army Group North; thirdly, Army Group South. Deployed between the Baltic and the Black Sea. First objective, the Dnieper; and then a thrust on Moscow and on to the Urals. Another thrust—the Crimea, the Caucasus and on to the Caspian, to the Near East and Central Asia.

16

These were the dispositions.

Gentlemen, you can imagine yourselves—what an immense landmass it is, and what tremendous demands there are on the supply system. But we have thought it all out and we have the organisation for it. Trucks and more trucks, everything on wheels. You must remember there aren't any railways—the gauge has to be changed first—and there are no roads or hardly any roads, and they will have to be built first. But we have, we have . . . German organisational skill. The world is going to see miracles.

Firstly, disposition of troops.

Secondly, supply organisation.

Thirdly, communications.

And then we have thought out how to administer the occupied territories—we have a huge field to work in.

Moreover, farther back we have Reichscommissariats under army commanders. We have the Reichscommissariat for the Baltic and for the Ukraine (the commanders have been appointed), the Commissariat for the Caucasus (the commander is standing by in Munich), the Moscow Commissariat (the commander is standing by in Coblenz), the Commissariat for the Urals (the commander is standing by in Frankfurt-on-Oder).

Further, we have the greatest military commanders of all time and the most brilliant organiser in history as our Leader. We have everything from the operational and organisational point of view to place the productive resources of this immense territory at our disposal.

Ores. Oil. Mineral deposits.

There will be a division of spoils on a large scale, an unheard-of scale. We'll take whatever there is to take. But what are we to put in its place? That's naturally not the question under discussion; the people at the top are still scratching their heads over it. And now, gentlemen, if I may, we will visit the signals installations—telephone exchanges, teleprinters, radio stations—to hear a lecture from the chief signals officer, General Fellgiebel.

Thereafter—a lecture by the Chief of Staff, Lieutenant-General Paulus.

Thereafter—tea with the C-in-C of the Army.

That was in Zossen, and now it's going to be the same

17

in East Prussia. Yesterday it was a Finn, the day before a Slovak, tomorrow it will be M. Antonescu from Bucharest, the day after the Japanese Ambassador from Berlin—in any case a mixture of truth and fiction, as Goethe called it, and somewhat premature laurels; in short, propaganda. That's it—and it may be all very fine and necessary at this minute, but I'm not going to play any more.

"No, I'm not going to play." This time the lieutenant-colonel said it aloud, so that the captain who travelled with him and the young staff officer glanced up out of their dozing sleep. But since Vilshofen said nothing further the captain had nothing to say either. He thought, the long journey is making the lieutenant-colonel jumpy. He took out his watch—it was two in the morning. The staff car in which the three officers sat was one of a whole column of MT. It was the advance party from GHQ, which was itself on the move and would arrive next day in special trains. The twelve-hour drive from Berlin to the triangle of territory in East Prussia which lay between Rastenburg, Loetzen and Angerburg was nearly at an end. They had already turned off the main road and were driving along the special road which the Todt Organisation had newly built to lead to Hitler's HQ. Right and left of the road thick forests slipped past. Then there came a road-block. Sentries from a defence battalion looked at their passes. Another short distance—a fork in the road and a signpost which said: Fritz. The board pointing in the other direction said: Quelle. The latter was the code-name for the Operational HQ, the former for the Deputy Chief of Staff's camp to which Vilshofen's car now turned off. The camp was in the heart of the wood. Huts stood under the trees with cement shelters scattered among them. Orderlies pulled open the doors of the cars and led the new arrivals into their quarters, carrying their kit boxes behind them.

*　　*　　*

The lieutenant who had been in the car with Vilshofen looked round his new quarters. He stood in front of the table; a sketch-map of the installations in the triangle had been put under the glass.

In a word—absolutely magnificent, just the job.

18

Concrete roads, a whole network of them, light railways, airfields, whole villages tucked away under the thick cover of the leaves—and in front of his window ancient trees, the ground between them raked and tidied like a park. A delightful little room, small, like a ship's cabin; varnished wood, a built-in cupboard, big drawer under his bunk, electric light, running water. When you thought what had been put into it—a whole army of men from the Todt Organisation and the Labour Service had worked secretly like gnomes in a fairy-tale—in a few months, almost like mushrooms, you might say, this miracle had sprung up on the soil of East Prussia. And everything bears the mark of the great far-reaching mind. The Fuehrer can work wonders.

*   *   *

Lieutenant-Colonel Vilshofen had washed the dust of the journey from his hands and face and was settling in. He hung his things in the cupboard and laid his papers on the table.

There are still the tanks, he thought; after all, it wasn't just for fun that you had spent your time and wits learning how to use them.

An officer in silver-braided epaulettes with a golden star on a crimson ground—a German general staff officer in this year of grace 1941, who had gone to war for "greater Germany". Not a figure of any great importance, but a man who felt behind him—however far he might have come since then—the cathedral at Ulm, that symbol of a thousand years of German civic life, with all its bourgeois virtues. He had something else in mind, too —the badge which is the trademark of a firm in Ulm, a firm which, under three generations of Vilshofens before him, had become a symbol of industrial progress and strict business integrity. And that was what was wanted now— not sales talk and the verbose publicity of a mushroom concern. After all, it was the quality of the firm's products that had opened the world to it and won it a name. And this modern Vilshofen still held to it that a good cause speaks for itself. But now he was a mere propagandist for things that didn't even exist. First of all it must be proven that we really have got something to show and then I'll be with you.

19

I want a command in the field.

No, said his chief. No, said the Chief of Staff, not for the moment, we can think about it again.

Well, that conversation was some time ago, so Vilshofen has been thinking about it again.

"Breakfast is served, sir." Lieutenant-Colonel Vilshofen walked to the mess over a yellow gravelled path under the old trees and sat down with the other officers of the advance party.

The orderlies had not yet brought in the second course. A great roar of engines rose in the air. It was the German bomber, dive-bomber and fighter-bomber squadrons flying past over the mess and over the trees, gaining height.

"How long is it till they cross the frontier?" said the lieutenant, turning to a captain from the staff of the C-in-C Air.

"They have about fifty miles to go—that's twenty minutes, so they'll cross the frontier at 0304 hours."

A tank officer turned to Vilshofen.

"If you can talk your chief round now, Vilshofen, they'll find a place for you right away. You can have a battalion. But you'll have to hurry. It won't last long."

* * *

The wood wasn't bluish any more, nor was it any longer just a shapeless mass. There were trees and branches in it now, and the thick roof of leaves was held aloft by a branching hundred-armed giant.

The birch-tree in the clearing with its tender pale-green leaves and drooping twigs seemed to have been born of dew and mist that very hour. Under it stood three men.

"Now that is something—'Ariston Lux'—cost twelve pfennigs each. Where did you win them, Lemke?"

"Got them from the General."

"Von Bomelbuerg—is that so? Does he smoke that sort of thing?"

"No—he can't any more—since they shot him through the kisser—he can't smoke any more."

"I see—so he just has them for his friends—not bad, either."

"Well, I only hope things move quickly and we get back to our unit. If they haven't forgotten us."

"The General will see to that. He rings three times

20

a day—rang an hour ago. The lieutenant had just lain down—then the phone rang again—from division—the aide. We weren't to let ourselves get dumped here by our old battery. We're only on loan, that's what the General said."

Yes, General Bomelbuerg—the four 105-mm guns here in the clearing with their limbers behind them, the horses from Hanover and East Prussia and Holstein picketed under the trees, the pointed tent at the edge of the wood with the troop commander, Langhoff, and his wireless operators, runners and signallers, and the three men standing under the birch-tree, even Sergeant-major Lemke's curling beard (for the divisional commander held that a real mounted sergeant-major should have a real beard out of World War I): all this and the blue curling smoke of the "Ariston Lux" existed only because of a whim of Bomelbuerg.

"So now we have another war."

"At least we know now why we formed the horsed troop in France."

"When we think what we went through—first of all ready to go into England with mountain guns and mules, and now with 105's and nags."

"Don't say nags, say horses."

"What I mean to say is that you get fond of your nags."

You get fond of your horses—and that was just what had annoyed the whole regiment when, on orders from the divisional commander, all the stables had been combed out for the new horsed troop that was going to be formed. The divisional commander wanted the troop to be decently mounted. They needed twenty-four Hanoverians, twenty-eight mounts, four horses for the number ones on each gun, two for the section commanders, two officers' chargers, two more for the mounted orderlies, sixteen for the limbers, and the field kitchens and supply waggons were to be four-in-hand. Then there were the draught horses which would come with time, and the commander wanted if possible all the teams to be the same colour—brown or dun or bay. And they hadn't only to get horses but saddles, riding-boots, harness, saddle-blankets, equipment and gun-crews into the bargain.

Bomelbuerg had wanted it like that and there was nothing else for it. Everything had to be got in the twinkling of an eye. The inspection a few days after the troop was formed had been a tremendous do. But the men who stood there exchanging memories under a Russian birch-tree had only heard about it at second-hand; what they did know was that they had had to dismount at a crossroads and let others, who had had a fine laugh over it, get into the saddle instead for the ride past.

"Ah, yes, the ride past at La Guerche."

"It wasn't necessary in any case. They say he can't see any farther than his nose."

"That's true, too—after his head-wound he sees nothing but a sort of shadow. And when he sits over his map he needs spectacles and a magnifying glass as well."

"So he couldn't have seen the horses or anyone on them, far less have any idea how they rode."

"But he feels that sort of thing—he sees that sort of thing instinctively."

"That's true, too."

"It's getting light already."

"It must be about time."

* * *

Langhoff, the troop commander, looked through his bifocal telescope. He could observe the whole village street. He had a woman in his field of vision, magnified several times. She was drawing water from the well—filled two buckets, hung them on a yoke and went off. Langhoff threw away the cigarette he had just lit. It was an "Ariston Lux".

The man at the field telephone smoked the same brand. The fact was that Sergeant-major Lemke had them in a present not from the hand of the General but from the troop commander. The signaller threw his cigarette away, too, but not without snuffing the end with his fingers.

Langhoff looked at his watch.

There were still three minutes till the attack.

"What are you stubbing your cigarette like that for?"

"There might be a forest fire, sir."

"How right you are."

Another glance at his watch, then the question: "Ready

22

for action?"

The signaller repeated into the telephone: "Ready for action?"

"1 Section ready."

"2 Section ready."

The sky thundered as a squadron of planes flew over the wood towards the east. The roar lasted a full minute and died away towards the horizon.

"Troop ready for action," Sergeant-major Lemke reported. From the OP came the order: "Troop—six rounds—fire."

The barrels recoil. A flash of fire from the muzzles. A crack from four iron mouths. Smoke. An echo returning.

"Troop—fire."

Another recoil, another flash, the echo returning. And then the echo was no longer from four pieces alone. In the neighbouring wood a troop was firing 100-mm guns. Farther away were other troops in action—howitzers, mortars, gun-howitzers, long-barrelled pieces. From the rear there came the roar of railway guns, and at longer intervals—each time it was a growl like the crack of doom —the great 60-cm piece, "Karl", bombarding the citadel of Brest-Litovsk. At this moment the front opened up from the Baltic to the Black Sea, one long wall of fire. The noise of the guns and the echo blended and rolled together into space.

Like wild geese flying at night was the thought that went through Riederheim's head as the shells from Langhoff's troop went over the trees. He even managed— it was after the second salvo—to say so out loud. "You can't help thinking about that song 'Wild geese rushing through the night'," he said to the runner, Feierfeil, the man from his own village, who lay beside him.

First of all they aren't wild geese, and secondly it's broad daylight, thought Feierfeil, and thirdly where has August gone and tucked himself away? For he had to keep in visual contact with the section of riflemen lying at the edge of the wood under their platoon commander, August Gnotke; and the place beneath the tree-trunk, where Gnotke had squatted so long, was obviously empty. Well, anyway, he thought, Riederheim is just as cracked as he was when he was a boy in Klein-Stepenitz. He has

23

read too much—that's what does it.

The image of wild geese rustling through the air certainly did not bear any resemblance to what was happening. Report and echo came together. The depths of the wood and the whole country behind them roared. Round about the smaller calibres were firing—the mortars throwing burning oil canisters into the village on the other bank, the 37-mm anti-tank guns firing on the Russian frontier tower with tracer, shells falling with an odd quacking sound in the marshy ground, earth rising in the air, scattering and falling back again. Everything was in uproar; a terrible grinding process was taking place.

"Well, this is it, Emil."

"Yes, this is it," Feierfeil answered and discovered Gnotke again. He had lain down beside Lance-Corporal Heydebreck. He's always doing something with Heydebreck—well, he's a nice kid, always willing to please, doesn't really suit a tin hat, but tries hard. We'll have to help him a bit to find his legs.

Gnotke and Heydebreck lay at the edge of the wood. The whole company lay there stretched out in a long line. In front of them they had the strip of meadow falling down to the river; it was twenty yards to the Bug. On the other bank there were bushes and beyond them fields of rye and oats. The huts in the village of Shuraveka trembled in the morning light. A stone church towered over the straw roofs.

"A cow has run away," said Heydebreck, "the herdsman is driving it out of the rye field with his belt. There's a women drawing water and she doesn't know."

"That's right," said Gnotke, "you feel better when the stuff comes whistling over from the other side. But what's the use of thinking too much?"

The moment had come—yellow mushrooms of smoke rose between the huts. A fountain of earth rose and fell tottering back. In the midst of a quickly spreading bank of smoke there were flashes of fire—that was the burning oil they had shot over.

Thick, oily smoke, the fumes of bursting shells, fiery showers spurting into the air. For ten minutes the fire from all weapons lay on the village, then it lifted on to more distant targets.

The line of infantry lay at the edge of the wood—behind them was company HQ with Riederheim and the company commander. There were no more instructions to give—all the orders had been handed out. When the fire came down on the targets farther on, the company attack began. The sappers brought the collapsible boats down to the water. The infantry climbed in. At bows and stern a sapper squatted with a paddle.

Dark, transparent water—there's no use thinking, but you do just the same. This dark running water is the line drawn by fate. Life has been left back there on the other bank.

The boats had reached the other side. Heydebreck sank up to his belly in the mud of the bank. He pulled himself up by a crooked branch. Not a shot was fired, even when they had gone through the bushes on the bank and then farther on there was no sign of the enemy.

"Get on there—get on."

Their way took them over a field of rye. Gnotke's platoon had the frontier tower as its first objective. Its second was the church in the village of Shuraveka. On Gnotke's left, 2 platoon, under command of a sergeant, moved forward, too, through high rye ready for reaping. Behind both platoons, 3 platoon followed under a lieutenant at an interval of a hundred paces.

A little distance from the tower lay the sentry who had been brought down from his perch. A rifleman turned him over and they saw a strong Mongolian face, ash-grey in death. Everything went according to plan. The little bodies of infantry reached the edge of the village and plunged into it. Gnotke raised his signal pistol and so did the commander of 2 platoon. Two white flares—the signal for company HQ to move forward.

"On your feet—up."

The company commander, Boblink, Sergeant Riederheim, the runner and a medical orderly got into a boat, too. It was not until they reached the other bank that Feierfeil got a command from Riederheim: "Emil—go to the heavy MG platoon—tell them to move forward. Platoon commanders to report to us."

Feierfeil, bicycle in hand, had himself ferried back and rode to the heavy MG platoon's position. When he had completed his mission and was back again on the east bank of the Bug, company HQ had already disappeared far forward in the cloud of smoke shrouding the village. Feierfeil trotted after them looking at the trodden rye: "Wild geese," he said. "In this rye it was wild pigs, but war is like that."

The village was no longer standing; nothing was standing. There was a wardrobe with long flames licking out of it, then a stone chimney place—a whole row of stone chimneys. Women were dragging things out of the flaming heap—a horse-collar, a sheepskin, a mattress, and were putting the stuff in safety at the back in the vegetable gardens. And where are the Russians, where on earth are the Russians? And why doesn't anyone shoot at us? Yet they said there was a whole battalion quartered in the village. Nothing—no resistance. A village knocked to pieces when they were driving the cows out to the fields. There was a woman who kept on pressing both fists against her temples; perhaps it was her grandmother who lay before her with no hair and no face. But that shouldn't matter to Emil, the veteran Emil, who was in Berlin in 1930 and in 1933, in the first SA battalion, when plenty of house doors were broken down. This isn't the first time he has dumped furniture in the street. And then, quite apart from the campaign in the west, there was the Polish campaign—a few things had happened then, too. But here there was the freshness of an early summer morning, the stench of burnt flesh and you didn't know whether it was the flesh of a cow or a woman. Either you never got used to it or else you had to get used to it all over again each time.

A breath of wind moved over the earth. The thick smoke rose like a black back-cloth. A pig ran squealing across the scene. A bare-footed old man stood with a few household goods under his arm. A car churned slowly through the sand. Feierfeil looked at the staff officers sitting in it (what are they doing so far forward?) and noticed their chalk-white faces. He recognised the commander of the flanking regiment, Colonel Zecke. He was shouting at the driver: "What's the meaning of this—get a move on." The car moved slowly away; its wheels sank deeper.

So that's how it is, then—it makes them sick, too. Let's get out of here, not see anything; out of the village, out into the fields. You breathe better there.

Feierfeil found company HQ behind the shell-torn church. Captain Boblink had a map-case in his hand and was marking it up, but it didn't seem to matter much—everything was going according to plan.

* * *

Hasse didn't fit in anywhere on divisional HQ. He had been taken from the divisional pool and posted as observer in excess of establishment; but he had not had any duties assigned to him, was neither G1, G2 nor even G3, and so the others called him the G17—but that was on mess evenings. His actual job was to hang on to the General like a burr and, given the enfeebled state of the latter's sight and hearing, he was really Bomelbuerg's eyes and ears.

The last few weeks, which had been a period of hard work for the staff, had scarcely left the G17 a free moment, for although he had no regular job in any special branch of the staff he had not been able to leave the General's side, and the General had had a hundred jobs on hand. So on the night of the attack, in spite of his youth, Hasse found himself almost at the limits of his endurance.

Another twenty-five minutes—that was the thought with which, although determined to stay awake for the great moment, he had fallen into such a deep sleep that he heard neither the artillery nor the railway guns, and had slept long past the time when the General had asked to be called.

He woke only when the sun was shining in at his window. When he entered the operations room it was still too early. There were only the duty officer and some orderlies in this, the biggest room in the peasant house. The duty officer sat at the map table with a telephone to his ear, marked up the situation and automatically passed it back to Corps.

100 Infantry Regiment has reached western side of Shuraveka, no opposition—101 Infantry Regiment has crossed the Bug, south of Triangle Wood, light opposition —no enemy artillery fire so far.

A wireless message from the unit on the right flank.

Attack developing according to plan—weak resistance.

Hasse learned that the General had been with the senior staff officer in charge of operations until after three o'clock and had then retired again. So he could go back to his own room and wait to be called.

Some hours later he came back with the General. At advanced HQ things still looked very much the same. Nothing exciting. Everything was going according to plan. The duty officer marked up his map with a charcoal pencil. The senior staff officer, Lieutenant-Colonel Neudeck, was wandering up and down.

"100 Regiment mostly across Bug and pushing on. 101 Regiment also mostly over. 1 Battery of divisional artillery preparing to move to new positions on the other flank. All going according to plan. Shuraveka clear of enemy."

So the duty officer reported to the General as he entered.

"In that case I propose to move the HQ forward. What do you say to Shuraveka?"

"I think it is very early to move, sir."

"All right, then, hang on." Waiting was not in Bomelbuerg's line. He took a few turns round the room, stopped behind the duty officer, watched him marking up the map and without saying a word left the room—naturally with Hasse at his side.

The officers who were left in the HQ heard a motor start up outside and a car move off. But no one thought any more of it, and—for the moment—no one remembered how once before in the French campaign he had driven off and been brought back in an ambulance, and how everyone had thought they would never see him alive again. But five months later he was back with them. The bullet had entered between the eyes at the bridge of the nose, had gone through the base of the skull without damaging the brain and come out slightly to the right of the occiput. The results were disturbances in his hearing, his sight, his sense of smell, of taste and of balance. He saw nothing at all now with one eye; the other distinguished only shadows. But what weighed upon Bomelbuerg even more than the physical disfigurement and the resulting damage to his powers of perception was

28

something else—what that was he had let out to one of the younger officers the evening he came back to the division. "My good man, my good Langhoff," he had said, "I expect you didn't recognise your General any more."

"But a couple of scars don't make so much difference, sir," was the answer.

"Is that so? Thank you, but then you see, old Bomelbuerg thought he was bullet-proof, and now a great hole has been shot in that idea."

"But, sir," Langhoff hastened to add, "allow me to contradict you, sir, and say that I think quite differently. Anybody else with a wound like that would never have survived it. But you, sir—if that isn't a sign that you're bullet-proof!"

"My dear boy," were the words which burst from the General's lips, and he took Lieutenant Langhoff by the shoulders and shook him, "you don't know what you've done to me by saying that. Thank you, my dear good boy, thank you." And from that day on Bomelbuerg really was convinced that he was bullet-proof.

That was Bomelbuerg, and such was the face the officers of his staff had by now got used to. But at this moment, as a staff-car drove away behind the house, none of the divisional staff, not even Lieutenant-Colonel Neudeck, thought of that other time, that distant fateful morning when he had driven off. The duty officer took down message after message and made constant changes on the situation map. Lieutenant-Colonel Neudeck lit a cigar and walked up and down. Sometimes he lifted a telephone and talked over the situation with Colonel Zecke or Colonel Schadow, the two regimental commanders, or with one of his opposite numbers in the neighbouring divisions.

He halted at the map table.

"Tell me, what are the reports from the observation balloons?"

"They reported ten minutes ago. Observation hindered by mist and rising sun."

There was nothing one could do—the whole thing went on on its own.

Isolated pockets of resistance—a few prisoners—no losses—slight losses—according to plan.

Corps rang. They asked for the senior staff officer.

The Chief of Staff came on the line: "Well, how are things with you, Neudeck? Everything according to plan, everything all right? Now listen, my dear man, in twenty minutes the Army Commander will arrive at your HQ —just to put you in the picture. Good-bye."

The Army Commander, the commander of Fourth Army, Field-Marshal von Kluge. Neudeck rang the liaison officer: "Listen, Butz, the Army Commander will be here in twenty minutes. Report to the General at once."

The news went through the house like wildfire. Everyone buckled up his belt, tugged his jacket straight. The duty officer had himself relieved by another officer for a minute to put himself to rights.

Major Butz came into the Ops room.

"The General isn't to be found."

"What? Impossible." As he shouted the words, Neudeck knew that it was very possible indeed and had a vision of that terrible morning in France.

"The General isn't there, the staff-car and driver are gone. So is Hasse—he went, too, of course."

Major Butz disappeared to search further. But the noise of an aeroplane engine could be heard already. A Fieseler Storch circled the house and suddenly settled in a strip of meadow hard by. Major Butz ran over to show the Field-Marshal the way; the Army Commander was accompanied by a staff officer. Neudeck met them half-way, but he never managed to give his message.

"Well, Neudeck," said the Army Commander at once, "how are things here? I see—Shuraveka's taken—no opposition worth mentioning — everybody pushing on. Where is the General?"

"The General is—I mean to say, has gone forward in his staff-car, sir."

"*What* has he done?"

"Yes, sir, just a short trip, he'll be back right away."

"Then we must do without him. Let's go in."

They went into the advanced HQ.

"Don't let me interrupt you," said the Field-Marshal to the duty officer and went over to his table where the situation map lay.

"So they're pushing on everywhere—hardly any opposition, eh, Neudeck?"

"Yes, sir, very few losses—gratifyingly so."

Hearing this remark repeated, the attendant staff officer wrinkled his brow in a worried way, and one could see that the Field-Marshal was anything but delighted at the report of such gratifyingly small losses.

"But things will gradually get stiffer—they must begin to wake up on the other side sometime."

"You have the observation balloons here—what do they report?" asked the staff captain.

The duty officer rang the artillery regiment.

Lieutenant-Colonel Neudeck and the captain in the observation balloon discussed the situation further. The Field-Marshal stood beside them and merely listened. He himself said little: "Fine—not so good—we'll see —you think so?" and so on.

"The report from the observation balloons has come in, sir."

"Well?"

"Scattered enemy artillery fire from area of the Fort. Motorised columns moving east from nearby barracks."

"And is anything coming west?"

"No movement westwards can be observed, sir."

"Impossible. Get through to them again."

The duty officer rang again and this time got a line straight to the balloons. Lieutenant-Colonel Neudeck took over the receiver and spoke to the captain who, from his balloon nearly four thousand feet up, looked far and wide over the open country. The captain stuck to his guns: "MT columns moving east—no movement in this direction."

"Tell him it's not possible."

"That's not possible," said Neudeck, passing on the message.

"Well, if that's so and if the people down there don't want to believe it they'd better come up themselves; I can only say what I see," they could hear the captain say from his balloon.

The faces of the staff captain and the Army Commander looked worried. There was something wrong somewhere —either in the reports on enemy activity drawn up at Corps and Division, or else in the weeks of work on the

31

maps of enemy dispositions. Going by the maps they had reckoned with tremendous resistance right away and had located the Red Army right on the frontier where it could —or so they hoped—be quickly brought to battle and defeated.

The Army Commander and the staff captain decided to fly to the flanking division, 45 Infantry Division, which reported heavy resistance from Brest-Litovsk and its citadel. Lieutenant-Colonel Neudeck and the divisional liaison officer accompanied the officers to the landing-place and stood in the meadow until the Storch had taken off and disappeared in a northerly direction.

"And now, Butz, stir yourself and see that you find the General at the double," said Lieutenant-Colonel Neudeck to the liaison officer.

* * *

A fluid advance was the best description for the manœuvre Bomelbuerg's division was carrying out. It had crossed the Bug, trampled the fields of rye and oats, taken possession of the smoking heaps of ash—all that was left of a village—and gone on over plough, over marshy meadow, through brush and small trees, by-passed the fort, taken a block of empty barracks, crossed the Brest-Kobryn road and so drawn an arc round the houses and towers of Brest-Litovsk which rose on the horizon. To the south the division had covered its flank, and to the north-east its forward elements were near a tributary of the Bug—the east-flowing Muchavetz. Here, in the rear of the town of Brest-Litovsk, where there was a bridge over the Muchavetz, lay the battle HQ of Schadow's regiment—barely two thousand yards short of its objective. This was the spot where, between eight and nine o'clock, a motor-cycle and sidecar tore past without paying any attention to the pennant marking the regimental HQ, only to be held up a thousand yards farther on by a shout from a runner.

The combination braked sharply.

"Halt—you can't go any farther forward." The runner was Corporal Feierfeil.

The motor-cycle had been spotted by regimental HQ as well.

"I say—what's that there? There's a pair of red-striped

pants on the road." The regimental commander, Lieutenant-Colonel Schadow, made the remark to the officers of his staff. They, too, looked over towards the pair of red-striped trousers—the badge of the general staff officer—and recognised the stocky figure of Bomelbuerg, standing in the middle of the road in the midst of a crowd of infantrymen. Schadow, a lean, very tall and somewhat irritable gentleman, seized his walking-stick and, followed by his liaison officer, went over to the road near which Captain Boblink had set up his company HQ.

Boblink had reported the situation to the General, informed him that the battalion HQ was about four hundred yards farther to the right and had then been dismissed. Now he stood there with a pair of binoculars to his eyes and watched two platoons of his company work their way forward against weak resistance to take the bridge over the Muchavetz. It was an exciting moment. Would they get the bridge intact or would it go up first? Boblink noticed, too, that the flanking company was pushing forward to the right of the road. I hope we get there first—I hope my boys get the bridge, he prayed. A couple of MGs hammered away at a clump of bushes on the other bank and silenced fire from them.

Lieutenant Hasse was at the General's side acting as his eye-glass. He passed on everything worth knowing to his chief.

"Sir . . ." General Bomelbuerg leant his head a little to the side. "Lieutenant-Colonel Schadow," Hasse prompted.

"Ah, my dear Schadow, now we must watch them take the bridge intact." It was not only Boblink's company that lay here before the bridge, but a whole regiment cramped in a deep gully. Zecke's regiment meanwhile was covering the operation to the south. The third regiment of the division was still in reserve.

"Sir, the senior staff officer has been asking us several times whether you had looked in on us," said Schadow, turning to Bomelbuerg.

"Yes, yes," said the General. "All right." Nothing mattered at this particular minute that didn't concern the bridge. Machine-guns rattled. Hand-grenades and charges exploded. The artillery came down on the far bank of the

M.—B

33

Muchavctz. From Brest came the thunder of howitzers and the detonations of the great siege-gun "Karl". The mud-covered figures of the infantry rose from the marshy ground, pushed forward and fell again. Over the river a Russian biplane came curving down in flames. A dark bundle broke away from the plane; a parachute unfolded and drifted over the river with the wind.

"We can see everything beautifully from battle HQ," said Schadow once more. He had to roar in Bomelbuerg's ear, but the latter motioned him away. "No, thanks—I'm very happy here with the men of the forward company."

"From battle HQ you can see how the flank battalion is getting on," said Schadow.

"My dear man, don't disturb me. Do go back to your HQ if you want," was all that Bomelbuerg replied to the repeated invitations. In the end Schadow had to go back with his LO.

Meanwhile the red stripes on Bomelbuerg's trousers acted like a magnet. After Schadow had left, the commander of the artillery regiment made an attempt to get the General back from the front line. Admittedly he didn't go himself; he sent his liaison officer, Holmers. He knew the old boy had a soft side for Holmers.

The bridge was taken in the face of light opposition, undamaged, according to plan. Holmers reached Boblink's position as white signal flares went up beyond the river.

"White flares," prompted Hasse.

Hasse was pale, and no wonder. He had lived through some exciting moments and was worried about further unpredictable developments. He had driven as far as the Bug in the staff car, had crossed the river in a collapsible boat, had come through the smoking ruins of Shuraveka in the motor-cycle combination and had had to go flat on his face when MG fire spurted out of the fort—all the while at Bomelbuerg's side. He had been going about with him since four in the morning, and after all he was not bullet-proof.

Maybe the General was, but he did not think he was himself.

"White flares, sir."

"White—then it's all right, we've taken it." Bomelbuerg

stretched out his hand and laid it on the shoulder of the person who had that minute arrived. He put his face so close to the other's that the tips of their noses almost touched. It was Holmers. "Holmers, my boy! There you are, you see—we've done it again. I knew Schadow would manage it. Now we must see that a message is put through to Corps right away."

"Yes, sir. There's a gunner officer in an OP in the bushes there. He'll send a signal at once."

"And now where is your CO?" Bomelbuerg asked Holmers.

"He is farther back, sir. He's doing a recce. You went past us like the wind, sir." Holmers was even better than Hasse at telling the General things. "Our battle HQ will be with Schadow's regiment," he said and watched a Russian prisoner being led past. It was the Russian airman shot down a few minutes before. A sunburnt face with light eyes. He had a gold-embroidered star on his sleeve. So he was a commissar. He obviously didn't know what was in store for him. A thousand yards back there fluttered the pennant of the regimental HQ. "Forward of regimental HQs. . ." It was a damned shame.

"And what is it like farther back—how far have they got with the bridging operation?" the General inquired.

"That's not going so well, sir. The east bank is terribly marshy."

"But they must put a move on."

Bomelbuerg turned to another figure on which he also laid his hand: "Ah, Butz, it's nice to see you. Tell me, why aren't they getting on with the bridge?" It was Butz's turn—now that he had found his commander— to explain to him that the extent of the strip of marsh on the east bank of the Bug had been underestimated and that the bridge they had prepared was not long enough.

A shot rang out on this side of Schadow's HQ. Holmers looked over and so did Butz. When Holmers tried to catch Major Butz's eye the other turned away. "I'm just going over for a minute," said Butz, "to try to get through to division," and went off to report to Lieutenant-Colonel Neudeck that he had carried out his orders and found the General.

Holmers was still thinking about the spot forward of regimental HQ. So that was the beginning. And if things went on like that? He remembered his conversation with Langhoff and the latter's sermon on the parallelogram of moral forces. What had he said? What you do yourself affects not only the other chap but recoils on yourself. And this shot, too, would recoil on their own heads. One thing was certain—that the man who had been shot down half an hour before and now lay forward of the regimental HQ was a combatant, and as such had, according to international law, a right to be spared and to be taken prisoner.

* * *

The sun, which that morning had risen blood-red out of the Pripet marshes, now stood high in the sky. The marsh under their feet was like a warm mush. A road —a bad one, full of muddy holes, which apparently wound about just as the cows had trod it out ages ago —ran parallel to the Bug, skirted the fort and a big block of barracks, ran through a wood and so on to the high embankment leading to the Muchavetz. There, half of Boblink's company lay. Their task had been accomplished, and the most important objective of the day was already reached. Now there was a halt while the rest of the company combed the banks, the brushwood, a couple of peasants' huts and the nearby sawmill, looking for hidden Russians.

The air was full of dust and smoke. An evil-smelling exhalation rose from the earth. It was good to be able to stretch your arms and legs and lie on your back. It would have been better still if you could have stayed here until the sun set behind the wood in the west—the wood from which the company had advanced that morning.

The infantrymen lay side by side—Heydebreck was there, with August Gnotke a little farther away, and Emil Feierfeil and some people from the anti-tank section.

"Boys, this is going to be a lovely campaign," said one of the anti-tank gunners, a Berliner. "All that cardboard stuff the Russians have—I've shot up seven of them myself."

"Take it easy, Hermann."

36

"Well, if I didn't get all seven, the rest of them fairly sprinted."

"Shut up," Gnotke shouted over.

The Berliner had in actual fact shot up an armoured car when they were working their way round the fort. Gnotke had had a look at it close up—a light armoured car with an MG.

"What I mean to say is that if the Russians have stuff like that it won't be so bad."

Gnotke laid his head on the damp grass and tried to sleep. The embankment was like a little hill, but at this time of day it threw no shadow. There was a sound of firing from Brest-Litovsk. Then there was a terrifying rumbling noise from the road leading out of the town. In thick clouds of dust the German tanks moved east.

"Has anyone seen anything of the other division?"

"Of course—we're in contact. Look, there are the tanks going forward—a pincer movement, they're making a big pocket."

Gnotke was thinking about the conversation with Hans Riederheim. I wish he'd leave me alone with all that old stuff. It's over and done with. I don't want any more to do with it. What does he want with Pauline anyway?

"Tell me, Emil," he turned to Feierfeil, "I was thinking about that postcard Hans wrote yesterday—what has he to do with Pauline?"

"Don't you know he's been after her for ages?"

"I see—and Pauline?"

"I can't say," answered her brother.

In the sky there was a droning of engines. The flak roared on all sides. The planes fanned out—signalling to the ground. Their own planes returning from a raid.

"This is a fine war—shooting up our own planes."

"Oh, shut up," said Gnotke again.

All sorts of things happen in war, and you couldn't worry about everything. Whether the flak was German or Russian, you were resting, but you didn't know how long it would last or how soon you would be up on your feet again.

The conversation died away—they all lay stretched out on the short, damp grass. That morning, waist-deep in water, they had climbed ashore on the marshy bank of the Bug. They had gone on through plough and swamp and ashes and tilth again. Their clothes had dried on their bodies and become soaked again with their sweat. Now they lay deep in their fatigue. An hour passed and the sun had reached its zenith when the earth under them trembled. At first it was like a train rumbling along out of the distance, then it became a roar which filled earth and sky.

* * *

In his search for the General, Major Butz had first gone to Zecke's regiment. He had passed through the block of barracks which had once been a Polish training school for officers—it was still burning. There were buildings of white brick, red tiles, flower-beds before the houses and pines beyond. The artillery had made a target of it. Great holes gaped in the walls; here and there flames billowed out; a curtain fluttered from a window. Women and children stood about with puzzled faces. Butz passed a dead soldier. There was a dead woman in the dust. Russian prisoners squatted in front of a house with their hands on their heads as if they had no idea of what was happening. From the sentry guarding the Russians Butz learned the whereabouts of regimental HQ. He had a good way to go before he saw the pennant of 101 Infantry Regiment fluttering in front of a house. He went in and looked for the liaison officer, Emmanuel.

"Hallo, Emmanuel, where is the colonel?"

Lieutenant Emmanuel sat in a chair with glassy, staring eyes. When he raised his face it seemed even more blank than those of the captured Russians. Someone took Butz by the arm and led him out of the room.

"Shell-shock—like at Niederkorn."

Emmanuel had had a nervous breakdown at the beginning of the French campaign, when the regiment came under heavy fire at Niederkorn and regimental HQ had lost some men. Thereafter they had sent him home and the matter had been hushed up. Zecke had taken Emmanuel back—he had once studied theology and was besides an unwearying worker—and made him regimental LO. Now the same thing had happened again. When they were driving through Shuraveka he had broken down completely.

Butz found the regimental staff behind the house. There were trees, and under the trees stood tables and chairs; the officers sat together. They had bottles of beer from the Russian mess, and there was bread and sausage, too; an NCO had just come back from a foraging expedition and was laying a tray with another course on the table.

"This isn't half bad—I thought it would have been worse."

"The beer isn't up to ours—a bit more bitter—but not bad."

"Look, taste this—wonderful pralines—and the biscuits aren't bad."

Bomelbuerg hadn't been seen here, so Butz drove on. Then he came across the General at 100 Regiment, with Boblink's company, rang up Lieutenant-Colonel Neudeck and—since the General still wanted to visit Zecke's regiment—perched himself on a motor-cycle.

This time there were two motor-cycles—in the sidecar of the first sat the General, while Hasse sat behind the driver. Butz rode pillion on the second. They drove through the barrack block and there were still the same women hanging aimlessly about, the same Russian prisoners squatting with raised hands, abandoned vehicles. The motor-cycles drove past the regimental staff's MT, drove on under the pines and stopped almost exactly opposite the tables under the trees.

Hasse helped the General out of his seat.

"Morning, gentlemen," crowed the General. "Good-morning, sir," they answered in chorus. "Morning, Zecke." He didn't see him, but he must be there. "Well, what's new with you?"

"Lieutenant-Colonel Neudeck has rung several times and asked for you, sir," Zecke was heard to say. Zecke, who had not been long with the division but, on the strength of an acquaintanceship of long standing, had been effusively greeted by Bomelbuerg on his arrival, always maintained that he had a special line to the Old Man—but very often, as on this morning, it proved to be otherwise.

"Well, then, Hasse, please put me through to Neudeck."

The General turned to Zecke again. "Well, what's new,

39

Zecke?"

"All objectives taken, sir—may I show you on the map?" Bomelbuerg came up to the table and leant forward—just a little, not in the least like a man who had to have his nose on the map to see anything at all.

"The first battalion has made contact with Schadow's regiment. The second battalion is facing south here on the edge of the barracks, 3 Battalion lies next to it, facing south-west and holding a line as far as the Bug," Zecke reported.

"Yes, yes," said Bomelbuerg testily. Everything according to plan, slight losses—that wasn't what he really wanted to hear from Zecke; he remembered what Hasse had just said to him before they drew up. He pointed at random but lighted, quite correctly, on the rear wall of the house where almost a hundred Russian prisoners squatted in the sun.

"And what is that supposed to be? You know, Zecke, a prisoner-collecting point like that, right under the nose of the regimental commander, isn't quite the thing."

"They're going to be taken off right away, sir. It's only temporary."

"I see. And what else is there?"

Butz had been there already and obviously the General had heard about Emmanuel, but Zecke didn't mention it. "Well, sir, something rather unpleasant has happened," he said. "3 Battalion has just reported that it has come under fire from some of our own tanks."

"That what?"

"Under fire, sir—most unfortunate, two heavy anti-tank guns with crews put out of action."

"But that is a frightful mess, Zecke. How did it come about?"

Zecke explained. Tanks had been sighted to the south, and the heavy anti-tank guns of 3 Battalion had opened fire and knocked some of them out; then the tanks had opened up on the anti-tank guns and put two guns and their crews out of action.

"There was nothing said about tanks approaching from the south, sir."

"What do you mean—nothing said? I suppose they know German from Russian tanks? An unbelievable mess,

I tell you."

"Sir," it was Hasse who spoke.

"What is it, Hasse?"

"Lieutenant-Colonel Neudeck, sir."

"Give it to me," Bomelbuerg took over the receiver. "Listen, Neudeck, we've just seen Schadow's people take the bridge—a first-class job again by Schadow. . ."

Zecke stood at his side and had to listen to a whole panegyric on Schadow. Then Neudeck apparently reported on the situation.

Bomelbuerg's face grew gloomy behind the glasses of his huge goggles and he nodded deeply as though Neudeck was standing there before him.

Neudeck was explaining that there was no opposition worth mentioning and that the casualties were everywhere light. Where there had been losses they were to be put down largely to the Russians fighting contrary to all the rules of strategy and tactics. There was firing from positions which had already been taken. The fort, for instance, which was completely surrounded and lay there absolutely silent, suddenly opened fire again whenever a truck went past. ("I had to go flat on my face myself," the General murmured.) And in Brest-Litovsk—Nuedeck had this from the flanking division—it was worse still, and the fortress was really worrying the divisional commander. "It looks as if we aren't going to have the losses in the front line in this war but in the rear," said Nuedeck. He went on to speak about something else— a certain nervous excitement which was noticeable in the reports from lower formations. "One of the reasons is that there is hardly any resistance. It's absolutely uncanny. Of course, there is firing from the fort, on the Bug, on the Muchavetz, in the woods. But whenever there is a shot anywhere on the road or in a village they say 'franc-tireurs'. And everybody starts shooting wildly and people start killing each other. That's what happened on the Koden road—some of our tanks came up from the south. . ."

"Yes, I know about that mess, that happened with Zecke's lot. What are you saying? Of course they must be stopped from shooting each other. Once we get 102 Regiment across, they will go over the ground again. Once this handful of Russians is disposed of, all this excitement will cease and there will be no more spooks. Tell me, Neudeck, how is the bridge getting on? . . . I see, marshy bank, no bottom, not enough equipment—and the sappers couldn't tell that beforehand! Anything else?"

"Yes, sir, Corps has just rung up. 18 Armoured Division can't use its proper advance route because the ground is a complete marsh. They're being turned north from Koden and pushed forward over the bridge we took on the Muchavetz and then along the Brest-Kobryn road."

"That's fine—so our success is bearing fruit nicely. But what happens to us then? We must sit where we are. The panzer divisions have priority on the roads."

"We must look for a gap and try to filter our troops through, sir. I have told the transport officer to report to the bridge."

"Well, we'll see. Get on to them back there and have the bridge over the Bug finished. Anything else?"

"I was thinking of moving over with HQ early in the afternoon—I would suggest moving into the barracks there."

"Fine, I'll get everything ready. I'll tell Butz and Hasse and they can see to it. Good-bye then, Nuedeck."

* * *

The telephone conversation was over—it was only now that the General realised that in actual fact things were going all wrong. The men are shooting each other—well, they'll soon stop that. But it really is frightful that the bridge is taking so long. 18 Armoured Division—fine, but then we're left hanging about and that isn't so good; in fact, it's annoying.

There was Zecke again.

"Well, what is it, Zecke?"

Lieutenant-Colonel Zecke made his report—it was about Lieutenant Emmanuel. "I see, Emmanuel—the LO—completely out—collapsed, you say." That was too much. The delay with the bridge, the fact that the division got left behind to let the armour through—it all suddenly added up. Bomelbuerg put his face close to the colonel's. He took off his goggles and turned his lacerated yellow eye-ball, his four-fifths blind, weeping eye, on the colonel as if he wanted to have a closer look at him.

"I told you so. But you wanted to have Emmanuel at all costs. Well, you've had him now. And I'm supposed to clear up the mess. I haven't the slightest intention of doing anything of the kind. That's the third mess you've made of things. . ."

"But, sir. . ."

"There's no excuse—the third, I said. First, the prisoner-collecting point beside regimental HQ. Second, your anti-tank guns open up on German armour and let themselves be overrun by German tanks. Third, the LO should be in an asylum. Words fail me to describe such a state of affairs in any regiment."

The General put on his goggles again. He had had a good look at Zecke—he had wanted to for a long time. And he had told him his mind clearly.

Zecke had understood that Bomelbuerg was needing to work off steam again. Let him. Zecke's sharp-featured face remained immobile during the whole row.

Bomelbuerg grunted again and, turning round, groped in a vacuum, but after a few paces contrived to reach Hasse's side. Zecke spoke up again, about accommodation for the divisional staff.

"If I may suggest, sir, there are a couple of quiet, well-lit rooms over there beside the mess."

"No, thank you. It's far too crowded here. Butz will have been looking round."

His aide had discovered a little clump of huts surrounded by pines and bushes on the road to the bridge. Bomelbuerg had himself taken there.

He sat at the window. Time went by and he did not move. He was thinking or sleeping—you couldn't tell exactly which, through the big goggles with the tinted lenses. It was hot and dusty and midges rose in swarms from the bushes by the window. Midges did not disturb the General; he didn't notice them, at least not until his hand went to his nose or cheek and found a bite there. But they disturbed Hasse. The billet Zecke had offered with the open space in front of the window had, of course, been incomparably better—but at that moment you could only offer the General a billet which was at a reasonable distance from Zecke's HQ.

"Hasse," said the General—it was really a question.

43

"The armour, sir," Hasse replied.

18 Armoured Division was there—the whole division, waiting to pass and be channelled over the bridge. Having opened the way for the armour, Bomelbuerg wanted to get some idea of what it looked like, so he stood in front of the house with Hasse at his side. The armoured cars, running like hounds a couple of miles ahead of the mainguard, were already past and thundering over the bridge.

"The advance guard, sir."

Heavy tanks, gleaming tracks, oily fumes, dust.

"A motor-cycle company, sir."

"The commander in his staff-car, sir."

Tracks, dust, stench. A rattling, roaring hell. Hasse might have spared himself the trouble, for no human voice could make itself heard. Bomelbuerg stood there a long time, then he went back into the hut and sat at the open window, his face still turned towards the dust-covered world outside.

* * *

The stream of tanks thundered over the bridge.

The infantry lying at the side of the road were covered with dust. When there was a halt the men of Gnotke's platoon could have a good look at the tanks. Only the driver sat inside; the crew sat on top—the commander on the edge of the turret with his headphones on, the others behind him.

"Look at that, they've all their kit hanging about on the outside."

"Of course, everything goes bad in the heat with the stink of oil."

Cooking utensils, drinking water, sacks of bread and rations—they all hung dangling on the walls of the tanks. Behind there were petrol tins, and no tank was without its boards and beams, its wooden matting to lay on soft patches. Then there were tanks with trailers.

"Like gipsies," remarked one of the infantrymen.

"What's that, mate?" One of the dust-covered faces turned towards him; there was a flash of white only from the eyes and teeth—the rest of the face was masked with dirt. On the brows it made great curving lumps; it clung to the mouth with the spittle, and on either side of the nose it descended in a black furrow.

"I was saying you could keep everything nice and clean behind the turret."

"Mind your own business. D'you think this is our first campaign?"

That was the end of that. The others entirely agreed. "They don't look very beautiful," said one. "They have half of Poland on them." "Maybe the infantry is better, after all." "Everybody has to carry his stuff somewhere." "Yes, but they carry it on their tanks." "Well, the main thing is, they've got to let us through soon so that we have the high road to Moscow under our feet."

The column went on, there was a halt and then it started again, rolling ahead at ten miles an hour. An armoured division has about five thousand vehicles; put them spaced out at the regulation interval with all the auxiliary units and it would cover more than a hundred miles. Perhaps a third of the division had crossed the Muchavetz and gone forward. It had been passing for hours, and there was no sign of its ending.

* * *

A couple of miles away a man still sat at a window. "Hasse!" he called.

"Yes, sir."

"They're singing. What is it?"

" 'The whole wide world is tottering', sir."

"Well?" He wanted to have it recited to him, and Hasse said it through right down to the lines:

> *"Masters today of Germany,*
> *Tomorrow the world is ours."*

Bomelbuerg did not hear what Hasse was reciting, nor did he hear what they sang outside on the road, but he sat there listening and said at last: "The boys sing wonderfully."

The tanks halted. Bomelbuerg went out again. He spoke to a lieutenant standing in an open turret. The lieutenant could not grasp what the general wanted of him.

"Lieutenant Vohwinkel, sir."

"Where from?" asked Bomelbuerg.

"The Black Forest, sir."

"Fine. Your first campaign?"

"No, sir; I was in Poland and France."

45

"And your crew, too?"

"Only the wireless operator, sir."

"Grand—hurry up now and get over the bridge so that we can have a clear road."

"Yes, sir."

The tanks rolled on. Bomelbuerg stayed where he was. He stood there by the elder bush and thought what an extraordinary, confused day this was, the sort of day that suddenly became too much for one. He thought of the First World War when the tanks, at least on the German side, hadn't been so important; he thought of his garrison service in Potsdam, for the Republic naturally couldn't bowler hat a Bomelbuerg. Finally he thought of Frau Charlotte Bomelbuerg, his wife, whom he didn't often remember.

He stood there and neither saw nor heard. He could not shut his eyes, for he had no sense of balance and would have begun to sway like a reed in the wind. He could smell nothing and taste nothing. And so it was all very much the same to him—even his food and Frau Charlotte Bomelbuerg in Potsdam. There was only one exception—the great machine of which he was a part; as far as that was concerned nothing left him cold, and he saw and heard and had clearly before his eyes all that went on, all that was happening that very minute.

There was no sign of the sun, which must be sinking, for all this rattling and roaring and whining and screeching which crept by blotted out the day. The long stream of armour and the long wake of thick dust it stirred up stretched as far back as the Bug and over the Bug far into the heart of Poland; far forward it must be near Kobrin and the HQ of a Russian army. So it rolled on along the road through Brest-Litovsk, Minsk and Smolensk, rolled along the military highway to Moscow —the highway they had seized and would now irresistibly sweep clear. It was a beginning, and in this beginning he and his men, and not least the men of Schadow's assault regiment, had played their part.

* * *

In the afternoon the LOs of 3 Motorised Division had brought the orders for the attack. D-day was 22nd June, H-hour 0305 hours. There was an appendix to orders that if the message "Wood for hutted camps not to be touched" came through, the attack was off.

The division was concentrated in a wood east of Tilsit. In the evening the soldiers listened to dance music from Berlin and the voice of the announcer saying Goodnight.

Then a great stillness settled down from the tops of the pines and fell on the camp. Solitary sentries paced up and down under the trees—almost everyone else lay sleeping. Here and there someone took up pen and paper, but few real letters were written. A few scribbled lines and the paper was stuck into the envelope and someone passing took the brief greeting and handed it in to the post orderly.

Soon after three the roaring of the planes set in, then the thunder of the artillery—then the tumult of the front, a great confused din rolling eastwards, a noise which would not stop but keep on through the years. There was still no movement in the divisional area. For them at least, the "wood for hutted camps" lay where it was for two days and nights. The order for the attack had been withdrawn; instead came an order two days later to move to Duenaburg, over ground which had already been flattened by an armoured division and SS regiments.

On the morning of the third day the tents were struck in the woodland camp. The twigs crackled underfoot. The troops embussed. The branches began to move, paths opened up on all sides and everywhere loaded troop-carriers appeared. The trucks lurched along a forest path and took up station. An unending line rolled over a pontoon bridge across the smooth-flowing water of the Memel, and so it went on through the watermeadows of an evacuated zone six miles deep, with the white mists of night still lying on the grass. The sun glinted on the polished parts of the trucks; little swastika flags flew brightly on the radiators. A loudspeaker gave the Wehrmacht communique. They were advancing, all along the eastern front things were going according to plan. The German forces involved were advancing quickly on their first objectives.

Suddenly the Wehrmacht communique was drowned by the roar of propellers, a long-drawn whistle, the crash of exploding bombs. The column stopped. The men climbed out of their trucks, lay down or scattered over the meadows, which offered no cover. A second attack—more bombs, more earth whirling upwards; hot black smoke drifting along the line of MT. There were calls for stretcher-bearers. Lieutenant Engel of the signals platoon lay under his truck and said: "The flags, damn it, take off the flags."

The swastika recognition flags were taken off the radiators, rolled up and stowed in the vehicles. They turned off the secondary road and on to the main road—not the main road through Kovno, but a branch road leading north through Seta between the lakes round Zarasai and on to Duenaburg. On they went at six miles an hour until there was a halt. On again, and then another halt. So between stopping and starting the first day passed. But they moved by night, too. Next forenoon the long column stopped for what must have been the hundredth time.

"What's up in front there?" they called to a despatch rider as he passed.

"The Old Man's command-vehicle has got stuck," said the DR, opened the throttle and was gone.

Down the road a bomb-crater barred the way. A command-vehicle belonging to the regimental commander, Tomasius, trying to drive round it, had stuck up to the axles in soft ground and was being dug out to be pulled clear on mats. There seemed to be no end to the waiting. The men squatted on the trucks or lay in the grass, sunned themselves and dozed; on either side there was an endless line of tall vehicles reaching to the lowest twigs of the trees.

Suddenly from behind there was shouting which grew louder and louder—firing—movement. The wary ones jumped for cover. A truck roared past with a machine-gun sticking out of the back, which rattled and hammered away. (What was all this about?—they had only stopped for a halt.) Bullets went through radiators, cabs and windscreens, hitting anything that moved behind the windscreens or the sides of the trucks.

"Russians," someone roared.

"Just what I was thinking—there must be Russians hereabouts."

"Shut you mouth."

"But this is Russia, sir, and there must be Russians."

"Stretcher-bearer!" came the cry. A truck was burning. A tongue of fire flared from a petrol-lorry. A yellow cloud of smoke drifted over the trucks. Then word came up from the rear: "Russians—stop them—stop the truck."

Ahead the MG still rattled. Now there was a noise of firing from behind. An automatic dual-purpose gun. Wheels tore past; there was a whirling cloud of dust and the sharp report of a gun. An armoured car tore along the column firing at the truck.

The road curved. The Russians had the armoured car behind and in front the crater and a clump of MT. There was no way round and no way out. For two Russian soldiers it seemed their last moment had come.

* * *

Gregory Subkov and Pyotr Ryevsky belonged to the same company. Subkov was sergeant and platoon commander; Ryevsky, lieutenant and company commander. Weeks before they and their men had been given their marching orders — through Vilna and on through Lithuania, for manœuvres. Or so it was said. Equipment had been left behind. There were no mortars, few MGs and those Maxims from the First World War. Every third man had a rifle and as much ammunition as he could carry. There were few horses and so the supply train came forward in bounds. Half the train was dumped at the side of the road and had to wait until the teams came back to bring them forward. So the horses had to cover the journey twice—thrice, if you counted the journeys empty. And what applied to the horses applied also to the Red Army men. The harder life is on manœuvres the easier it is in the field—so Suvarov had said. By day they advanced, by night they retired; thus a move of sixty miles was made up to a hundred and eighty with all the extra marching. So weeks went past and a certain Sunday came. The company was in a prepared position consisting of earthen ramparts thick enough to be splinter-proof. Over there were the German "rest areas"—which was what people called them when the subject of the Germans came up during the manœuvres. It was known that they had gathered an immense army on the western

49

frontier.

The story was that they had been moved into East Prussia, into Volhynia and as far down as the Carpathians —to rest. The political commissar who visited the various companies explained it thus. First of all, he said, there was a treaty of friendship between Germany and the Soviet Union. Secondly, Hitler, even if he wanted to, couldn't make such a sudden switch in policy; besides, he was getting ready to attack England and his troops were too scattered as it was—he had just sent a whole army group to the Balkans. There weren't enough men for anyone to pick a quarrel with the "invincible Red Army"— certainly not in Germany. The commissar, who of course didn't have a direct line to Moscow but had his instructions from the highest authorities through Army, should have known. But, nevertheless, early one morning there were the Germans on the ground and in the air. There was nothing else in the air—not even one ancient plane. And on the ground—well, there was 3 Company on the bare sandy soil of Lithuania with a few rifles in their hands and a few cartridges in their pockets. The last noodles had been given out the evening before because the supply train had had to be left behind. There was no water in the position. At crack of dawn there came a rattling on the nearby road. There was nothing to be seen through the white layer of mist, but when Subkov came back from the street he was waving his hands in a most unmilitary manner and saying: "Fritzes, Fritzes—as thick as sand and in a hurry, they can't get east quick enough."

When the ground mist cleared, Lieutenant Ryevsky could see the road running past a hundred yards away. Trucks and more trucks without end, big buses among them—big as the barges on the Neva. The troop-carriers were both wheeled and tracked; they rushed quickly on. They were in a hurry—it seemed that the men they carried were so intent on their goal that they did not even look at the country on either side of the road. Sometimes a couple of them would climb down from a halted vehicle, take a few steps off the road, let down their trousers and turn their bare backsides to the well-camouflaged Russian positions. A well-aimed shot from a rifle and they fell

50

on their noses or else limped back to the truck without pulling their trousers up again. And so it went on—such little incidents did not hold up the roaring stream on tracks and wheels. At last—the Red Army men had waited a long time for it—there came a distant rumbling from the east drawing nearer under the blue sky. The corps artillery was bringing the road under fire. Subkov counted the salvoes. There were exactly eight of them. Then it was all over—the ammunition was used up.

The only telephone line from the detached company went directly to Division—sometimes it didn't work for a whole day, sometimes for only a few hours, but it always worked in the end. The company waited for the help it had been promised. At night they stole a few boxes of their own ammunition from the dump at the railway station which the Germans had taken. But the patrols could not bring back rations or any first aid material. Sometimes the water-carriers were killed or came back wounded. The men turned their pockets inside out and scraped together the last fragments of black tobacco. And they counted their losses. So many had been killed already that there was now a rifle for each man. On the fourth night, at the very time when the wretched survivors were assembling to march back across country, a captain turned up in the company position and said he was a liaison officer from Division. The Fatherland was in great danger, he told the assembled Red Army men, but in general the position was not serious and the Red Army was advancing everywhere, and had already taken a lot of prisoners and captured a lot of material. Only on this sector of the front had the Germans succeeded in breaking through. Help was at hand and until it came they must hang on and stay where they were.

Stay where they were. The men had shoes with flapping soles on their feet; but that didn't matter. It was equally unimportant that they wore uniforms which had served generations of soldiers before them. The carts of the supply train had been stranded on the road and it was five days since the last meal. And there had been a war on for four days—a war which threatened to swallow them all up, just as it had swallowed up 1 and 2 Companies and all the rest of the battalion. The days were

51

long and hot and there was no water. Earth from a muddy water-hole was strained in a cap and a few drops of liquid filtered out. There was no sign that any sort of HQ was looking after the troops.

While the captain was speaking to them, enemy shells were bursting in the position. In the distance there was the bark of German tank-guns. The rattling of trucks had never ceased on the road near by. Over their heads there hung a flare from a German plane. Two-thirds of the company lay dead, unburied under the open sky. Yet under these circumstances they were supposed to stay where they were—only a traitor could speak like that.

The line they had all thought was dead began to work again and Division asked to speak to the captain. What was Ryevsky to say?—that the LO from Division had been killed? That the Red Army men had cut his throat with a knife? He hesitatingly spoke of an accident but on interrogation had to confess to a crime which neither he nor the platoon commander had been able to prevent. There was a silence at the other end of the wire. Then the order came through that Lieutenant Ryevsky and Sergeant Subkov were to report at once to Division in Seta. The appointment of a substitute was by now an unnecessary formality. The men were swarming over the countryside in search of water, and many of them—half mad with thirst—would never return. Before first light Ryevsky and Subkov crossed the railway line. They took over the dead captain's truck which stood parked in the woods. No one believed them when they said they might collect some rations at Division and perhaps bring back a couple of mortars. For them there was no coming back. How beautiful the earth is curving under the sky of a new day when that day is to be your last.

"What hurry is there, Comrade Lieutenant?"

"Yes, what hurry is there, Gregory Petrovich?"

Ryevsky used Subkov's first name and patronymic—an unusual form of address in the army—just as if Subkov were no longer a sergeant of the Red Army but had become a closer acquaintance, perhaps foreman in the textile factory in the little town of Plyess on the Volga.

"We can stop under the trees and fill our caps with berries," said Subkov.

Later they sat together on the soft moss with the berries between them. The noise of the road, and even their hunger and thirst, lay behind them. From the trees a stillness descended. From the depths of the woods there came the mating cry of a bird. It would be like that next day, too; it would go on being like that. Wooing and nest-building—there would still be a girl called Natalya Ivanovna in Leningrad and one called Maria Antonovna in Plyess when all trace was gone of Pyotr Ryevsky and Gregory Subkov.

"Plyess—a nice little town with woods all round it. The people come from Moscow to take the air. There's a convalescent home called after Chaliapin, and then there's the textile factory."

Subkov is talking nonsense, of course—what interest can he have in a convalescent home where other people are still lying in chaise-longues in the sun, and what interest can he have in the factory? He has said good-bye to Maria and Lydia and Galyna who is only three.

The stillness in the wood was almost unbearable.

"We had better drive on, Pyotr Nikonorevitch."

Drive on and get it over quicker.

In silence they watched the play of the twigs which hung down into the roadway and were disturbed by the truck as it passed. A couple of times they came out into open country and drove along between fields of rye. Then suddenly—they had been too quick about it—they were on the road to Seta. It was only when they had been driving for a while that they noticed trucks in front and behind. They had got into a gap in a convoy.

Green uniforms—Germans! There were no two ways about it.

Subkov slowed down. How long could they go on like this? Something must happen. "They drive well—they leave the left hand side of the road clear—you could drive past," said Ryevsky. You could, but you wouldn't get to the far end of the column. Or maybe that was the way to make a decent end of things. Yes, of course, fight and die as others have done before. And on the road here would be a better way than in a courtyard in Seta against a stable wall.

"Gregory Petrovitch."

Subkov came out of his reverie—he had just thought of the stable wall and of the white church in Plyess in the spring, and how on a still day it is mirrored in the Volga with its domed towers.

"Yes, what is it, Pyotr Nikonorevitch?"

"I'll get into the back and mount the MG. There's nothing else to say—oh yes, there is, damn it—Grisha!"

Pyotr Ryevsky had a bright face with big blue eyes. He jumped into the back. Subkov still felt the kiss on his cheek. He took a tighter hold of the steering wheel. To hell then—poor Maria left by herself, and Lydia and Galyna. And this had to happen during manœuvres. May, June, July, he had reckoned, and in August when the water-melons ripened he would have been back home. You shouldn't make plans; they never come out the way you want.

Things never work out the way you want—so Ryevsky thought, too. The money had never stretched far enough for the lovely things behind the shining windows of the great food-store on the Nevsky-Prospekt—neither his own nor Natalya's, nor both together.

So two Russian soldiers began their war against a German division. Strange faces, green uniforms, shouting, confusion. The old, tired Maxim rattled away—if only it didn't jam for once. But suddenly the end came. A clump of vehicles, motor-cycles, huge trucks, one beside the other. No way out any more. Subkov took his hands from the wheel—the devil himself took it and slewed it against a tree. The truck tore on for a bit, stuck fast and hung there with its bonnet and cab protruding from a clump of bushes. Far below there was the gleam of high grass which turned to clear, clear water; then Subkov saw no more.

* * *

From all sides the German soldiers came running. The Russian driver sat in a great cloud of smoke. The machine-gunner jumped over the tailboard, broke away and fell, cut in two by a burst of machine-gun fire.

When Lieutenant Engel reached the smoking truck the dead man's pockets were being gone through for documents. A Russian lieutenant with a young face. In the cab a soldier wrapped in a cloud of smoke.

"Get back from it—it might tip over."

"Give him another burst."

"He's dead—keep your ammo for the living."

The machine-pistol sank again.

"They're absolutely mad—how can people sacrifice themselves like that?"

"That isn't how you fight a war and it isn't even brave."

"What is it, then?"

"That's what I'd like to know."

So the talk went to and fro over the dead man as he lay peacefully in the grass.

"Somebody should shut his eyes."

A signaller bent over the dead lieutenant and closed his eyes but thought it best to add: "So that he can't grin at us like that."

"Have you had another look at the truck, sir?"

"Of course, our Opels are a different job—but I thought they only had a Ford licence and here they are building their own cars."

No, it wasn't a Ford or a Citroen or a Peugeot, like many of the cars in the convoy. This Russian truck didn't look much but it was a serviceable job—you had to admit it. "Nice and high off the ground—just right for these roads."

"Look at this hell of a great air filter—the Peugeots and Renaults don't have any. And the springs—they've at least got decent springs." The convoy had already had its first broken springs and axles.

Engel and a lieutenant from the artillery signals troop walked up and down together. So the Russians built cars —you had to have seen it yourself to believe it.

"Well, there can't be many of them—and in any case they'll have a revolution here in three weeks at the latest."

The convoy crept on again at a snail's pace. The wheels churned on the soft patches. The staff car of the signals company went up and down like a boat in a rough sea. Amid all the dust and noise, the tossing and bumping of the trucks, the spluttering of the motor-cycles with their throttles half-shut, the signallers tried to sing:

"How will we go to heaven?
Captain, tell us that. . ."

One of Engel's signallers was the first to spot the planes

and the first to jump over the tailboard and get down beside the truck. Dangling from his parachute, a shot-down pilot drifted across the road and landed in the meadow. Several motor-cyclists raced across, left their bicycles and ran across the grass. When they were half-way there and saw that the Russian wasn't simply going to let himself be taken but had jumped behind a tree and opened fire with a machine-pistol, one of them—it was the signal company's DR—turned back.

"You won't get an Iron Cross for that," someone scoffed.

"I'm not that daft to take on a private war with one Russian," said the DR; but he had to take his lieutenant on his pillion all the same and drive back towards the tree, where a real gun-fight was going on.

"These Russians, sir, you never know what they're going to do . . . and the motor-cyclists will manage quite well."

"Drive closer," said the lieutenant. And the DR, having left his cycle at the side of the road, had to follow his officer. But they did not reach the tree until the firing had stopped. The wounded motor-cyclists came stumbling towards them and on the grass lay the Russian pilot. A ricochet from the tree had torn away half his face. He had sprayed them all pretty effectively with his machine-pistol but it was mostly a case of slight wounds, except for one man who lay dying on the grass.

The endless column crept on.

There was another halt, then it moved on again—more Russian planes, more shouts of "Stretcher-bearer", more hours standing still and mounting again and moving on at a walking pace. A caterpillar on wheels and tracks creeping into the villages and emerging again at the other end, distended here and there with ration lorries and petrol lorries and hundreds of men spread out over the fields, stretching from horizon to horizon, leaving on either side dust and churned-up earth like a brown smear—so the column travelled from the Memel to the Dubisa and on over the meadows, through marshes and woods, with an armoured advance guard rolling ahead and driving before it a mass of peasant carts and a crowd of people. After two days of it the main body of 3 Motorised

Infantry Division drove through Seta.

This place they called Seta had been a little town up to two days before—until the Stuka attack. Now it was only rubble and dust trickling among the ruins; not a fence, not a tree standing. Among the ruins of a stone building, where the HQ of a Russian division had been, a poster was stuck on the door (one wondered where all these posters had come from amidst all the confusion) showing a German soldier having his teeth knocked out by a Russian. Another poster had an inscription in Cyrillic characters: "You cannot die two deaths—one is not too many for the Fatherland."

The soldiers still sang, then suddenly the song broke off in the middle. Lieutenant Engel let his camera sink in his hand.

For at that moment a cry seemed to rise from the earth itself—an unending lament. Bare-headed men and women with kerchiefs over their bowed heads carried open coffins of undressed pine-boards which rocked like boats on a sluggish stream; the lids were borne by those behind. There were flowers and a scent of death; wax-white hands folded on breasts; collar and tie under the sharp unshaven chin of a dead man; a young woman with straw-coloured hair; the pretty face of a girl under white paper frills. Dead men's faces with blue lips and eyelids. From under the wavering load came the sound of sobbing. No one in the procession had a glance for the soldiers of the motorised division as it rattled past.

The procession came past the regimental commander's staff car. Colonel Tomasius took a handkerchief from his pocket and wiped his face. He caught his liaison officer's eye.

"Extraordinary," said the LO.

"Yes, an extraordinary land."

"If only we got somewhere and the men saw some action—we can't go on like this."

"What do you mean, Hanke?"

"I mean, sir, there's no resistance, no fighting in the open—but there's shooting going on all the time, in front, in the rear, half-way down the column. And it's not only bomber-attacks—the division has to keep fighting a continual war against the odd couple of mad Russians.

57

And when one lot has been dealt with there comes another handful of them. And that can't go on, sir."

"No, of course it can't."

"The men see nothing but executions—because that's what it comes to when they shoot down one of these maniacs. And a funeral procession like this—with girls looking like Snowhite under white folds of paper—they don't do anything to help morale. The inhabitants should be forbidden to parade their dead like that and carry them about in open coffins."

"I do recommend that the customs of the inhabitants should be interfered with as little as possible."

"Yes, sir, but then it all adds up—there are the Fuehrer's special orders which are carried out in front of everyone."

"I have already told you what I think of them. This order about the commissars is typical of Himmler. I can't understand how Brauchitsch let it go through. In my regiment as least the order will not be obeyed. Forward of regimental HQ! I'm not having any of that. Prisoners will be escorted back to Division—including commissars."

"But according to the order on commissars the regiment should do more than that."

A vein swelled on the Colonel's brow.

"Up to now we have kept our hands clean and I don't want it to be otherwise. And I will not have any eighteen-year-old lieutenant passing sentence of death on civilians old enough to be his father, either. The divisional commander has the final word and all difficult cases will be sent up to him. You understand me, Hanke, we cannot give youngsters the last word on life and death or—just because they are local commanders—have them making decisions which affect whole villages for good or ill."

Hanke understood perfectly well, but he did not see how it could be done. Meantime he was perfectly happy with what his commanding officer had said—he could push all the unpleasantnesses on to Division. There the IO would have to deal with them—perhaps not an eighteen-year-old second lieutenant but a full lieutenant of twenty-eight.

* * *

The charred ruins and ashes of Seta were left behind

by the clattering tracks and churning wheels of the column. On it went to the main road to Duenaburg; on either side of the road and deep in woods lay the lakes of Zarasai.

Days of bright sunshine on the meadows and the leafy sea of the woods, which stretched out hour after hour. Ghostly white nights, which allowed no sleep and no rest to the nerves.

The division marched on.

Ahead the advance guard, then the mainguard, the first and second regimental groups, the artillery, the sappers, the field ambulances, the regimental staffs, the divisional staff with the leading regiment. Then followed the second echelon with long convoys carrying petrol, ammunition, rations, spare-parts and clothing. Lastly, the field hospital with ambulances and trucks and more trucks.

The forward elements were in sight of Zarasai. In front was meadowland stretching to the banks of a lake. Clear, blue water with whitewashed houses beyond. When the road curved and came out of the wood into open country, the leading trucks of the second regimental group —and with it Lieutenant Engel and his signal platoon— could see the meadow and the lake and a bit of the little town. Nothing moved—not even the reflection of the church with the slim tower or the white houses; there was not a breath to stir this midday hour.

There was a hold-up ahead.

The trucks closed up and stopped, one after another. The men jumped down and took a few steps into the grass. The signals platoon sat near their truck. One of them shuffled a pack of cards.

Lieutenant Engel was sitting in a staff car, just beginning a letter when a DR brought an order from Regiment. Engel stuck the letter in his pocket and turned to the card-players on the grass.

"Get ready for action."

He pulled out of the column and drove down the long convoy. It was not so easy—some of the trucks he had to drive slowly round, and at last he stuck fast in a hopeless tangle. On either side of the road stood lorries and motor-cycles—a whole petrol company. Soldiers lay about in the fields in hundreds. There was nothing for it—Engel left his car and tried to make his way forward on foot. The trucks belonged to the 2nd Echelon of the advancing 8 Armoured Division. He went on past groups of soldiers, past quarrelling convoy-leaders till at last he saw Colonel Tomasius's command vehicle with a built-in map table, a desk and a card-index, with telephones and a leather-sofa which took up all one side. And since the tall broad-shouldered man, Colonel Tomasius, was known to the whole regiment as "Uncle Tom", it had been an obvious step to christen his monster vehicle "Uncle Tom's Cabin".

When Engel entered he saw the colonel and his staff captain, Hanke. The divisional commander was there, too, and a lieutenant, von Breitenfeld by name, from the recce squadron.

"Beg to report, sir—thank you, sir—thank you, sir," was all that Engel heard from the lieutenant—phrases which came out one after another on top of short remarks by the colonel or the General. Each time the graceful figure of Lieutenant von Breitenfeld stiffened and his hand went to his cap.

Tomasius took a long pull at his cigar, blew out a thick cloud of smoke and let his big blue eyes—everything about him was big, eyes, nose, mouth, hands and feet as well—rest reflectively on the lieutenant. Engel could see clearly that there was something in the air. It wasn't only the presence of the colonel and the General which had brought a scarlet flush to the face of the nineteen-year-old lieutenant and left him quite out of breath. Lieutenant von Breitenfeld had pushed ahead with his armoured car and had come under fire from the wood.

"I saw quite clearly, sir," once again a slight bow and the hand flashed up to his cap. "Yes, sir, I saw shell-bursts."

"Tell us again—in some sort of sequence."

"Beg to report, sir. I came under rifle and machine-gun fire. I also came under fire from light anti-tank guns."

"I see—light anti-tank guns."

"Yes, sir, I came under fire from all sides."

"Slowly, young man. Here, have a cigarette first," said Tomasius.

"Thank you, sir."

"Now, show us on the map where you got to. And where are the points from which you came under fire?"

"Here—and here—and here. I came under fire from all sides, sir."

"But you don't mean to say," said the General, turning to the lieutenant, "that you were under fire from all calibres for three miles and got back here without any damage to your car."

Tomasius interrupted good-naturedly: "I expect he was stepping on the gas a bit. Isn't that so, Breitenfeld?"

"Yes, sir, I was stepping on it quite a bit."

"Well, what do you say—how strong is the enemy, what are his intentions—what are the Russians up to?"

"I think, sir. . ."

Von Breitenfeld broke off—general, colonel, captain and lieutenant, they all listened to something outside. The roar of a propeller passed overhead. Tomasius glanced out of the window and up at the sky, then looked at the great mass of blocked vehicles. There was one solitary Russian plane to be seen; it disappeared over the horizon.

"Let's hope for the best and that he doesn't bring his mates."

"Come on, then, Breitenfeld, what do you think?"

"I beg to report, sir, there were masses of troops in the wood—I saw them taking up new positions across the road. I take it they are planning an attack on the road to take us in the flank, sir."

The General stood behind the map table.

"It still isn't a very clear situation—I suppose we will have to put in enough troops to clear things up?" It was a question directed at the colonel.

"Well, sir," said Tomasius, "maybe it's another of these mad attacks."

"Well, I'll go over to the HQ. I shall put in the forward regiment." The General paused and looked at Tomasius but the latter kept his eye on his cigar and said nothing.

"Well, what do you suggest—what artillery will you use, Tomasius?"

"I think the two light batteries should be enough, sir. The battery forward with the regiment can take up firing positions right away; I'll bring up the other one. I think we can do without the heavy battery for the moment."

"All right—one infantry regiment and two batteries. Deny the road over-night and clean up in the morning," said the General putting his hand to his cap as he left the command vehicle.

The colonel turned to Engel.

"All right, Engel, get ready for action. Let me have a line to Ops right away."

Tomasius had not got far with his orders when the door was torn open and someone shouted in: "Enemy aircraft."

"Out with you—take cover."

Without touching his cigar, Tomasius moved it into the opposite corner of his mouth and climbed out of the vehicle—he was the last to leave. He took a couple of steps with his somewhat clumsy gait and saw that there was nowhere to go because there was no cover.

"Air attack." The shout echoed over the fields. The air was already full of the roar of propellers; at least one squadron came tearing down.

"It's incredible the number of trucks there are standing about—it simply attracts the planes." Tomasius stood beside his staff car; then he climbed in. He wanted to see what went on—both hands on the windscreen, wearing an old leather coat with a big braid cap which shaded his eyes, he stood there for everyone to see amidst the confusion. The bombers still came in—machine-guns firing furiously, bombs screaming down, causing a continual roar of explosions. In the clump of vehicles farther down the column every bomb found its mark. In the air there were bits of trucks, water-tanks and petrol tins.

"Sir, there is a little hollow ten yards to the left—may I suggest, sir, that you take cover?" Tomasius made a gesture in the negative, so Lieutenant von Breitenfeld had to make it a point of honour to stand bolt upright beside the car. It was an incredible scene; he saw bomb-bursts, fountains of sand rising into the air, a great clump of earth with wheat growing on it whizzing past. The troops had completely lost their heads; instead of taking cover in a ditch or getting down on the ground, they ran out into the open—drivers, tank crews, men from the supply columns, infantrymen, all mixed up together.

"Why don't you start firing—even with your rifles.

Don't let a couple of fighters put the wind up you," roared the colonel. No one heard him in the confusion.

"Sir, may I suggest," said von Breitenfeld again. His words were cut short as a terrible detonation shook the air and a tongue of flame shot up. A black mushroom of smoke darkened the sky and threw off balls of smoke. Men rushed across the fields; some were burning brightly; others rolled on the ground trying to smother the flames with blankets or whatever came to hand. The petrol column of 8 Armoured Division—all but a few vehicles —had gone up in smoke. The destruction was immense. Everywhere there were calls for stretcher-bearers. Another plane screeched past; then the air was still again.

When Hanke got up off the ground he saw his commanding officer standing under the drifting clouds of smoke—his hands still on the rim of the windscreen and the stub of his cigar in the corner of his mouth. Beside the car stood von Breitenfeld with his head inclined forward a little and his hand to his cap.

Hanke hurried over.

"Hanke, get over and sort out this mess. The battery with the forward group to take up position right of the road and the other battery to move up. Everything else must get off the road and into the woods. That applies to our own troops and the armoured division's echelon. So get on with it, Hanke."

The burnt-out trucks were left where they were. The rest moved off. In the fields and on the road, as far as one could see, there were trucks everywhere backing and turning, with wheels and radiators dipping down into the ditches and climbing up the other side again. Twigs cracked, saplings—and here and there even grown trees— were shorn off. Hundreds of trucks pushed their way in under the thick roof of leaves, worked twenty or thirty yards forward and halted. The crews settled down for the night. But the leading regimental group moved forward, ready for action. For a while they went on along the road and then turned off into the positions they were to take up, and the men began to dig in. There followed tractor-drawn 100-mm howitzers and machine-gun platoons; they, too, moved along the road for a bit and then turned off to their positions, their OPs and their command posts. More than half the division was deployed. An hour later the countryside lay quiet. From the lake the croaking of the frogs came through the pale dusk of the night.

Between seven and eight thousand men lay and waited for the day. At three in the morning they advanced to the attack. They were to occupy a wood which lay surrounded by marsh and commanding the road to Zarasai. Colonel Tomasius, who took the whole thing very lightly, lay on the black leather sofa in his command vehicle. When, shortly after three, troops of 100-mm howitzers began to fire, he opened his eyes. After a time he turned to his staff captain, who sat in the light of a half-shaded lamp at the map-table.

"Well, Hanke, anything special?"

"No, sir, the infantry is combing the place out. Absolutely no resistance, or none to speak of."

"All right, when something happens, please wake me."

Tomasius turned to the wall and fell into a deep, sound sleep. Neither the crack of a rifle nor a burst of machine-gun fire disturbed him; his snores could be heard not only in the farthest corner of the command vehicle but outside in Lieutenant Engel's staff car as well.

About six o'clock the telephone buzzed again. This time it was the General wanting the colonel.

"Sir. . ."

"What is it, Hanke?"

"The General is on the line."

Tomasius sat up and took the receiver. A big, thick-set East Prussian, his jacket buttoned-up, his heavy cheeks red with sleep. "Yes, sir, very well, sir. . ."

"There you are, Tom, I told you so. They got five men in the wood. The IO has just interrogated them. According to them there were about eighty of them— the remains of a Russian battalion."

"Eighty!"

"That's right, eighty—and they literally threw the whole division into confusion. Half the division deployed, slit trenches dug, artillery in action."

"It's a silly kind of war," yawned Tomasius. It had been the General's idea in any case, and if *he* hadn't put the brake on things they would have had the heavy

64

artillery in action, too.

"You can't get any sort of picture, Tom. It's absolutely impossible. It looked as if a large formation was going to make a flank attack. Well, there were eighty men, and now they tell me that one prisoner said that only thirty of them were fit to fight at all; the rest hadn't even got rifles."

"Only thirty of them, then?"

"Yes, against all rules and regulations."

"We still lost a whole day through it, sir."

"That's right—it makes you tear your hair."

And that was Uncle Tom's conclusion, too. When the phone-call was over and he had climbed into his ortho-paedic boots (they had a zip-fastener at the sides so that they opened all the way down, and he didn't pull them on but literally climbed into them), he was ready to go out and ginger things up so that his regiment would be ready to move at the earliest possible moment. But it was some time before the convoys rolled on again. They went through Zarasai and on through woods and past little lakes, which turned dark under the clouds of dust from the marching division.

Two more days went by before the churches of Duenaburg came in sight through the muzzle-flashes and smoke as 8 Armoured Division and the SS Death's Head Division went in to the assault. 3 Motorised Infantry Division was also deployed and one of its regiments was put in.

But an hour earlier a short conversation had taken place in Tomasius's command vehicle between the colonel and Hanke. Hanke had come back from Division where he had been given a picture of the division's losses up to date. Summing up, he had said to his commanding officer:

"We haven't been in action yet and we have more losses than in France already."

"That isn't the most worrying thing," Tomasius had answered, and added: "We have taken a week for a move that should have taken two or three days. We have lost valuable time."

PART II

"Not a single locomotive, not a single truck, not a kilo of wheat, not a litre of fuel must be left for the enemy. The collective farm peasants must drive away all the livestock. Partisan units, both mounted and on foot, must be formed to blow up bridges and roads, to destroy telephone and telegraphic communications, to burn down woods. . ."

J. V. Stalin, 3 July 1941.

It will be no easy task for future historians to reconstruct and analyse what in those days was described to the world as the "Double Battle of Bialystock and Minsk". The reason is that only on one side can the lines of manœuvre be traced; on the other, the Russian side, the campaign was characterised by inability to deal with the onrush of events and confusion spreading right up to army headquarters. The commanders of the Russian armies in the west found themselves faced with tasks for which the means at their disposal were completely inadequate; neither offensive nor defensive operations progressed much further than the planning stage. The net result was the continuous movement of defeated and fleeing troops—a movement which ran from west to east and was everywhere expressed in the same words: "Go home, go east into Russia."

* * *

Three Russian armies and four armoured corps (one fully equipped and three forming) plus special technical troops, and the military formations of the NKVD— altogether about 800,000 men were deployed in a piece of territory 200 miles long by 250 to 300 miles deep. That is to say, in the area bounded on the west by Grodno, Bialystock and Brest-Litovsk, and in the east by the White-Russian town of Minsk.

The staffs of these numerically superior army groups found themselves facing unexpectedly strong offensive forces; their formations were split up by quickly advancing armoured spearheads and in part overrun; the whole area was surrounded by a great pincer movement, by a steel net, but one so thin that it was broken even by the planless eastern movement of disorganised bodies of troops, and would scarcely have offered any real resistance to an organised Russian retreat.

In fact, however, only 100,000 of the 800,000 men escaped through the wide meshes of the net. In addition troops from the Moscow military district, from the Upper Volga, from the Urals and even from the Far East, who,

in the first days of the war—and many even earlier—
had been detrained at Vitebsk, at Lepel, at Polotsk, on
the Dvina and the Duena, and had begun to move west,
were all engulfed. The Beresina and the western Dvina
were the riverlines across which the defeated troops sought
safety—but only one in ten reached it. Their weapons
were left in the west.

Amongst those who stayed behind were the Communist
youth, who, even before the war, had been grouped in
their units as activists, and were now held together by a
fanatical faith which stopped short of no sacrifice—they
and political commissars whom a pitiless order of the
Fuehrer's barred from captivity, and for whom there was
no other choice than to fight to the last with hastily
formed bodies of troops. There stayed behind soldiers
who asked "Why fight when our industry, which only
produced for defence and gave it such priority that for
thirty years it couldn't let the people have a cooking
spoon or shoes or clothing, leaves us without a weapon
when it comes to the point? Why fight, and against
whom?" There stayed behind NKVD incendiary squads
and collective farmers who stood in a daze beside their
burning huts, watching their cattle being driven away
in a cloud of dust and last year's grain harvest, which
they had delivered to the state granaries, burning in the
distance. There stayed behind defeated, hunted, fleeing
people; there remained the double pocket of Bialystock
and Minsk. Yet it was not a pocket, nor even a double
pocket, but five or six great concentrations of encircled
troops, which moved from place to place, merged with
each other, were split again and disintegrated completely
like bubbles in porridge. One hundred and twenty
thousand square miles of earth were transformed into
a fiery furnace.

There stayed behind Colonel Semyonov, Chief of
Operations on an army staff. There stayed behind Alexey
Narishkin, the commander of the same army. There stayed
behind Captain Kasanzev, Captain Uralov and Nina
Mihailovna, Uralov's wife; there stayed behind Morosov,
who commanded a tank regiment, and Sergeant Subkov
who was dragging himself away from the crashed truck
on the Seta road on his burnt feet.

At the moment of which we are speaking, Colonel Semyonov was standing at the window of his house in Bialystock and looking down the street; it was completely transformed. Morosov, the tank commander, was running to the orders group in the tent at divisional headquarters. Captain Uralov was collecting his battalion in its camp in the woods. And Subkov—yes, Subkov still had everything before him.

Subkov still had everything before him—the first clatter of the Fritzes hurrying along the road, the crumbling of the positions in the Lithuanian dunes, the drive through the wood in the early morning, the meeting with 3 Motorised Infantry Division, the crash into the tree and the ensuing uproar of which he was barely conscious; then the awakening in silence so complete that he thought he heard the wing-beat of an owl.

Naturally he could not hear the owl's gliding flight, but he could see it. The owl had put on its summer plumage and adapted itself to the clear northern nights; its fleeting image was caught in the retina of his eyes, which had been open all the time and presumably had registered other passing objects, although these had remained outside his consciousness. From that moment he saw again and felt the stillness which lay over the land.

"Akh, batyushka, an owl."

He said 'batyushka', little father, but that was only a manner of speaking—he had the habit of carrying on solitary conversations with his grandfather in the village, for it was the latter who had taught him to understand not only the flight of an owl but the form and movement of a cloud, and had spoken about things which were better left unsaid, and which Subkov's father had kept behind tightly pursed lips. Yet in the end such caution hadn't helped him.

The owl skimmed low over the ground. A clump of grass with ripe, swelling ears bent down, for it was more than time for the reaper; a figure advanced over the meadow from the edge of the wood, but it was only white vapour. Once before, with the same immediacy and the same amazement, little Gregory Subkov had become aware of the faces and objects which surrounded him—when he still lay in a bast cradle hanging from the roof of a village

71

hut. Grandfather, an owl and grass in the meadow.

He had to tear himself from the place where he lay, and that was not so easy. His feet had suffered from the fire which had broken out under the bonnet. With an effort he managed to get on to the back of the truck, and as he climbed down and let himself slide to the ground everything that had happened flashed through his mind. Lieutenant Ryevsky looked the same as he had when he was alive—under the veil of mist his face looked even more delicate. There was nothing he could do— he must not stay and bury him. The rattle of tracks on the road broke the brief stillness of the night and warned him to be on his guard. But he did something inexplicable, he made the sign of the cross over the dead man. Grandfather would have done it, too—it could do no harm. Another glance at the comrade he was leaving behind and he slipped over the road like a shadow and dived into the standing rye.

Where was he to go now? To Seta?—no, not to Seta. They say you can die only once—the proverbs with their store of simple wisdom were another thing he had from his grandfather—and he had already died, here on the road. There was no need any more for the swift, summary sentence of the divisional court martial. So if not to Seta, then in the opposite direction—out of the divisional area, the corps area, to the south into the swamps and woods. Up to now it had been a case of luck—perhaps everything in the past had been luck, too. Meantime there would be berries in the woods and mushrooms, and perhaps a lot of other things in his path. Human beings he tried to avoid, and only when he had left Lithuania behind him did he go into a village here and there. When he did, he spoke only to the old people.

"Aye, there are going to be great changes," he heard them say more than once in these days. Such talk was quite common, and there were people who made no secret of what they meant by changes. "That stupid Georgian has fooled us long enough," one man said, "but now it's all up with him and we won't have to take our caps off in front of his picture any more."

One day Subkov was lying in the reeds, watching a pair of herons. As they wandered past calmly and idly, almost under his nose, he brought one down with a shot. He had cleaned it and wrapped it in clay and was just roasting it over an open fire, when he turned and saw a figure amongst the trees. He recovered his calm at once, for there was nothing to fear from this man, standing there motionless in bast shoes, with a long white beard and thin, dangling hands. So he signalled to him to come nearer, which the old man willingly did.

Vassily Nikonorevitch Shulga might have been ninety or over—yet he was much younger than that.

"I'm sixty and a bit more," he said, and added, "I'm quite alone. If my sons are still living I don't know what has become of them, and if they *are* still on this earth they know nothing about me. I have lost my nearest, my family and my home—it was God's will. And how is it with you, my son; where are your men, the other soldiers?" he asked.

Subkov could only raise his hand and point vaguely: over the reeds and the river and the open land beyond to a high cloud of dust which had been standing for hours in the sky.

"They're over there somewhere," he said.

"No—that's the others." Shulga knew all about it.

"And ours, too—they are in the fields either side of the road."

The cloud of dust was indeed due to one of the endless German convoys; beneath the long, moving cloud lay the road leading from Vilna to Minsk. Shulga had been there and had watched the passing vehicles from a ryefield. Dazed by the roaring and the dust and a wild hope he had returned to the marshes.

"If they could use me I would do anything for them. But they don't need my weak efforts. All I can do is to pray to God to give them wings to get to Moscow more quickly."

"As far as the wings go, they have them already. Where I was we saw nothing but German planes—ours weren't to be seen. But listen, little uncle, isn't this *our* land they are driving over—behaving as if they were at home, in their own country?"

"Our land!" said Shulga in amazement. "It once was our land. Until the Reds came into the village we lived

73

in peace and there was enough land for all."

Subkov looked more closely at the old man but it was not really necessary—you could see at first glance that he was a "has been", that he belonged to a class that no longer existed. Probably he had done his stretch in the Far North and was now wandering about like this. What was there left for such a man—no collective farm, no factory would employ him, not even for the most unskilled labour. A lot of them went back to settle near their old prison camps—the only place where they could stay undisturbed.

But there was the heron and it was time to think of the food and of breaking off the clay crust. For the meal Shulga proposed another spot standing a little higher, where there was water as well—not marsh water but running water from a spring. So they set off; but first they trod out the fire. The new place was everything Subkov could wish for, and he at once began to separate the black gleaming clay from the roasted flesh. But Shulga would not eat until he had thanked God for the meal. Well, this wasn't a junior officers' mess in the Red Army, and grandfather in the village had had the same ideas about prayers and no one had objected. The blessing hadn't done the heron any harm, they discovered, for it tasted like chicken.

"Do you come from these parts, little uncle?" said Subkov, resuming the conversation.

"No, I had a married daughter hereabouts. I wonder where you are now, Lena — and your husband Ponomarenko? He had a windmill not far from here. I wonder where he disappeared to. You see, the Ponomarenkos are a family from our village. It is in the Kursk governmental district."

There you were—so he was a "has been", still clinging to the old administrative terms. "You mean in the Kursk *rayon*," Subkov could not refrain from correcting him. The old man gave him a friendly glance from his big blue eyes.

"That's right—in the Kursk governmental district," he repeated, "a big town surrounded by wooded steppe and fields of rich black earth. There were two churches and a school with three classes, six shops and three windmills."

Shulga was glad to be able for once to speak freely and gave an exact account of everything—the number of farms, the way the houses were built: "They were of wood and the roofs were thatched with straw, but quite often they had tiles, and then each farmer had his own garden, and where the fields began there were oaks and limes and yew-trees, hundreds of years old. We were proud of these old trees, and our gardens were famous throughout the countryside. And our beasts were well-kept. Each of us had two or three draught-horses, two or three cattle—not counting milch-cows—and up to fifty sheep. We slaughtered twice a year and every house had two or three fat pigs."

So this village, to hear him speak, had been a sort of paradise; but Subkov knew better. "The workers on the farms had to work fourteen hours a day for the landlords and got fifty kopecks for it," he interposed, "and everyone knows that the workers were terribly kept down and earned twenty-five to thirty roubles a month—today their pay has gone up to three hundred and fifty roubles."

"So you say—but are you sure?"

"I know. I read it in my schoolbook."

Evening had come on; fireflies rose from the meadow and flew about like little fiery particles. Shulga and Subkov had eaten; they had water close by in the basin of a little spring. From the spot where they lay they could look out over the open country on which a last gleam of daylight still lingered. On the southern horizon a great fire glowed. A town was in flames—or perhaps it was a village nearer at hand. But in any case there were many who saw in the flames not the consuming fire of defeat but fiery portals leading to a new life.

"Our Russian tongue will be consecrated again, so that you will be able to take up a book and know that the words are there in the service of truth."

Shulga spoke like grandfather in the village. And Subkov was not so simple as to take everything he saw in print for gospel, or not to know that the *Short History of the CPSU (b)* was too short for it to contain the whole truth. Maybe workers in England and Germany were exploited by the factory-owners, maybe they did have wretched lives and bad pay and have to live in damp

75

cellars and die of consumption—you could well believe it—but that didn't alter the fact that in the Soviet Union you couldn't get shoes, and, if you really had to have them, that you could only get them on the black market and for more money than a worker could ever scrape together. But what was the use of speaking about it when talk changed nothing, and careless talk could only make matters worse?

"My own father," said Subkov, "was always a good worker and a loyal Soviet citizen and always held his tongue. But once, when mother served us thin cabbage soup again, he got angry and made such a row that it could be heard out in the street and there was nothing for it—he had to pay for what he said. They sent for him a couple of times and then he didn't come back. You see it is the same everywhere—not only in your village."

"You must understand the villages to understand Russia," Shulga said. "After the Revolution things had got a bit more settled. Of course there were rumours, but no one took them seriously, although some things should have made people think. The village communities were divided into three groups—kulaks, medium peasants and poor peasants. Tradesmen, millers and all the well-off peasants were included among the kulaks, and they had to deliver more produce to the State. Once they had delivered it, they were asked for more, and so it went on until they couldn't deliver what was demanded. Then came the moment when their plant and machinery and even their houses were confiscated. They themselves were arrested and transported far away.

"The rest of their family were arrested with them, or a little later. If it was not at once, they had a chance to escape from the village and thus perhaps avoid the fate of the head of the house, but I can't remember a single case where they succeeded. We all thought then that these were just local excesses, that only the people in power locally were to blame, and that the regime didn't know about them. We were so simple-minded about the deliveries we couldn't meet that we used to buy produce or borrow it from neighbours to try and make up the right amounts, until at last we had nothing left—no money, no

76

belongings, no corn; and the others, who had helped us, had nothing either to meet the demands of the State. Yes, it was a situation you couldn't escape from, and it was a long time until I really understood that hunger and poverty were the basis of this accursed regime.

"It was a black day in our village when the first twenty families were arrested and rounded up—I call it a black day because first of all it was possible for it to happen in front of the whole village, and yet the others held their tongues and let it happen. No one suspected that these unfortunate families were only the beginning of a general landslide. No one understood what was really happening. My neighbour, and a lot of people who thought like him, said: 'With four cows I'm not a kulak and so I have nothing to fear and nothing to hide.' So they thought, and the others thought the same, and when the day came that they did understand what was happening to the whole village it was too late for them and for us all.

"One misfortune followed on another—we were driven haphazard to the end of the village to be deported or, if they wanted it that way, driven into the mass meetings to raise our hands and vote for some new measure, or else join the collective farm, which nobody was interested in. Apart from one or two who had nothing to lose, hardly anyone put down his name for it. Then new waves of oppression began. One day this man was arrested, the next day someone else—so in a little while about three hundred peasant farms were destroyed. The only crime of all the people arrested was that they didn't want to join the *kolkhoz* and made no secret of their dislike of it. And it wasn't only the peasants themselves but their families, too, who were put into the camps to die in misery.

"Those members of their families who were ᴺleft untouched were driven out of their own homes. They could take nothing with them except what they had on their backs. In summer they could still manage, but in winter the wretched people froze to death on the roads with their children. I've told you about the Ponomarenko family. I had become distantly related to them through my daughter's marriage. Among those who were spared

77

in their family was a young woman—she was called Lena like my daughter—with her little girl. One night it was bitterly cold, bright with stars and very still. When someone tapped at my window I knew at once who was asking to be let in, and all their suffering came to life before my eyes. It was the young mother wrapped in a blanket covered with hoar-frost, with little Lena pressed close to her breast. The little one was just at the stage where she was speaking her first words and her days were full of new discoveries. She never stopped crowing with joy, she was such a happy child by nature. I stood behind the closed window and tears ran down my cheeks. The neighbours wept too, but no one could do anything. If you helped enemies of the people the same disaster fell upon you and so you couldn't even help. I hesitated for a long time. When I couldn't bear it any more, and did at last open the door, I was so beside myself that the poor creature who had been driven from her own home had to comfort me. After that I waited from day to day for my arrest, but my special knowledge of fruit-growing gave me a reprieve. Meantime something like eight hundred peasants had joined the *kolkhoz* with all their beasts and equipment in order to escape from the constant threat of arrest. But nothing could hide the fact that the structure of rural economy had been completely destroyed. To make up for what had been done to the land it would have needed a new measure by the government— a new kind of New Economic Policy, but a proper one this time, which would have given the peasant back his security.

"But that man—I can't find a name for him," old Shulga raised his hand which protruded skinnily from his frayed coat and pointed to the east, "he had pushed on so far that he didn't want to go back a single step along the road to disaster, and he had other ideas. What tremendous presumption that one man, born of woman, should set himself against all Christian men, who are as numerous as the corn in the summer wind on our Russian earth, and make hunger his ally and so reach his goal with the peasants crushed beneath his feet like vermin! People speak of eight million victims, of ten million even. No one counted them, there were so many trodden underfoot—and those who remain are still vermin and cannot rise again although each one has his memories and hopes."

Night had fallen over the wood in which Shulga and Subkov lay encamped. It lay on the fields below them like a silken robe. The glow of the fire on the horizon had shrunk—a great glowing eye remained to mark the spot. But elsewhere the flames shot up and at one point a burst of tracer flickered over the fields. Subkov lay on his back with his head on his knapsack; his eyes looked up the long trunks of the firs to a little space which the topmost twigs left clear, and to the stars which gleam high above our human destinies. In 1933, too, the same stars had looked down, unmoved by Death's great harvest, on the fields and villages. In Plyess a brigade for collecting hidden grain had been formed in the higher classes of the secondary school, but when it reached the villages there was no more talk of collecting grain.

"We ate cats and dogs and the bark of the trees and we swelled with hunger," Shulga went on. "Hunger hardened people against the fates of others, even when it was the fate of their own kith and kin. That was what that monster had brought us to. He wanted men and only managed to make men into animals and worse, for animals help each other. It came to the point where even the fear of death was lost. There were corpses everywhere and no one buried them—there was no energy left for that, and besides, why should you do it when you would die yourself tomorrow? At last the chairman of the Kursk Soviet came to our village—not to feed us as we thought in our suffering—but to pick out those who could still move. They got five hundred grammes of bread and soup twice a day and had to gather the corpses from the huts and the roads and the fields and drag them away. They were buried fifteen, twenty, even thirty together—no proper grave, no cross, nothing to remember them by."

Shulga saw that his neighbour had fallen asleep. A single star hung in the west like a stable-lamp; soon it would be light. He too shut his eyes for a little. When they awoke the land lay below them in a white mist. Beneath its thick blanket they could hear the clatter of tank tracks.

"It sounds as if there were a lot of them," Subkov remarked.

Grey backs emerged on a little rise which was clear of the ground mist. The tanks were like a troop of elephants peacefully grazing.

"Perhaps they are going towards Minsk—or maybe towards Lepel," said Subkov, and added after a while: "I'm going to Minsk."

Shulga said: "I have been thinking it over—it's merely an idea I have but I think I must go to Minsk, too."

* * *

Colonel Semyonov looked down the street. There wasn't a single person to be seen, and at this time of day—it was about four in the morning—that would have been its normal aspect, but at that moment a murderous shrieking noise swooped down, tearing open the sky and lashing the earth. He thought the town ought to rear up under such blows, the streets scream and twist, but they lay peacefully transfixed; as if they did not understand what was happening to them.

He stood at the window in his pyjamas, trying to comprehend the scene. The falling bombs, the sudden explosions, the pillars of fire above the park, the fountains of earth and rubble—these things meant war. A war which neither he nor the Chief of Staff, nor the Army Commander, nor anyone had expected.

Colonel Semyonov threw off his pyjamas, pulled on his underwear and his trousers and seized the telephone. As he tried to get through he felt his wife take his arms, slip on the rest of his things and help him into his jacket. He could not get through so he ran out of the house. He scarcely knew how he got on to the street. He felt that he had forgotten something and should turn back to say something very important to his wife. And he hadn't said goodbye to his grown-up daughter, Irina; hadn't seen her the night before because she had been out.

The damned ack-ack—what was wrong with it?—it hadn't opened up yet. Semyonov began to run. He must get to General Utkin, the Chief of Staff, without a moment's delay. General Utkin lived in the same street, and a little farther on, at the corner, the Army Commander, General Narishkin, had his billet.

A Ju 88 dived almost to street level with a terrifying howl—so that was it, a Wagnerian performance in the early morning. They would have to get used to this imitation thunder, and the troops would have to get used to it, too. But Semyonov couldn't help coming out in a sweat. When he reached Utkin's house his mouth felt parched.

The sentry at the garden gate looked like a ghost. Motor-cycles rattled along the empty street—they drove past the house towards the Army Commander's. Anastasia Timofeyevna, Utkin's wife, opened the door for Semyonov. She was holding her head and ran off at once.

"Terrible—bombing—bombing."

"Where is the General?" asked Semyonov.

"In there, he's telephoning."

An officer showed him the door to the office, to the little music-room, as it had been under the former Polish owner.

Utkin was telephoning.

"A bloody shambles—look at this mess, Semyonov—no one answers—is this supposed to be an HQ?" Utkin was using two and sometimes three instruments; his wife was helping him to get the lines. "This is Utkin speaking, Utkin—General Utkin—give me HQ—HQ—fatheads."

The earth quivered. Everything in the house rattled. Something fell on the floor above. The door opened and two children in nightshirts came in crying with fear and bewilderment.

Utkin was foaming.

"That bastard ack-ack officer—he should be shot, and some of 'Stalin's falcons' too—a dozen of them—shot at once."

"Andryushka, darling, here's someone on the line."

Utkin snatched the receiver. "This is Utkin speaking—General Utkin—listen——" and he went into obscenities.

The children howled. Utkin cursed, and threw the receiver on to the carpet.

"I give up. Let's get out of here, Semyonov. Get over to HQ."

"But Andryushka, what are you doing, what are you thinking of, where are you going? Don't you see that everything is on fire?"

Over the park, over the former seat of the Polish governor, where the Army staff were billeted, a thick bank of black smoke was indeed rising; from the window they could see blinding flashes rising through it.

In the house everything was rattling again. Pictures fell from the walls. This time it was due not to a bomb but to the firing of an anti-aircraft battery. Utkin jumped with joy.

"At last, at last—they've woken up. Now we'll show them."

"Are you mad—what have you done, putting the ack-ack at our front-door? Go out at once and send them away with their stupid peashooters. They'll bring everything down on top of us! Now we'll have all the bombs to ourselves!"

"Annushka, darling."

"The things I have to go through—I wish I'd stayed in Ivanovno!"

"Be calm, Annushka. In any case get ready, collect the children—I'll send you a car. It will be here directly."

"What are you thinking about—are you out of your mind?"

What did he think she was going to do? Clothes, jewellery, furs, silver—for two years she had been collecting valuable stuff from every shop in town and from the towns round about. There was the grand piano, too, Chopin's fingers had touched its keys. And he calmly said get ready; a car was coming!

The ack-ack guns fired as fast as they could be loaded, but the attack continued unchecked. "The trumpets of Jericho." Ridiculous—how did a cultured Soviet citizen come to think of such a thing? The walls swayed. Rubble and earth rained from a darkened sky. Utkin ran a few steps, then the floor gave way under his feet. Anastasia Timofeyevna, for all her fifteen stones, felt as light as a swirling leaf, and her face was as white as a sheet of paper. She felt she was going to faint, and her outstretched arm came into contact with a portrait which had fallen from the wall: the arrogant face of a Polish nobleman. Her hand went through the canvas, which was rotten with age, and she sank to the ground beneath the picture in its heavy gilt frame.

The bomb had obviously fallen in the street outside. The damage in Utkin's house was considerable. The family was literally sitting among the ruins, amidst blown-in windows and broken furniture thrown higgledy-piggledy. Miraculously no one was hurt, not even the two children, who were quite dumb with fear.

"Now it's all over—it's all over here, Anastasia. Leave everything and go. Let's get away from here."

"Yes, away from here," Anastasia Timofeyevna repeated. She was now as docile as a lamb, quite ready to leave in the same state as she had arrived.

"Get a car for yourself, too, Semyonov."

"Yes, for Maria Andreyevna and Irinushka," said Anastasia. "We could send an officer, Andryushka, to tell Maria Andreyevna so that she loses no time in getting ready."

Utkin stumbled over the broken floor-boards to the door and shouted some orders. Soon he returned. "We must go now, Semyonov. We've stayed too long already. Whatever is waiting for us won't be much fun."

Utkin and Anastasia had not been long out of the house when the officer returned. He had not been able to discharge his errand or find Maria Andreyevna. The lieutenant was pale and trembled as he spoke.

"The house isn't standing any more, there's nothing left—only a pile of smoking ruins."

* * *

The little hunting lodge in the park at Bialystock, assigned as billets to the forty political commissars who had arrived that afternoon, pitched like a ship on a rough sea. There was a shrieking and cracking and banging, but Captain Kasanzev was only marginally aware of these phenomena. Suddenly transferred from the desolate marshes on the river Bobr to take part in a conference, he had had an unusually enjoyable evening; he had been brought back to his billet with a thick head and now lay like a log on his camp bed. There was a shriek and a whistle—bombs, he said to himself, bombs undoubtedly. Well, Timoshenko had taught them to train the troops on exercises just as if it were a real war. As far as he was concerned he had nothing to do with it—for one thing because he had come here as a delegate and had

83

got leave from his regiment for that and nothing else; so he turned over on his side and fell asleep again.

He was vaguely aware of people who came and shook him, but he was unable to open his eyes. Their efforts to awaken him merely stirred up his recent experiences in his mind. He tasted the caviare and the vodka again— the vodka had been iced and there had been French brandy and white and red wine, three kinds of red wine. They didn't live badly in garrison, in the occupied territories of Poland. And the scene at night in the park had been lovely. Under the leafy roof of the trees, green in the electric light, the little table lamps with their silk shades were like brightly coloured moths.

"May I offer you a brandy, Miss Irina?"

How did you address a woman like this, anyway— Comrade or Miss?

"Miss Comrade, a herring on ice then?"

Irina Petrovna, daughter of a Polish colonel, had refused. Sheathed in a thin silk dress, her smooth dark hair parted in the centre, her bare arms and shoulders as white as alabaster, she looked just like the Polish princess in the golden frame in the gallery. Kapustin had introduced him to her. No, she didn't want vodka or a herring on ice, but she didn't mind dancing. After that she danced with a long thin fellow, with whom she disappeared and didn't come back. She wasn't in the park, nor in the gallery, nor on the dance floor; she was nowhere to be seen.

Kasanzev rolled about on his bed and looked for Irina Petrovna. Kapustin, the long thin man, majors, colonels, even generals—all ranks passed through his dream just as the evening before they had walked to and fro on the gravelled path, with the ladies of the garrison on their arms, to disappear at last into the deepest green where no lamps burned.

Kasanzev had had no one to walk to and fro with— that is, apart from Kapustin, with whom he had fought in Finland and had come across again here. In their search through the park they had come to a big grey house with several wings and a lot of trucks drawn up in front. Three or four hundred of them. There would be plenty to do—there were any number of dangerous anti-social elements in Poland. He and Kapustin had found themselves in a huge hall, full of tobacco smoke and the clatter of plates and knives and forks. There was a tremendous din and everybody was eating and drinking —sergeants, officers, privates, all mixed together with NKVD men and political officers. The NKVD troops were armed to the teeth.

Kasanzev had not known—nor had Kapustin—that they had walked in on a banquet given by the Secret Police in honour of a plenipotentiary from Moscow. They had partaken of the liquor, which flowed abundantly. Then Kasanzev, urged by some inner restlessness, had gone on alone and made his way through the empty corridors. It was not ghosts whose footsteps he heard echo in the empty rooms, but startled couples.

He had not found Irina, but he saw the tall thin man again—actually it was not quite the thing to talk simply and disrespectfully of "the tall thin man" because he was the Judge-Advocate-General. He sat in a pavilion, far gone in drink and quite alone, and played the piano with his long bony fingers. A ravaged face in the night, but the melody which welled up under his hands was so delicate than Kasanzev burst into tears.

The first air attack Kasanzev slept through.

Now the second attack was thundering over Bialystock. Kasanzev opened his eyes but shut them again against the brightness of the bare, swept sky. There was a continual whining in the air. A fresh wind was blowing. Almost by accident he picked a handful of glass splinters out of his hair.

Kapustin's voice came to him from an immense distance, calling his name.

"Are these glass splinters, Kapustin?"

"Yes, they are glass splinters, you idiot."

"What's up, then?"

"War—the exiled Poles," said Kapustin.

"The exiled Poles—the ones in London?" asked Kasanzev in amazement.

"Yes, they have attacked us along with the Germans. Come and look here, you can see there is no roof any more."

No, there was no roof any more, the roof had flown

away—and there was war into the bargain. That was enough to make you lose your wits—he had at least to think over the new situation, and he let himself fall back on his straw mattress. Kapustin was really furious now and ran off. Soon Kasanzev pulled himself together and stumbled to the door, feeling his way down the stairs into the cellar where he found the canteen and ordered a vodka and a herring. The vodka he drank at one gulp. The herring he merely stared at, and in that position, his head in his hands, fell once more into a doze.

Hours went by and others came into the cellar and sat down at the table. Their talk gradually woke him up. So there were no communications with Moscow any more—no, that was wrong, it was only that telephone and telegraphic communications with Moscow were destroyed. And the railway to Grodno was no longer running. The bridges over the Nemen were down. And what about the conference and the operation for the "Pacification of Poland?" The conference was off, he learned, the plenipotentiary from Moscow had gone back and the political officers from the various regiments had to return to their units.

"But how do I get to my regiment if everything is destroyed as far as Grodno?"

"You'll have to get them to tell you all that at the Special Branch. If you haven't been there yet, then it's high time you went. Everyone else has his movement-orders in his pocket."

The Special Branch was in the two-storied house at the end of the park. The Junkers roared over the tree-tops spraying bursts of machine-gun fire interspersed with 20-mm cannon. Leaves and branches rained down with splinters from ack-ack shells.

The house was well-chosen at any rate—it was lower than the other buildings and completely hidden in trees. The wild-looking types in leather jackets lounging about were part of the crowd he had met the night before at the banquet. He must be able to get haversack rations for the journey here, and for a good long journey too— these chaps had plenty. It would be even better if he didn't have to go back to his lousy regiment at all and could be used here with the security forces. The big car park in front of the house was already empty and the trucks that were still left were being loaded up with typewriters, telephones, radio transmitters, files and other office paraphernalia. The Special Branch was apparently moving. Admittedly it didn't look as if they were advancing—the trucks, loaded high, drove off in an easterly direction. A small convoy, drawn up a little to one side and made up of five or six cars, caught Kasanzev's eye; it was worth having a closer look at. Trunks, personal belongings, sewing machines were piled on the cars, in which some well-dressed women were sitting—and officers, too. The whole lot looked decidedly anxious, and no wonder—first the bombs, then this pack of half-drunk fellows, who were taking a high-ranking officer, a lieutenant-general, out of one of the cars. He looked pale and dirty.

"Lieutenant-General Masanov—he deserted from the front," Kasanzev learned from one of the leather-jackets. This captain—they were all captains and above—then pointed out a colonel who was just arriving, a short man with iron-grey hair. He was pale as death but walked upright disdaining to take cover under the trees. The young liaison officer who accompanied him had no choice but to walk on, holding himself upright, through the hail of shrapnel.

"Colonel Semyonov—he has had bad news, his house is in ruins. No, you don't need to go into the Special Branch, not into the house. All delegates from the front have to report in the hut over there."

Kasanzev, on his way to the hut to collect his movement order, saw the General who had run away from the front led off to the wing of the house where the head of the Special Branch had his office. Colonel Semyonov was being taken there, too.

* * *

What the Chief of Staff demanded was certainly not easy. Reality had surpassed any of the traditional textbook situations. The classic example—that of a division entering a railway station under fire and having to be detrained and deployed—was inapplicable. And there were no generals available to collect round the situation map, to ask questions and wait for objective answers. But there were generals who had lost their heads, departmental heads busy packing off their wives and belongings, staff officers with nervous breakdowns, duty-officers with chalk-white faces, telephone girls running to and fro wailing, doors left open, papers scattered in the corridors, secret documents fluttering down the stairs.

Headquarters was like an overturned wasps' nest.

It was high time to leave the building, which was under constant bombardment, and move to the camp which stood ready in the woods east of Bialystock. None of the telephones worked any more—a runner had to be used for every message, even the most unimportant ones. Radio was the only means of communication which still functioned, either for rear communications—with Minsk and Moscow—or for communications with the front, with corps and divisions, if these units were still there and had commanders. But what units were still in position and what commanders were still in their HQ's? Semyonov had sent liaison officers forward to find out and, having got through to the Army Commander, had given these officers full powers—telling them to act on their own initiative and take over the command of units which had no officers left.

Semyonov stood in his office and signals were brought to him—from supply depots, from forward airfields, from operational staffs in Moscow and Minsk. But what he saw were the ruins of his house. Ammunition, barbed wire, petrol—but there was nothing left where a house had stood that morning, only a heap of broken walls and smoke rising from the crevices.

"Is there still no report from the pioneer platoon?"

"No, not yet."

"Tell them to send 1 Platoon of HQ Company as well."

"Yes, Comrade Colonel, at once."

A division wants to withdraw, a corps wants to withdraw. An infantry regiment has had sixty per cent losses and wants to take up a position farther back with what is left.

Marusya is dead—war demands victims.

"The division is to hold on. The corps is to hold on. The regiment is to defend its position to the last man." This was the usual instruction and the only one he could give; it was the only instruction he had from Moscow.

A pioneer platoon and 1 Platoon of HQ Company—a hundred Red Army men are digging—what will they dig up? Marusya and Irinuschka.

"A regimental commander wants MT to move his wounded, Comrade Colonel."

"No MT can be allocated at this time. The commander must rely on whatever is available locally until further notice."

"Lieutenant-General Masanov is on the line again—it's urgent, Comrade Colonel."

"The division must stay where it is."

"There is a good prepared position on the edge of a wood. Lieutenant-General Masanov proposes to withdraw to it with the remains of his division. It has only twenty per cent of its strength left. The rest has been wiped out, Comrade Colonel."

An order from the Army Commander is laid on his table:

"All officers and other ranks detached from their units are to be stopped; they will be formed into units and sent forward without delay.

Signed: Narishkin,
General."

A man stood before him and talked and talked—a man with the rank of general, talking about the advance of the "invincible Red Army" towards Warsaw—but as he talked he could barely conceal the shifty movement of his eyes and the thoughts of flight coming and going behind them. At last he came round to his own affairs. It was a question of some trucks which he needed urgently. Semyonov sent him to the transport officer.

"What news is there, Comrade Captain?"

"Two hundred planes have been destroyed on the airfield at Byelsk, Comrade Colonel."

What will they dig out?—it is only two days since she came back from the Black Sea, as slim as a girl and bronzed with sun and wind.

"The airfield at Volkovysk is asking for petrol."

"They must use their iron reserve—it should all be there according to plan."

"Yes, Comrade Colonel, it should all be there. But

when they opened the tanks it wasn't high octane petrol but a mixture planes couldn't use."

Ammunition, petrol, barbed wire, MT. Resistance by the Polish population. A captain murdered, a major and two lieutenants murdered, a truck with wireless equipment destroyed.

"That's something for the Special Branch."

A man with big bones, a healthy complexion and a beard tinged with red was brought in. He came from the other side.

"Take him to the Intelligence people—let them deal with him. What news of Masanov?"

"There has been no contact with him for hours, Comrade Colonel."

More ammunition, more petrol, more regiments, divisions and corps wanting to withdraw. And what does the Special Branch want?—a lieutenant from the Security Forces stood in front of Semyonov.

"Comrade Colonel, I have been sent by General Ristin. It concerns a certain Lieutenant-General Masanov—we have stopped him."

"What do you mean—I'm wanting him—why stopped?"

"The General has sent me for you to clear up the situation. You must come at once, Comrade Colonel."

Accompanied by the lieutenant, Semyonov went through the park. The Ju's were almost touching the tree-tops. In front of the grey house stood whole fleets of brand-new trucks—he could use those for carrying ammunition and petrol; he had nothing at all for the wounded. And he could use all these officers lounging about in front of the house—all senior officers, hardly a captain among them; but no, he'd rather not. How did they all manage to get the same brutal expression? Why did they all have leather jackets? In any case, after their special duties they are no use for commanding troops. The Special Branch is the dog-whip of the Army Command—how will it work in war? War is too serious an affair—they can hardly submit every decision to police supervision.

He thought of Maria Andreyevna again and was ashamed of it—for these cigarette-smoking women interrogators with their complete lack of femininity bore no resemblance to his poor Maryusa. One of these
90

creatures with ruby-red finger-nails and the rank of major took another pull at her cigar; but she left it behind in an ash-tray when she went into the office of the chief of the Special Branch. Semyonov felt uneasy—after all, this wasn't a moment to be wasting one's time in outer offices. Ammunition, petrol, MT—and when you do find some ammunition it isn't the right calibre and there is no transport. Then the convoy sets out and the corps isn't where it should be any longer, and the ammunition column falls into the hands of the Germans. Unimaginable confusion and sheer inefficiency as well, but these are minor worries. There's no keeping the troops in their positions. When things get too hot they simply run away, simply withdraw without orders. And all our equipment is in danger of being left behind. When will the order at last come from Moscow allowing certain units to be withdrawn and regrouped in the rear?

The cigar-smoking woman interrogator was there again. She opened the door of her chief's office with a courteous grimace, but she couldn't quite bring it off with that face of hers.

General Ristin was not sitting behind his desk; he was sitting on top of it. Semyonov did not care to look too closely at the faces in the background—the light of day didn't suit them. The young woman with the rank of major stayed in the room, too, with her cigar this time and a shorthand pad. The Judge-Advocate-General was there, too, wandering up and down the long room with his new boots creaking. Ristin was still busy reading something. Semyonov shook hands with the Judge-Advocate-General without looking him in the face. This man plays the piano wonderfully, he thought. Maryusa always said he played so well.

Ristin read through the document and handed it back without a word, making only a gesture with his hand, which seemed to say: "That's settled."

"Now, Colonel Semyonov, what is happening in your army? What is this story about that heroic son of the fatherland out there—what has he done?"

The Judge-Advocate-General stopped his pacing. The other creatures in the room pricked up their ears.

"Lieutenant-General Masanov is a divisional com-

91

mander, Comrade General."

"I know that, of course—but what has he done, what sort of an officer is he?"

"Lieutenant-General Masanov commanded one of our best divisions."

"Well, you know we are here to fight a war—not to transport our womenfolk to safety. He arrived here with women, belongings, sewing machines—in four or five trucks."

"And cars," someone interposed.

"We can use the trucks for other purposes, I believe. I want an explanation from you, Colonel Semyonov."

"I can only repeat—up to now Lieutenant-General Masanov was a capable commander and he has the complete confidence of the Army Commander."

"Where is the Army Commander—why has General Narishkin not been brought here?"

"General Narishkin is not at his headquarters."

"Where is Narishkin, Colonel Semyonov?"

"The Army Commander, General Narishkin, has gone forward to the Narev where an enemy break-through is reported. He wishes to see the situation on the spot and take the necessary measures immediately."

"We'll have to do without Narishkin. We've taken too long over this affair already. Comrade Judge, what is your opinion?"

"We must examine the divisional commander personally."

"Bring him in."

Lieutenant-General Masanov was brought in, between two colonels. Both took up positions beside Masanov, who was almost a head higher than they.

Ristin still sat on the table.

"Lieutenant-General Masanov, why did you desert your troops?"

"I did not desert my troops."

"Explain to me the present situation of your division."

"I cannot give any such explanation—my division has been wiped out. We used up all our ammunition and when we asked for more received none. We had nothing left to hold on with. The troops ran back bare-footed. I could not stop them."

"And you yourself packed your womenfolk into cars —that's a swinish way to behave."

"Comrade General. . ."

General Ristin took his place behind his table.

"I am not your comrade any more and you're not a Lieutenant-General any more. How does our oath go? To fight to our last drop of blood for the Fatherland, the Party, the State. But you fight for staff-cars for wives, womenfolk and sewing-machines. Where were you off to, you scoundrel?"

"Colonel Semyonov, I call upon you to bear witness."

Semyonov knew that he had not been able to send him any help, that he had even had to refuse to allow him to withdraw the remains of his division to prepared positions on the edge of the wood five miles to the east. He had been unable to give him any other instructions— he himself was bound by the same orders.

"I wanted to take up prepared positions in the woods."

"I could not allow withdrawal to positions farther in the rear," said Semyonov.

"Shut up," roared Ristin, and it was not clear to whom. Semyonov's face was a white mask.

"Comrade Judge, what is your opinion?"

"Guilty," said the Judge-Advocate.

Ristin nodded slightly in the direction of Masanov. *"Rastrelyat,"* he said.

Rastrelyat—to be shot.

"Colonel Medvyed." One of the escorting colonels seized Masanov and led him out.

Semyonov was dismissed. He left the building by the main entrance. The little convoy still stood there. The officers had disappeared; only the women were still in their places. One of these well-dressed women was Masanov's wife, waiting for her husband to come back.

Semyonov walked past without looking up.

* * *

Kasanzev was completely sober when he came out of the hut. On his movement order it said that he had to report to his regiment in the marshes. And he hadn't got any nice rations for the journey from the Special Branch stores. He had to march off, with his empty knapsack— not towards the east, the way the Special Branch trucks were going, but to the west, to the river Bobr; then he would probably have to trail after his regiment—perhaps southwards, towards Moscow. So far he was still in Bialystock. After some halts, because of the bombing, and taking cover a few times in shelters which weren't up to much, he was now standing on the bridge over the Biala, a little stream dirty with discharge from the factories. On either side he saw ravaged houses with open porches full of litter. The wave of attackers roaring over the town was now aiming at a more distant objective so that he could stand upright on the bridge and watch the monsters storming over the roofs.

But one more bomb did fall.

The cross on the nearby church swayed as if it were not on the top of a tower but on the very tip of a bending mast. But that was merely an optical illusion as the black smoke of the explosion swirled suddenly past. When the smoke had cleared, church and cross still stood in their place as before. Now people were running to and fro in the rabbit warren of the old town with bundles, barrows and trunks, stopping to look up into the air and venturing at last on to the square before moving off to the east. The children of Israel, who lived in this part of the town, were leaving. But Kasanzev saw not only Jews but Russians too with their whole families. Majors and even colonels were dragging trunks, tables, chairs, even pianos, and stowing them on trucks along with their wives and children. The women weren't so well dressed now as in the park the evening before. They probably thought—rightly—that the journey before them might be long and difficult. Off you go then—east to Russia and home. I am marching west—getting out of the town as quickly as I can, away from this unending roar and confusion. Out there you at least know that you are at the front. Keep along the Biala and you'll soon find the protection of a wood and a peaceful camping place for the night.

The groups of soldiers coming from the opposite direction disturbed him. Apparently there were a good many deserters from the front—too many at least for him to stop them. Soon he struck off along a side path, and by the time he had reached a suitable wood there was already a first star in the pale sky. He pushed the undergrowth carefully to one side—and touched a machine-pistol which pointed at him threateningly.

"Halt, hands up," came the command.

This was shameful and almost too much for him.

"One, two . . ." the other counted; at three he would fire, you could see that. Kasanzev raised both hands. The other was an officer with a pockmarked face and bright red hair. A battalion commander going the rounds of his sentries, as Kasanzev learned later; and he seemed rather inclined to shoot down on the spot this man who had tried to slip noiselessly through his guards.

"Keep calm, I'm a captain like yourself."

"You are a German parachutist. Come along and I'll show you where you'll find some more of your pals lying about."

Kasanzev had to go on ahead, farther into the wood. He was brought to the Special Branch where he produced his movement order and identity card as an officer of the Red Army. Everything was there—his party card, the document showing he had the Order of Lenin and finally his special pass stating that he was an officer on special duties.

"Apologise to him, Uralov," said the Special Branch officer after looking through the papers.

Captain Uralov muttered something incomprehensible.

"And now let him go or keep him in your battalion, since we are all going in the same direction."

But Captain Uralov first took him to his Colonel.

"All right—if he's going towards the front at this time of day, he's as good a soldier as yourself, Uralov. We'll soon see if he knows the areas as well as he should according to his statements."

The Colonel called Uralov back.

"Give him something to eat," he added.

So Kasanzev arrived at an armoured battalion which lay in the wood, well camouflaged, and was only waiting for darkness to fall before moving off. Uralov was the commander of an infantry battalion which rode on the tanks—four or five men to each. That same night the tanks reached an area Kasanzev recognised from the marches his regiment had made on manœuvres. It was after two o'clock and the first light was showing in the sky when Colonel Morosov, the tank battalion commander, sent for him to report to the armoured command vehicle.

"Who are those people I keep seeing over there?" asked Morosov.

"They are forced labourers, Comrade Colonel. They are building an airfield ten miles from here." The forced labourers travelled close to the road but, like timid deer, kept out of sight under the trees.

"But they have no guards."

"Yes, that's odd—and they're not going to their work but in the opposite direction."

Before the reason for this strange movement could be discovered, Morosov's vehicle, which drove at the head of the second column, was surrounded by more strange figures. There was no doubt about it—they were deserters.

Morosov gave the order to halt.

"What are you doing here? Where are you from?"

"From over there—from the river."

"We're going back—we have no officers—we don't know what's happening."

"Where are your officers?"

"They drove off, Comrade Colonel. Off in cars—they're gone."

"And what's happening up at the front?"

"Thousands of Germans—heavy fire from across the river—we couldn't hold on—we're going back."

We're going *back*! A terrible word in Morosov's ears. He jumped down from his tank.

"Look at this—a Klim Voroshilov tank weighing fifty-two tons. There are thousands of tanks like this on your side."

The men did not seem very convinced—but more and more came up.

"Have you had anything to eat?" asked Morosov.

Now they came alive, throwing off their apathy—if they were to be believed they hadn't seen a field kitchen for a fortnight.

"Give them something to eat at once, Uralov. And then get as many up on the tanks as there's room for. And all the rest of you listen to me. This is an armoured corps moving up—we'll break any resistance."

96

A few grumbled. "We've heard that already—our officers said the same—invincible until they heard the bullets whistle." Morosov ignored them. "We're going forward," he said, "first to the river, then across the river and farther on still. To Warsaw, to Berlin."

He managed to make many turn back again, not very willingly, hesitant at first—but they began to face west once more. Many were undecided and could not make up their minds what to do. A staff car, travelling east, passed them and halted. The artillery commander from the over-run division was in it.

Colonel Morosov went up to him.

"What is wrong, why are you retreating Comrade General?"

"You have no idea what it's like, Comrade Colonel. Go forward and see for yourself what is happening. You'll see our men retreating without boots to their feet. The supply trains have been left behind. We have the guns all right, but no ammunition, it's all expended. From Army HQ we only get promises, but you can't fire promises. How are we to hold on with nothing?"

"What do you need? Tell me the calibre and the number of rounds. Our corps can give you as much as you want. Look at your map—do you see the crossroads? Turn left there. Three miles farther on you will come to a small hill with a wood on it. You'll find our HQ there. You'll get all you want."

"We can still save the guns. The enemy hasn't crossed the river yet, although there is no resistance because we have no troops there."

"Where is the enemy exactly?"

"I can't say exactly. His fire is coming from the other side of the river."

Morosov and his tanks drove on.

The artillery commander followed the directions he had been given. He drove past units of the armoured corps. A powerful force and immensely impressive—two armoured divisions, an infantry division and an airforce division in their rear. That was a corps which at least had equipment—the sort of stuff he had only heard of. When you had material like that it was easy to talk like the colonel back there.

A rifle regiment on motor-cycles went ahead of Morosov's battalion, took a bridge by assault and held it under the enemy's concentrated fire—held it even when the unit was down to half its strength. Further support arrived—a motorised infantry regiment with some tanks—and the bridgehead on the farther bank was extended. The infantry, which had previously retreated in disorder, advanced again under cover of the tanks and took up their old positions.

The way was open for the armour.

Towards midday Morosov's battalion crossed the bridge. On the farther bank they formed up for action. They went forward in groups, overrunning German ack-ack and anti-tank guns and driving the infantry before them.

"Close up," signalled Morosov.

Ahead in the rye tanks had appeared. For a time everything seemed peaceful—a herd of great animals calmly grazing.

"Hold your fire—let them come closer."

The German tanks too seemed to want to close the range. At four hundred yards they opened up a well-aimed fire, but the German shells bounded off the Russian armour like peas off a wall. Morosov ordered the squadrons on his flanks to cover him with fire and with the rest he made a rapid advance, giving at the same time the order to fire at will. The effect of the Russian 76-mm guns was terrifying. There were blinding flashes; earth and clumps of rye rose from the field together with tank-tracks and fragments of destroyed tanks. As one fountain subsided another sprang up.

The Russian divisional commander, in overalls which were sweaty and filthy with dust, had the whole wide field of battle before his eyes. The midday sun shimmered on the rye, on the backs of the tanks deep in the high grass, on the muzzle flashes and smoke from the guns, on the wrecked hulks and on fleeing German tanks, many of which were left behind.

"We're smashing them," the commander exulted.

For the first time the hurrah of advancing Russian infantry rang out under the hot sky.

*   *   *

Lieutenant-Colonel Vilshofen had got permission to

leave GHQ and had been posted to an armoured division and given command of a battalion. One of his first tasks was to destroy a body of enemy armour, take a bridge and form a bridgehead on the other bank.

After the advance march the battalion went forward in extended order through fields of standing rye. Vilshofen stood in the open turret with his glasses to his eyes. Russian tanks had been sighted. Out of the shadow of the wood they came into the sunlit plain—too many of them to count, and they seemed to have a turn of speed. The shape of the tanks and the American Christy-suspension puzzled him. This was a type which had never been referred to in the handbooks of the German armoured troops. Close in quickly and make the enemy fight your way, thought Vilshofen.

A thousand yards, eight hundred yards.

The contours of these new tanks stood out clearly among the high crops. The Russians still did not fire—obviously the commander hadn't realised yet that he was going to have to deal with a respectable tank force. Vilshofen was cautious. He meant to deliver a quick thrust, make for the bridge and cross it and so form the bridgehead according to orders.

His two flanking squadrons of light tanks—Buzzard and Falcon—had closed in to six hundred yards. The heavy squadron, whose code-name was Eagle and in the midst of which Vilshofen drove, was about three hundred yards farther back.

"Eagle, Eagle. Enemy tanks ahead—fire at will."

The heavy squadron opened fire.

Six hundred yards, five hundred yards. . .

"Follow up, Eagle. Concentrated fire—all tanks fire at will."

In his heavy Mark IV tank Vilshofen drove on with the light squadrons on either side—Buzzard on his right and Falcon on his left. Concentrated fire—fifteen or twenty muzzles turned on a single enemy tank. There was no doubt they were direct hits. Again and again shells rattled on the armour plating—but they glanced off and the tracer streaked up into the air. The 50-mm guns of the Mark IIIs and the short-barrelled 75-mms of the Mark IVs could not penetrate. The heaviest calibres mounted by any

99

German tank were mere peashooters against superior armour.

A hot summer afternoon, dazzling sunshine and even brighter muzzle-flashes from the Russian guns. The report they gave was another unpleasant surprise. They must be enormous pieces—long-barrelled guns with penetration to match. On the other hand their fire was not controlled but scattered and erratic; whereas the excellent fire control of his own squadron commanders gave a tiny ray of hope. Vilshofen saw a tongue of flame go up from the next tank. A direct hit, clean through—only one man climbed out. Another tongue of flame on his left. To his right a Mark IV went up into the air. A Russian tank, hit in the track, spun round, stopped dead but kept on firing.

He must halt—there was no point in trying to advance farther. Over his wireless he gave the order.

The tanks faced each other at four hundred, even at three hundred yards. Vilshofen had something like forty guns in position. Every second eighty shells were fired—fifty or perhaps sixty found their targets. But the enemy tanks stood it out; if some stopped dead and ceased firing for a while it was only because of the demoralising, crippling effect of the accurate German fire.

The Russians received reinforcements from the wood. They came on in packs. Vilshofen ordered Eagle squadron to engage them at long range.

Retreat was out of the question. Vilshofen's orders were to destroy the Russian armour, take the bridge and form a bridgehead. Eight of his tanks were burning, now there were nine of them; a tenth got a direct hit.

It had all happened in a matter of seconds.

"Eagle, Eagle — make smoke. Buzzard, Falcon, disengage slowly."

The unbelievable order was given only after a sober appreciation of the situation, and was at once picked up and carried out by the squadron.

Keep hammering away at them—bluff them, keep them from counter-attacking. That was all they could try to do.

"Fall back — keep up your fire regardless of expenditure."

They must not let the Russians counter-attack, not let them break through.

"Eagle, Falcon, Buzzard—let them have it."

The hail of fire was not without its effect. The leading tanks, spattered with shot, went off their course and ceased firing; each time it was a little while before they discovered that they were still fit for action and could advance and fire as before. Others slowed down, too. The pursuers were being left behind. Vilshofen's battalion was now firing at extreme range; it withdrew to the edge of a wood and continued to fire from that position. Before them in the open country lay the destroyed tanks. Some of the crews were moving through the rye, trying to reach the shelter of their own lines.

The battalion stayed under cover where the enemy could not observe them. If their pursuers pushed on they were to let the enemy tanks come into close range and then take them under the massed fire of their guns.

The commander drove back into the village and went into regimental HQ. The CO jumped up and shouted at him: "What are you doing here, Vilshofen? What sort of a mess is this? What's wrong—where is your battalion? You had orders to take the bridge. We have to form the bridgehead by evening."

"Sir, I have to report that we are up against superior tanks. We were simply shot to pieces. We attacked all right, but our guns can't pierce their armour."

But the colonel wouldn't listen to what Vilshofen had to say about the streamlined contours and Christie-suspensions of the Russian tanks. Nor would he believe that the German shells had merely glanced off the Russian armour. He was red with anger as he stood opposite this battalion commander of his who had been so long out of the front line and a week ago had been sitting in the office at GHQ.

"Impossible—I don't want to hear anything about it. The whole thing is incredible to me."

"If you care to drive forward, sir, you can see the tanks from close up. I saw what they were like for ten minutes. About sixteen of our own tanks have been knocked out—they're out there still burning."

"You should have got a bit closer and concentrated your fire. Let them have it."

"We opened fire at four hundred yards and even then

101

couldn't achieve penetration. The Russians put a shell right through our tanks each time they got a direct hit. We have had heavy losses. My battalion is on the edge of the wood. I don't know how long it can hold on there."

"Our orders from Division are to take the bridge."

"I know that is the order from Division—but I don't know how we are to do it."

The regimental commander called Division: "The battalion cannot take the bridge. The Russians are on this side of the river with strong armoured forces. Between fifteen and twenty of our own tanks have been put out of action, we are up against modern tanks with superior armament and superior armour. We can't pierce them with our ammunition. The task cannot be carried out."

"Impossible—the Fuehrer himself has given the order. We must report by this evening that the bridge has been taken. Attack again with your regiment at once. Put in 2 Battalion as well. Report back immediately."

"Yes, sir. We have to attack again, Vilshofen."

"I must refuse to comply with the order, sir, it is nonsense."

"It is an order from Division, a personal order from the Fuehrer."

"We'll get the same drubbing and still not get the bridge. Unless the Russians pull out of their own accord —and that isn't likely."

"I repeat—the order originates from the Fuehrer."

"It is suicide, sir."

This time two battalions attacked, and came to a standstill as before. Eight of Vilshofen's tanks and fourteen from the other battalion were left burning—and on this occasion the enemy pushed forward farther than before and came unpleasantly near the village where the regimental HQ lay.

When Vilshofen and the commander of 2 Battalion reached HQ again, the staff had already been warned by wireless and had moved. The colonel had been ordered to report to Division.

Heavy losses from superior armour and greater penetration by the Russian guns was the explanation which the divisional commander had finally to accept and pass on. He added lack of air support as a contributory factor.

Lieutenant-Colonel Vilshofen and the CO of 2 Battalion stood once more at the end of the village street. It was evening. On the fields beyond, some of the abandoned tanks were burning; over others the flames had died down but smoke was still rising. High over the rye-fields, above the Russian positions and the forest behind them, circled a German reconnaissance plane.

"And we have never heard of this tank although it outclasses us," said the other commander.

"If their fire control had been up to the same standard we wouldn't be standing here now. They could have pushed through to regiment and divisional HQ," said Vilshofen.

*   *   *

The Great Bear shone over the tent which housed the HQ of the Russian corps commander; the two bright stars on the western horizon were Castor and Pollux. Down there lay the river and the bridge across it, and further over, just where the two stars touched the misty horizon, lay the two villages where German troops had lain that day and which were now evacuated.

The Russian patrols were unable to make any contact with the enemy and could apparently push farther and farther west. In the command tent, which lay on a wooded slope, the corps commander had gathered round him half a dozen generals, his chief staff officers. Opinions were hopelessly at variance and the picture only became a bit clearer when the first reports from the flanks came in. According to them, the Germans had crossed the river north and south of the point where the tank-battles had taken place during the day and were obviously trying to envelope the whole corps. It was a manœuvre which could be examined and dealt with. Admittedly the corps commander had to rely entirely on his own forces—but he felt he was in a position to do so. The formations under corps command were to be divided and sent in against both arms of the pincers. The tank units were strong enough and the motorised infantry mobile enough to carry out this manœuvre.

But one point had been long debated and was difficult to resolve. The Chief of Staff was of the opinion that the spearhead of the attack should be withdrawn across the bridge it had taken the day before. The chief of the Special Branch wanted the bridge to be held, and a large enough bridgehead to act as a base for further offensive moves. He was not satisfied with a compromise which would leave one tank battalion in the bridgehead in case of need. He wanted to have the entire spearhead—a whole division—concentrated across the river. There was nothing for it—the Chief of Staff and the other officers could argue but in the end they had to accept this proposal.

The orders for regrouping were sent out. The task was a difficult one and operational orders aimed in particular at keeping some reserves in hand at all costs. The darkest part of the night was already over and messages were beginning to come in from units which had taken up their new positions The staff officers bending over their tables looked up and listened. High over the tents they could hear the drone of engines—the noise of heavily laden machines. The flight passed over the camp. It was not long before the first bomb fell and others followed. The officers sprang up. They could see with their naked eyes what was happening some ten miles away in the forest to the east where all the mechanised columns of the corps were collected. The woods beneath them were hidden in a white incandescence. The heat was so great that waves of hot air and the smell of burning drifted up the slope to the staff tents. Explosions followed one after another: petrol tanks, ammunition dumps, whole columns went up in the air. Each explosion set off a chain of destruction.

The corps commander came out of his tent and looked over the top of the trees; there were still rumblings and explosions long after the bombs ceased falling. No messenger came from the supply columns. The staff officer responsible for supplies had come back without being able to give even an approximate idea of the extent of the catastrophe; he was now having an unpleasant interview with the head of the Special Branch.

Towards morning the camp sank into a leaden sleep. Only in the operations room the work went on. The re-grouping of the corps had been carried out according to plan. The force in the centre had not been able to hold the bridgehead—had indeed been forced to break through an enemy blocking force on the near side of the river, and was fighting hard to keep a foothold on the river line at all. The divisional commander who had carried out the attack on the previous day was asking urgently for supplies. Corps could give nothing itself— the situation in the forest was still obscure, although it was perhaps still too early to say that the supply park no longer existed. The airforce division announced catastrophic losses. Sixty per cent of the planes had been destroyed on the ground and the remaining machines could not take off for lack of petrol. The Chief of Staff turned for help to Army, demanding petrol, air support and ammunition. Army promised to do all it could to help —but could not promise anything that day.

"Bring it up again in twenty-four hours—better still in forty-eight hours," was the reply with which the Chief of Staff had to content himself.

There was a deep silence in the little wood. It was in the forenoon, between ten and eleven. In front of the tent of the chief of the Special Branch lay the corpse of the supply officer. Fat flies were humming over the dead man's face. A woodpecker hammered in the trees. The rattling of heavy trucks broke the silence, and a Voroshilov tank came up the slope. Officers appeared from all sides and the corps commander, too, came out of his tent.

A man climbed out of the tank—the day before he had looked like a fitter, sweating and black with powder, but now he seemed to have emerged from hell. It was the divisional commander who was fighting the battle at the bridge. He caught sight of the corps commander, went up to him and saluted.

"Major-General Tokarev reporting."

The corps commander raised his hand to his cap.

"What news, Tokarev?"

"Comrade General—my armoured division doesn't exist any more."

"What are you talking about? Are you drunk, Tokarev?"

Generals, colonels, lieutenant-colonels drew nearer— the chief of the Special Branch placed himself beside the corps commander.

"I am quite sober, Comrade General. I have come to report. I can hold the German mass attacks and hold them for a long time. But I need ammunition and petrol."

"Comrade Major-General, I can only tell you what I have already said in messages—that as soon as supplies arrive you will get everything."

"*Now*, Comrade General."

"Be sensible, Tokarev. Do you think it is easy for me to have to give you that answer?"

"*Now*, Comrade General."

"What the devil do you want?"

"Ammunition and petrol, Comrade General."

"Go back and hold on."

Tokarev turned away and in so doing forgot to salute. He stumbled back to his tank and took a radio message which a lieutenant handed him. "An urgent message from 1 Regiment, Comrade General," said the lieutenant. The message seemed to cause the Major-General to forget the presence of his superior commander and the collected staff. He pulled out his water-bottle and took a swig, then handed the bottle round—first to Colonel Morosov, then to the other five or six officers who were with him.

What was this? Were they really going to get drunk in the presence of the corps commander? The whole affair was so exceptional that even the chief of the Special Branch, that ponderous thick-set man, though he reddened noticeably, stood as if rooted to the spot. Morosov had a voice like a fog horn. "A wonderful weapon it was," he was saying, "a wonderful machine, a fine division." He took another swig at the bottle and passed it on. Tokarev had just received the message that the best regiment of his division was gone—not defeated in battle, but unable to move and so delivered up to the enemy.

Things couldn't go on like this. The corps commander's patience was exhausted. The chief of the Special Branch looked like having a heart attack. Tokarev was one of the most capable commanders and led the best division in the corps. On his file he was described as an exemplary Soviet patriot who, from being a *Besprisorny*—a stray waif —from the catacombs of Odessa, had climbed up to his present position of command. From that point of view much could be overlooked in him; but this was going too far.

Tokarev turned round and walked up to the General once more.

"Look, Comrade General, 1 Regiment is gone. 2 Regiment is going the same way. But we can't move any more. The tanks are OK. The troops are fighting. But without petrol they are just dugouts stuck in the ground, unable to move. By the time I get back there they won't even be that any more. The crews are dismantling the machine-guns and are defending themselves from all-round attacks with them. Comrade General, give us ammunition for the machine-guns."

But there was no MG ammunition either.

Tokarev had a pistol in his hand—he pointed it at his temple, pulled the trigger and collapsed. The quiet in the wood became more intense. The woodpecker began to drum again.

V Armoured Corps offered no further organised resistance. The tanks remained where they were. The tank-crews dismantled the heavy machine-guns, broke through the German blocking force and disappeared into the woods and swamps.

* * *

The Army Commander, Lieutenant-General Narishkin, and Colonel Semyonov, his chief of operations, together with part of the staff had come back to Bialystock once more. The troops jammed in the bottle-neck over the Biala, the chaos of supplies and communications, reports of the hostile attitude of the populace, had put Narishkin into such a temper that there was no keeping him in the camp in the woods. He had come to get into the midst of things, to try to disentangle the knotted mass of troops and MT and get things moving again. Of the bombed HQ there remained only the outside wall, so he had gone straight back to his old home.

This old stone house, which had once belonged to a Polish nobleman, was cramped but it would have to do.

Colonel Semyonov could hardly bear it; he sat in a room with ancestral portaits on the walls, with a collection of weapons and a suit of armour standing by his table. He had plenty of work to do, for over and above his own job he had had to take on the work of the Chief of Staff, Utkin. Yet the move to Bialystock did not mean a greater burden for him; on the contrary, for whole hours he was out of the confusion. Here he had to concentrate on one thing only, his commander's plans. But because he had passed two peaceful years here with his family, he once more felt the full weight of the sorrow which had befallen him. Since leaving his house that morning he had not gone back. Now he felt drawn irresistibly to the spot, although there was no hope any more. He left the papers on his desk, laid down his pencil and went to the window. But he couldn't even do that without feeling Maria Andreyevna beside him, just as she had stood that morning four days ago.

In the street the column of evacuees with prams, bicycles and barrows still trickled on. The air of this summer afternoon was full not only of dust and the smell of burning—the sense of doom was so strong that it had become part of the atmosphere. Semyonov, who had been in three campaigns, had a nose for the special quality of this hour. The catastrophe was there—it had materialised. The burdened figures in the street halted. People in a hurry suddenly had time. They laid down their loads and lined the sides of the street. From the cellars Poles emerged, hungry for bad tidings. "Has Ivan got a bloody nose yet? Will it last long, or should we lay into him?"

The Poles no longer looked up into the sky—they looked towards the west. From over the bridge on the Biala came the first great wave of Red Army men who had been sent on manœuvres with inadequate equipment: Maxims from the First World War, too few rifles, bandoliers round their necks, their trouser pockets full of small arms ammunition and a handful of dry bread in their knapsacks. That was the state in which they had run into massed fire. Barefoot and dusty, with soles worn away; with primitive bandages, torn from their shirts, round their heads; many of them limping on sticks, others with their arms in slings, they dragged along over the cobbles. The traffic block at the bridge had cleared and they could move on again. They filled every street, and a smell of sweat and of the marshes rose to the roof-tops.

They were marching again—the road to the east was free.

Now that the traffic block was overcome and everything was fluid again Semyonov felt relieved and let himself drift. For the first time for four days he followed his own impulses. Suddenly he found himself down among the crowd, on his way to the grave which had been filled in two days before. He must see it with his own eyes —touch it with his own hands, before he would be convinced of the finality of his loss.

Walls piled on each other with here and there a balcony railing, stones and dust—that was what Maryusa's grave looked like. His daughter, Irina, had been dug out. When the bomb fell she had been in the cellar where her mother had sent her to get food for the journey. The vaulted roof had withstood the pressure and after two days she had been released. Pale as a ghost, with an ugly wound running down her cheek to her neck, she had been brought to him, and next day he had sent her off with a personal escort from his staff towards the east, to Minsk, and from there on to Moscow.

Maryusa—two years in Bialystock, sixteen years in various garrisons. He had met her for the first time in Mariupol when he was a lieutenant, and now he must leave her here under the rubble.

Semyonov had now seen his wife's grave with his own eyes. There was nothing more to do; he had to turn back to life, to this confused business of living which seemed to have burst out of its normal framework.

He went along beside the crowd of men.

"*Kak dyela?*" he asked a sergeant. "*Kak dyela*—how are things?" He was almost frightened at the sound of his own voice, at the fact that he had left the street with his wife's grave behind him for ever and was back at his job. More than ever before he felt these soldiers were his family. The sergeant was walking with a stick, dragging a leg wrapped in blood-sodden bandages through the dust. He did not look up but moved his hand a little and answered: "*Nitchevo.*"

"*Kak dyela?*" said Semyonov, turning to another.

"Blisters on my feet, Comrade Colonel, *nitchevo.*"

A young face—a Comsomol. He looked up and saw a strange colonel. So there were still officers like that—

his own had run away.

"*Kak dyela?*"

"*Nitchevo,*" said the young Communist.

With bloody heads, with raw feet, without bread, without officers, without transport, with no aid for the wounded, camping in the ditches at night with their uniforms for their only covering.

Nitchevo!

The remains of a heavy artillery regiment passed by without their guns. Soldiers from Masanov's division, but Masanov lay shot behind the grey house in the park. His wife was still alive. Where would she be, what road was she wandering along in her thin shoes and fine dress? Tank crews from V Corps had their heavy machine-guns with them; Ristin had brought him a Captain Uralov from that lot to carry out a special mission. There were few officers to be seen—here and there a lieutenant or a captain; rarely anyone of higher rank. The soldiers drifted past. If they looked up they saw Polish faces, foreign faces, foreign streets in a foreign town—they wanted to get away from here, to get the road under their feet: to the east, to Russia, home. "*Domoy.*"

"The invincible army," scoffed the Poles.

"They've given you a bloody nose already, Ivan."

"Where are you hurrying to?—that's the wrong road. The other way goes to Warsaw."

The Poles were venturing out now and Ristin couldn't shoot them all. Semyonov went back to his office and sat down again at his table beneath the portraits of the Polish nobility. Next door an officer sat waiting; he was pockmarked and had bright red hair.

"If anyone can carry out the mission, Uralov is the man," Ristin had said.

At the other end of the room the door stood open; Narishkin could be heard raging and shouting.

"What are you talking about? Do you think you are here on leave—in the mountains in the Caucasus or something? Get out! Get out of my sight!"

A man appeared in the doorway and staggered to the exit—he looked like a circus clown with a face like a white painted mask.

"He's sitting on the equipment for three million

soldiers. And now it's too late—we can't get any wagons out of the station and there's no other transport. Now let's see Captain Uralov."

"Come in. You too, Semyonov. This job of Uralov's can't be put off—then we'll look at our own tasks."

Narishkin shoved over a packet of cigarettes.

"Help yourselves, comrades—things are a bit crowded here, Semyonov. But we're closer to the front—nearer to what is happening. We'll stay here until everything is across the river. What do you think of these fools? Only two hours ago they were reporting successes, sending through messages saying they were advancing in massed attacks, and now they're streaming past us. It's fear that gives rise to messages like that; in the last analysis it's an attempt to deceive Moscow. Intelligence has been a complete failure—what I must know is what enemy forces I have to deal with."

General Narishkin bent over a document and put his name to it. Semyonov took it from him, folded it and put a seal on the envelope—one at each corner and one in the middle. A top secret document—no one was allowed to open an envelope sealed like that, not even the police. If they arrested the bearer they must take him to whomever it was addressed to.

"You know what it is all about and understand how important your mission is, Comrade Captain?"

"Yes, Comrade General."

"You will carry out your mission—the lives of hundreds of thousands depend on it."

The task was to get through to 3 Army HQ in Grodno, or wherever it was now, and return with reliable information on the co-ordination of the movements of the two armies. A courier with the same task had already been despatched to Brest-Litovsk to the commander of 4 Army.

"It's a difficult task, Comrade Captain."

"I will carry it out to the best of my abilities, Comrade General."

"I have great confidence in you, Comrade Captain, and I am sure you will carry out your assignment brilliantly."

"For the Fatherland, for the Party, for Comrade Stalin!"

That was a formula at which both General and colonel had to jump up and salute. Captain Uralov took the document from Semyonov. Semyonov and Narishkin waited until he had hidden the paper on his person.

"You will go by motor-cycle as far as possible and then proceed on by any means available."

"One way or another, Comrade General. I don't put much value on my life."

The door closed behind Uralov.

"From him that isn't an empty phrase. But why must one first have lost one's father and mother at birth, and not know one's own name or the history of one's family, in order to be a devoted Soviet citizen?"

Narishkin obviously did not expect any answer to this remark. He was adopting a very unusual tone. What did it mean? One of his stars wasn't sitting quite right—but what did a star on a general's uniform matter when a whole army was being routed?

Semyonov didn't say anything about the General's star —he spoke instead about Captain Uralov.

"He got the Order of the Red Star in the Finnish War, the Order of Lenin in the Far East, and his extraordinary name at the technical school in the Urals where he was taken in as a nameless waif."

"I bet he couldn't stand it."

"Twice they killed their teachers and broke out. Little Uralov was mixed up in it. It says so on his file."

"These waifs—I remember a little devil like that on the Orient Express. You try jumping from one coach to another at full speed and you'll break your neck. But they did it, and lots of them were only six or seven years old. They fell under the wheels, too, of course, but enough of them survived. At every station they reappeared like migrant birds, and they pinched everything that wasn't nailed down. Well, our Uralov has learned to read and write, has got everything he possesses from the Soviet State—and doesn't know what the Soviet State has taken from him. Now he's ready to give his life and says: 'For the Fatherland, for Stalin.'"

Narishkin was behaving in an extraordinary manner. What was this all leading up to? They were surrounded by chaos and disaster—was this the time for a confidential chat?

"Let's sit down, Pyotr Ivanovitch."

Narishkin offered Semyonov a comfortable chair, sat down opposite him and leant back.

"How is Irina Petrovna, by the way?"

"She got away with superficial injuries, but she'll probably have an ugly scar on her face. I sent her off right away to Minsk and from there she should go on to Moscow."

"Let's get to work now. Petrol, barbed wire, transport, officer deserters, let's leave all that, Pyotr Ivanovitch. We have known each other long enough, so let's take time and look at our unusual situation from an unusual point of view."

* * *

The peculiarity of the task which General Narishkin had in mind for Colonel Semyonov lay in the fact that the former could neither give a clear outline of it nor a direct order stating the object to be achieved. Semyonov seemed to be suited to the task for two reasons. Firstly, there was a long-standing tie of personal friendship between Narishkin and Semyonov dating from military college and even further back; for they both came from the same town, Nikolayevsk on the Ob. So a great deal could be said by hints. Secondly, Semyonov was the kind of man who could be expected to show initiative and provide from his own resources something which, at the moment, was not coming from higher up.

"Pyotr Ivanovitch—let's talk like one professional soldier to another. Hold on, they say, hold on—of course we want to hold on. But we have no supplies and get no clear orders. The organisation isn't functioning. You know quite well you can feed the Russian soldier badly —but when you have nothing at all to give him then there's an end to good order and military discipline. There's no question of fighting spirit any more. When they are faced with this chaotic situation the officers try to run away. The soldiers fight, and not badly either—there's nothing else they can do until things break down altogether. We have been sending officers forward with orders to take over command on their own responsibility, and to keep the units on the spot. We can't carry on

113

with this kind of order any longer. It's no use trying to make them do the impossible: it will defeat our own ends. Look out of the window and see what a mess we're in already."

"The troops must break out."

"Excellent—that's the idea. They must be kept together and made to fight their way out of this."

"That's it, Alexey Alexandrovitch. But in what direction should they be moved?"

"You know quite well that we can't put the question like that. We have no orders to withdraw. But what do things look like in reality? I had the chief intelligence officer sitting here a little while ago—he couldn't tell me much about the enemy. But he does listen to enemy bulletins—according to them all our possible withdrawal routes are under heavy bombardment. Bombs are falling hundreds of miles to our rear—in Minsk and Borissov and on the Beresina. It looks very much as if we have got into a pocket. Listen, Semyonov, I have spoken to Korobkov of 3 Army. He sees the situation in exactly the same way as I do, yet Korobkov cannot put it to the Defence Committee—nor can I—that in view of the untenable position the armies should be pulled back. But we can discuss a re-grouping of forces. That is allowed. And that is the framework within which we have to work out our operation; we have to throw a sprat to catch a whale."

Narishkin took some slips of paper from his table—wireless messages from Moscow, from the Defence Committee, from the Supreme War Council. He looked at one or two and laid them back on the table.

"They are asking for the impossible. Advance, they say, hold on, fight to the last man and the last round. And we have chaos before our eyes. You are my chief of operations, Semyonov, you are a strategist. I must rely on you. You have a clear picture of what we are heading for—we can't stand by and watch without doing anything."

Semyonov understood perfectly, and he translated what he heard and what was asked of him into sober reality. He was to get all available troops on to a line further back, to transform the chaotic rout of the Army into an orderly retreat, although there was no order for such a withdrawal. He was, moreover, to act over the heads of commanders, many of whom had disappeared, but many of whom would re-emerge and look for a scapegoat for their own failure. And at best what he had were only the broken remnants of formations which in the eyes of the Defence Committee and the Kremlin still counted as intact divisions and corps.

"It means assuming a responsibility which we can't very well expect those at the very top to take on themselves later," said Semyonov.

"Listen, you are already in a desperate situation. Yesterday and the day before we passed on these ridiculous reports of successes. You have deceived the Kremlin, you have deceived Stalin. As things are, the Army is going to pieces in your hands. Will it not be something if you have collected the troops on a line further back, re-grouped them and so saved what there is to save?"

Semyonov was not feeling in a laughing mood but he smiled. He spoke to Narishkin as he used to speak to him at school in Nikolayevsk. "Listen, Alexey Alexandrovitch, you are an Army Commander all right, you've even got a name in the world of military science—but you are still the sly Siberian you always were. You don't need to try and fool me!"

"That's right, Pyotr, I like to hear you say that—if things weren't so serious I would open a bottle now and we would have a drink together. But this isn't the right time for that. There's a war on and a lot of people are dying. You have lost your wife. Your daughter has been spared to you. Well, think of the sons and fathers who are your responsibility. You and I don't want to have to say one day that we have them on our consciences. Listen, Pyotr, we went to school together."

That was true—in an old building of ancient pinewood; it stood high up on the bank of the river and from the window you could look down on the Ob. That was in the days of the Czars.

"Do you remember the big orchard?"

"Naturally."

"And the old watchman?"

115

"Of course I remember—and I remember the strategy we used. Or was it tactics?"

"Yes, we would split up into three groups. The old man ran after one group, then the other boys could get busy and in the end we all had our pockets full of apples. We solved the problem in those days."

"In those days strategy was easier—there was no one to keep interfering."

Narishkin laid his heavy hand again on the messages from Moscow. With a sudden jerk he swept them all under the table. "Useless stuff, Pyotr; that sort of thing is no use any more. Events have outstripped them. And this doesn't help either."

He handed Semyonov a piece of paper which had remained on his table.

You must conduct a merciless war, it said, *against all forms of defeatism. All persons causing disorganisation in the rear areas, all deserters, all persons spreading alarm and rumours are to be handed over for liquidation.*

"That doesn't get you anywhere. The supply officer is lying shot behind the wall of headquarters. But supplies won't move because of that. No materials arrive to put up defences, no petrol either. There's an artillery commander lying there, too. His death hasn't altered anything. The guns he put into position three hundred yards from the frontier—not because he wanted to but because he had to—are lost just the same. The chief railway engineer is there, too. But that doesn't alter the gauge of the railways here in Western Byelo-Russia or in the Baltic states, and the transport bottle-neck still exists. There's a battalion commander called Masanov lying dead as well. But however many men are shot, their deaths can't alter the fact that we have no effective defence plans— that the first plan didn't work, and that the second, based on the first, didn't work either."

"This man Hitler surprised us all—not only the planning staff," said Semyonov. "You know we all thought that he had enough on his hands—that he would behave reasonably and not take on another heavy commitment. But we didn't reckon with a madman."

"Never mind Hitler—he had nothing to do with our

defence plans. We have plenty to do coping with our own madness, with our own political follies. Hitler is hitting out like a maniac and is busy creating a world coalition against himself. In due course he'll be put in a strait-jacket—I suppose you have heard Churchill's speech?"

"I haven't heard anything except petrol, ammunition, supplies, that's all. I haven't had time for anything else."

"I see—but the slackers on your staff had time, and they're talking about nothing else. Churchill's speech made a bigger impression than any announcement from Moscow. Well, we have Hitler on top of us and he's hitting us quite hard. What we need is a breathing-space and a line to collect and re-form on. We're not allowed to have that line. You know yourself the other things we need. And what do we actually get? There they are, lying on the floor. Empty promises. Spit on them, Pyotr. No help, no one comes to see us. We aren't sent a single roll of wire, a single shell, a single tin of petrol. We're left to ourselves with the whole area from Bialystock to Minsk to defend. Here we are sitting in Byelo-Russia—180,000 of us with as many again on our right and as many with the army on our left. Altogether 800,000 men with the airforce units and rear elements. What is going to happen to us, Pyotr? Here we are with a strong enemy concentration facing us, surrounded on both sides and without support from the rear. We are left to our own resources. We are Russians and perhaps too patient—but I ask you, are we to bow our heads and wait for the blow to fall?"

To pull himself out of the swamp by his own pigtail, like Baron Muenchausen—yes, that's what he wants, thought Semyonov. Narishkin wants to have the troops he has left formed on a line further back, but he doesn't want to give the order for it. What does that mean in actual practice—what line is he thinking of?

Narishkin looked at the map which lay spread out under his hands. With a red pencil he sketched a vague line—there was no doubt about it, it was the old Russian frontier. Behind that line he put in a rough arc; within it lay the little town of Slonim. So Narishkin wanted to give up the whole western territory with its bad roads,

117

unconverted railways and unreliable population. A new line on the old frontier; an HQ in Slonim. That seemed clear even if nothing else were said, even without any direct order.

"The task is clear, Alexey Alexandrovitch."

General Narishkin stood up.

"And now, Colonel Semyonov."

"Comrade General."

"We go back to the camp in the woods—we leave in five minutes."

* * *

Five minutes later motor-cyclists pushed their way through troops cramming the streets. The men stood aside and made way for the armoured cars which bore the Army Commander and his staff from Bialystock to the camp in the woods.

In the camp Semyonov started on his new job at once. New positions had to be prepared and ammunition, petrol and supplies directed to them. Then he had to set up straggler collection posts and skeleton units. And for that any old officer wouldn't do—he would need men like Uralov who feared neither death nor the devil, a whole mass of such undaunted beings, devoted and intelligent enough for their grave task; but he had to use what he could lay hands on.

A few paces away steps led down into Narishkin's dugout. Three duty officers sat in the ante-room. A sergeant was laying a cable and kept going in and out. From the north came the noise of German artillery in action; the atmosphere in the ante-room was depressing.

In the biggest room—it was revetted with timber—Narishkin once more sat poring over the map. The old Russian frontier and the little river Shchara would do as a line to re-form on—but hardly for more than a few days. Everything now turned on what forces could be extricated from the collapse in the west and transferred more or less intact to that line; for the units being hastily formed from stragglers, and there were huge numbers of them, could only be considered second line troops and used as such.

"Alexey Alexandrovitch." The good Anna Pavlovna, who had for years been cook and housekeeper in

Narishkin's little mess had come in and seen the food left untouched. She had made meat dumplings and that was the sort of food for a Siberian like Narishkin. But there they stood on the table; he had not even sampled one of them. "Alexey Alexandrovitch, you can't sit up all night and eat nothing and simply smoke."

"Leave me alone, Anna Pavlovna; clear the things away."

Anna Pavlovna looked worried, but without a word she cleared the table. Soon she came back again bringing Narishkin comfortable shoes and a light jacket instead of his military coat.

She looked after Alexey Alexandrovitch—saw to his food, his clothes and his laundry, brought water to bathe his feet after a hard day, made sure that he got what was due to his family and himself from the quartermaster, dealt with the paymaster over special allowances, saw to a hundred trifles affecting his well-being and was the most respected person on the staff, being better informed indeed than many staff officers. Senior officers visiting Narishkin treated her with particular respect, shook hands with her and asked how she was; yet with it all she had stayed simple and modest, and friendly with everyone.

"Who has been touching the picture—the glass is broken?" said Narishkin. The glass over the portrait of his daughter, Anna, which stood on his desk, showed a crack. It had been overlooked by Anna Pavlovna, although she had removed the visitors' other traces.

"The MO was here with the paymaster, and the quartermaster came and joined them," she said. "They ate and drank and I suppose the glass got broken." Other things had got broken, too—a chair and some glasses. But Anna Pavlovna said nothing about them; she merely added: "They got quite merry."

"So I leave the place and they sit here and eat and drink. The MO would have done better to drive out and look after the wounded!" Narishkin suppressed a remark about the other two—the one looked after his household and the other provided the money for it. Anna Pavlovna was still hanging about.

"What else, Anna Pavlovna?"

She enquired about a major and a colonel who had

been almost daily visitors and had now suddenly stopped coming. "We don't see General Utkin any more, either," she said.

"It is war, Anna Pavlovna; lots of people get killed—some in one way, some in another." That was all that Narishkin gave her in answer. He was obviously not in a talkative mood and she withdrew.

Narishkin sat up for a long time.

Slonim as HQ—that was a good beginning. But what came next? A second red circle took shape under his hand—further east—round the little town of Baranovitchy. A third point on which the pencil lingered was Minsk itself. Narishkin himself probably did not know why his hand raised the red pencil again without leaving a mark. He could not know that for his Army Minsk was already unattainably remote, that it would remain for ever beyond the line terminating his own life.

Narishkin sat under the shaded lamp.

The whole thing stinks from the top down, he thought, and the catastrophe we find ourselves involved in didn't begin yesterday; it goes much further back. There is ammunition, petrol, everything—for other armies. Their advance parties have blank cheques for anything they want in Minsk. Strong forces have been brought up from long distances. Troops from the Ural military district have been detrained along the Vitebsk-Polotsk railway line. Troops from the Moscow military district are being sent to Lepel, and in the south they are joining up with troops from Orel. From Polotsk through Lepel, on to Borrisov and Bobruisk—that is the line of the Beresina, the forward line. Behind it lies the Dnieper, the new main defence line which has been planned from above—not such a new line either, for Tuchachevsky proposed it once before, and Voroshilov, the People's Commissar for Defence, turned it down.

Tuchachevsky was shot. The Army Commanders and corps commanders, even the divisional commanders of 1937 disappeared. Fortifications, army positions, airfields were set up near the western frontier—Tuchachevsky had wanted them two hundred and fifty miles further east because of the undeveloped transport system of the Soviets—and they were overrun in the first few hours, on the first day of the war. But the new defence line which is being prepared and supplied with material is no other than the old Tuchachevsky line. Polotsk—Lepel—Borrisov—Bobruisk—so the arc runs. Outside that arc is the fiery furnace, blazing so high that the *Hozyain* won't waste another cartridge, another field dressing, another drop of petrol on it.

The *Hozyain*—the boss. This is his hour.

It is two in the morning. All Moscow knows the lighted window above the Kremlin walls. There Stalin paces to and fro, smoking one pipe after the other, and broods. To him the sacrifice of eight hundred thousand men is just one of the unfortunate necessities of war. And it seems a modest figure to him—just a beginning. Once —and that was in peacetime—the number was eight million. They were peasants, and today the nameless children of those peasants are amongst his most faithful followers.

The *Hozyain*.

In the dugout the dim light of a single lamp fell on the table. The thick earth walls cut off all noise from the outside world. The deep silence of the night lay all around —the only movement came from the duty officers' room. The door opened and a major came in.

"Comrade General, Moscow calling."

"Let me have it then."

The major put through the connection and left the room again. And there he was—his voice was in the room as if it came from beyond the lamp, from the chair there in the half light, unmistakable with its Georgian cadence.

"Alexey Alexandrovitch."

"Joseph Vissarionovitch."

"*Nu kak dyela?*—How are things?"

Should he answer like the sergeant in the street: *Nitchevo?*—I'm done for, but that's not the point—it doesn't matter because Army Commanders grow on trees in this country. He had to answer *en clair* and the enemy was listening. But even *en clair* he would say what he had to say.

"*Nu kak?*—Well, then?"

"Joseph Vissarionovitch—the situation is serious. The

121

officers are doing what they can. The soldiers are fighting. But we get no supplies. We need ammunition, petrol, medical supplies, we need everything. I haven't had anything for a long time."

"A member of the Defence Committee will come down to you."

"There is no time to lose, Joseph Vissarionovitch. I have only forty per cent of my forces left—sixty per cent are lost. We are up against a strong enemy concentration. How shall I get material? I have reached a serious decision. The situation allows of nothing else. To save my equipment I propose to withdraw my formations, regroup them and form a new defence line."

Narishkin had to repeat his proposal. There was a short pause before Stalin spoke again:

"My armies are advancing. Only a traitor could make such a proposal to me."

The set went dead—the rough, hoarse smoker's voice died away. The chair in the shadow of the lamp was once more an ordinary chair.

Alexey Alexandrovitch stared at the closed door and the wooden revetting. It was like a tomb here within the thick earth walls. A picture of his wife, Lena Fyodorovna, and of his daughter, Anna, stood on the table in front of him. There was a crack not only in the glass but in the frame, too—the swine, that's how they behave when I'm not there. Lena and Anna had stayed in Moscow. So far, so good. Lena was old enough to belong to the past, and so long as there had been someone there to protect her and she was the wife of an Army Commander she had been able to continue to live "in the past". She had always preferred a second-hand book with yellowed pages—perhaps written in 1890 or 1900—to all the latest publications of the Soviet authors. And a visit to the Moscow opera or the ballet had always seemed to her more important than the construction of the Moscow underground or the May Day parade on Red Square. As for Anna—the girl had had a good education, she had studied, she was free with her pocket money and liked giving parties. They had need of a husband and a father able to cover up their unproductive existences with his name and rank.

He took his revolver in his hand and laid it down again. No, he had no need for that—he wouldn't use it. He would tread his path to the end, which might be tomorrow or perhaps a little later. And what would happen to Lena and Anna then? He could do nothing for them—he could leave them no security. A Soviet citizen who has fallen from grace has less to bequeath than a dead dog.

Lena.

But when all the lights in Narishkin's dugout had gone out and he lay down to sleep it wasn't Lena who was there.

"Alyosha," said Anna Pavlovna still half asleep. "What is it, Alyosha, darling?"

"Don't keep on asking the same thing," replied Alexey Alexandrovitch.

In the night he returned once more to his desk and signed some orders, among them the order to move the HQ. Semyonov had proposed the ruins of a monastery west of the river Shchara.

The couriers who had been sent to Korobkov in Brest-Litovsk and to Grodno, to the staff of 3 Army, had been ordered to report to Slonim with the answers on joint operations.

The mass of soldiers now making their way east would come up against the Shchara; here he would make them face west again.

The duty officer came in.

"What is it?"

"A German prisoner, Comrade General—shall I bring him in?"

"No, no more tonight."

The duty officer came back again.

"A message is coming through from Moscow, Comrade General."

"I'll wait for that."

The order was brought to him.

Top Secret—to be read only to senior officers:

Following an investigation by the General Staff of the Union of Soviet Socialist Republics, the Commander-in-Chief of 4 Army, General Korobkov, has been found guilty of treason, degraded, removed from his post and condemned to death by shooting.

After promulgation, the sentence was carried out by members of the Special Branch.

* * *

Nina Mihailovna Uralova was terrified by the bombs whistling down on Bialystock, terrified at her own physical fear—but most terrified of all at what she saw going on around her.

It was a nightmare.

She was waiting for the "important Government statement" which had been announced on the wireless; for it was from the Government, from the Kremlin, that the word must come to free her from her fear. The Government statement came and she heard Comrade Molotov's grave accusation against Fascist Germany, and she breathed again when she heard, too, that the enemy had been halted and thrown back with heavy losses.

But the nightmare remained.

Indeed, it almost seemed as if Molotov's speech had given it new life. Even more people were gathering in front of the shops breaking the windows and pulling out whatever they could lay hands on. Others had packed their things and were hurrying to the station with cases, sacks and baskets. Captain Peredovo, Captain Pustin and Lieutenant-Colonel Gortshakov didn't seem to have heard the important speech at all, so busy were they with their own affairs. There were lieutenant-colonels and even colonels, dragging things along like porters—not only trunks and cases but tables and arm-chairs—and piling them on to trucks. If the Jews were leaving the city they had their own good reasons which you could understand. No doubt the Russian families should be got away from the bombing—but it should happen in an orderly manner. Yet Pustin stood at the corner of the street like a bandit, held up a truck with his revolver and drove up to his house with it. And didn't the order say: Everyone must stay where he is. And for officers on leave: Everyone will return to his unit. But Lieutenant-Colonel Gortshakov had sent his adjutant to the front, while he himself collected his trunks, his children and his wife and last of all climbed up on the truck himself and drove away. Peredovo and Pustin drove off, too—yet the one had a battalion on the front like Nikolai and the other was on

124

a regimental staff.

Nina Mihailovna ran to the Party Office.

On her way she looked in on Olga Vladimirovna, a colonel's wife, who had often done social work and had even run the club for a time. But it was a strange meeting. Olga Vladimirovna was almost unrecognisable. You could not talk sensibly with her. She ran to and fro with her arms full of clothes, or with a pile of books; she brought plates, pots and pans from the kitchen; she tore the curtains from the windows, and everything lay piled in confusion.

"Olga Vladimirovna, the Red Army has thrown back the enemy."

"What are you chattering about—don't you see what's happening under your own eyes? We have all been betrayed—everything is lost already. You clumsy creature—" this was addressed to her Polish maid— "don't stand about there. Take a basket and pack everything and get downstairs with it quick. Take the broom, too, and these shoes here and the lamp and this vase—"

The maid went downstairs.

Nina Mihailovna tried to speak to Olga but the latter cut her short.

"You blockhead—you don't understand a thing. We must get out of here. The invincible Red Army—that's the sort of nonsense you keep coming out with. Later maybe, yes later—but here and now everything is lost. That slut —where is she?"

The maid did not return.

"You have offended her, Olga Vladimirovna."

"As if I had time for that—I'll apologise to her, you'll see, I'll apologise to her—I'll go straight down after her."

She ran down the stairs, Nina following. The maid had disappeared together with all the things she should have loaded on to the car.

"*Boje moy, Boje moy*—" Olga was even calling on the old-fashioned Deity to witness her misfortune! That was too much for Nina Mihailovna—she left her friend standing in the street and ran on towards the Party Office.

Here, where she had expected advice and moral support, the confusion was even greater, and her disappointment increased. Here, too, they were packing, and she found everyone preparing to flee. Rugs, card-indexes, lists of members, all lay mixed up together.

What were they doing, what did this mean?

"Where is the Party Secretary?"

"Don't interrupt, Nina Mihailovna, don't you see we're busy?"

"I don't understand—haven't you heard Molotov's speech?"

"We have no time to argue. Don't hinder us. You are in our way."

The Party Secretary had left already for Minsk—to get fresh directives, they said. The Assistant Secretary she found burning files, including a whole bundle of her own reports on cultural work in Poland and the state of the youth organisations, which she had put together with such care: all these she saw thrown into the stove. The Assistant Secretary was sitting before a heap of papers, and pile after pile was being brought and thrown down at his feet.

The door was thrust open—Anton, Vladislav, Venzel, Lydia and Maya, the whole district committee of the Polish Communist Party, came in. Nina thought for a moment that they had all got jaundice. Kasimir rushed to the Assistant Secretary, grabbed him by the tail of his coat and talked at him, swallowing whole syllables, whole words; yet he was usually an excellent speaker.

They had been looking for the Russian Secretary but he had disappeared. Now they clung to the Assistant Secretary.

"Instructions, Comrade, directives! Give us a report on the international situation. And the great pacification campaign in East Poland—what will be done about that? You're clearing out—you can't simply leave us in the lurch! Give us back the lists we drew up for the campaign."

"Let go of me—have you gone off your heads? I haven't any lists to give you—they have been passed on. There are no new instructions yet. Calm down—you'll be told everything in due course. You can see I have no time just now."

The Assistant Secretary went from room to room, and the whole crowd of melancholy figures streamed after him.

They were trembling now and their speech was incoherent. They were a pitiful sight. Yesterday they had still been invincible with their powerful ally at their side, but now the great ally was clearing out. What was going to happen to them now? And how would they manage to survive, left alone in their own land and face to face with the enraged people?

Nina Mihailovna realised that the Assistant Secretary wouldn't have any time for her if he did not even have a word for the leading comrades from the Polish Party. Suddenly she was surrounded by Poles.

"Nina Mihailovna!" She knew them, after all—she had spoken at their youth conferences about culture in the Soviet Union, about the new ethics of the Soviet Union, about love and marriage and children in Soviet society— she had written for the *Byelorusskaya Pravda* in Minsk and even for the *Komsomolskaya Pravda* in Moscow.

"Nina Mihailovna! Comrade Uralova! Tell us what to do—help us. We can't stay here alone at this difficult time. We can't stay here under any circumstances! We need documents, movement orders, cars. In Strabla they dragged one of our comrades along until he died. In Zabludov the Party Office was completely wrecked. Here in Bialystock we daren't cross the street!"

This stammering—these distorted faces! Yet Vladimir had always been an eloquent speaker. Venzel had written wonderful poems about Poland's rebirth, about its friendship for the great Soviet Union. She knew them as politicians, as organisers, as tribunes of the people. Nina Mihailovna could not bear the sight of this pitiable collapse. She looked round for a way of escape.

Everywhere it was the same: chaos and flight and fear. By next day there was not a single responsible comrade to be found. The Town Soviet, the Party Secretariat were bare and deserted and the bombs continued to fall.

Pustin and Peredovo had disappeared—miserable deserters. The Assistant Secretary drove off in a heavily loaded truck with carpets, trunks and typists. Lieutenant-Colonel Gortschakov got a box on the ears from a NKVD lieutenant at the roadblock outside the town and when he defended himself was shot. And Irina Petrovna, the daughter of Colonel Semyonov, that proud and somewhat pert young woman, was dug out of the rubble with her mouth full of dust, looking like a boneless rag-doll, and was carried away.

It was night—the third night already.

On the western horizon the sky was red, reflecting many fires which crept together and flickered up from time to time. There in the west where the sky burned, somewhere Nikolai was doing his duty.

Nikolai Uralov, with the Order of the Red Star and the Order of Lenin on his breast. When he turned round you could see his broad shoulders outlined under the thin military jacket. That was how she had seen him for the first time in the Park in Bialystock. There was so much sun that day, and so much light in his grey eyes. He had come as a delegate to a Communist Youth Congress.

A new day came and with it the moment when the leaderless troops from the Narev, from Bobr and from the woods came flooding into Bialystock. Nina Mihailovna was down on the street asking the soldiers for news of V Armoured Corps, telling them the number of Nikolai's regiment and battalion. She managed to cross to the other side of the river but then could not get back over the jammed bridge. So she missed the only moment when she might have seen Nikolai.

Nikolai Uralov tore through the streets on a motor-bicycle. He stopped in front of his house and leapt up the stairs. There was no answer to his knocking. Of course she's gone like all the rest, he said to himself, and that's a good thing—the best thing she could have done. He hurried down again and a few minutes later was driving away in a northerly direction along a field track. He wanted to try to reach Grodno from the east.

At this very moment a soldier was saying to Nina: "Your man is lying in the marshes back there. He doesn't look very pretty. Come with me instead—a young woman like you shouldn't sleep alone."

"You needn't hope any more—there's no point," said another. "If you still have a pair of trousers of his or a jacket give them to me. I need civilian clothes—I'm going home."

"We're through—we're going home!" That was what most of them said.

The mass of soldiers began to flow forward once more; pressed close together in the bottleneck they went on over the bridge with Nina Mihailovna in their midst. She overheard many remarks—some of them good-humoured, some of them coarse—and one malicious comment which made her think.

"She's well-dressed. Foreign clothes, I expect. We're paying for that now with our blood."

"Don't hang your head. You're too young to mourn. A young dove like you soon finds another mate. Stalin's finished and everything will get better." So another tried to comfort her.

There were soldiers everywhere; the whole front poured into the town. It was a nightmare; but this time Nina Mihailovna looked the phantom straight in the face. They had all been betrayed. Olga Vladimirovna had said so; the soldiers said so; the Assistant Secretary's pale face showed it; so did the shifting eyes of Pustin and Gortschakov and the Polish Communists, trembling in their fear. These were terrible acts of treachery, yet no one outside this chaos knew anything about them. Moscow knew nothing about them. And the man who should have learned about them first—the man who could banish the phantom with a wave of his hand—hadn't even been told!

Near the station the great storage sheds rose darkly against the reddened sky. There was a red glint, too, on the faces of the soldiers. They were cursing and yelling, surging against the sheds and falling back again. Then they stood still and hoped that the sheds with their stores of food would be opened.

Treason here, too.

These supply officials—they were wonderful when it was a case of arranging a party with some other officers, or of coming to the park in the evening to listen to the music and dance and drink. Now they were sitting on their flour-sacks and pointing out that they had no orders to distribute food, and that the sacks were still sealed and they were not empowered to break the seals. Yet beyond the burning town the rumble of the German guns could be heard. Did they want to let these immense stores fall into German hands still under bond?

Nina Mihailovna had suddenly a mission to fulfil. She

must get to Moscow and report. There was no time to lose.

People had been rude to her—in the Party rooms they had said: "Go away, you silly woman, we have other things to think about." Yes, everyone here in the garrison had other things to think about. They had got used to living well in an occupied country. Their wives had begun to dress differently. They had learned new ways, thought only of clothes, of good food, of comfort—even their babies had to be taken out in prams fitted with tyres and springs.

Their wives—and what about herself, could she make an exception of herself? Had not the soldier on the bridge noticed her foreign clothes, and was it not right what he said? She had thought of it as an innocent form of pleasure, and at twenty-two she had not been able to withstand the temptation. There had been an old woman living in Olga Vladimirovna's cellar—the former owner of the house, once a Polish countess. "My dear girl, at your age you can't go about in that cotton dress fastened up to the neck," the Polish countess had said to her, and had shown her the Warsaw fashion magazines, had told her the shops where the best cosmetics could be bought. And Nikolai had rather liked it. At first he had laughed when she appeared dressed up like that, but however tired he was from work when he came home, he cheered up again when she got dressed and liked going out with her. That had been the beginning—that was the way that led to luxury and comfort, and from there straight to treason.

Nina Mihailovna had already begun her journey. She scarcely noticed that she had crossed the railway and left the town behind her. On she went, with the drifting mass of soldiers. Behind them the German artillery drew nearer. She tried to stop a car, but no one paid any attention to her signs—they only thought of saving their own skins.

Soldiers and more soldiers—new faces kept emerging from the darkness. There was a truck halted on the roadside. Nina Mihailovna tried to get on to it, but she was not the only one. There were wounded men, soldiers with their feet raw with walking. More and more kept coming up, but they couldn't all get on to the truck. And those already on board made no effort to make room for more. Nina caught their eye, however—a young woman.

"I must go straight to Moscow."

"Oho, to Moscow—what's your business there?"

"It's very important."

"Show us your bit of paper."

"Show me *your* bits of paper," she retorted. "We know all about you. You have lots of important things to organise, but it's all a swindle. You aren't even taking a single wounded man with you. These soldiers here are all dirt to you. You have betrayed everything and instead of fighting you are driving off."

"Yes, we're driving off—but you stay where you are. Give our love to Moscow."

Then something happened. A captain with the badge of a political commissar asked for the driver's movement order. He had none.

"Out with the lot of you."

"Nonsense," said a major who was sitting beside the driver.

"Don't try to resist, major. I won't stop at a box on the ears this time—I'll try something else." The machine-pistol in the commissar's hands underlined his words. A pair of hands grabbed the major and snatched him from the truck. The driver got out by himself. While the major and the captain were still quarrelling someone else had already taken the driver's empty seat. A new set of passengers had boarded the truck. After a short tussle the previous passengers were ejected with the exception of one or two who had sat quietly in the dark. When the truck drove off again there were forty men standing in it, packed together, and Nina Mihailovna had been given a hand up, too. The captain sitting next to the driver was Kasanzev and he had a movement order. He had to report at the station in Volkovysk in order to get arms from the cavalry division stationed there, and, of course, rations too. That was why he had managed to collect some men.

The roar of engines overhead was unceasing. The trucks drove without lights through a sea of men and from time to time their vehicle rammed the one in front. Nina Mihailovna heard the men speaking softly to each other. The same things as she had heard everywhere. Everything

131

had been sold and betrayed—the officers had run away—Grodno, too, was already taken by the Germans. "And where is that officer in front there taking us to this time? We've had nothing to eat for days and nothing to smoke." "There's supposed to be stuff in Volkovysk." "I'm sticking to the captain, anyway, he'll do something—we're in a truck and we don't need to get any more blisters." "That's true, and we are getting east quicker—getting nearer home."

Slowly the truck made its way forward past armed convoys and crowds of refugees. Everywhere arms were raised; curses followed them as they drove past. In the woods, in the fields, in the midst of the tall rye, there were flickering lights.

"Look—spies."

"See them running."

"German parachutists."

A flare sank slowly down—it seemed to be suspended in the sky, The fleeing figures began to take shape. The chalk-white faces of Uzbeks, of Siberians, of Cossacks, of Turkmenians, appeared. All the races of Russia were passing along these roads. On the railway which ran alongside the road there was a crowded train; on the steps stood women with kerchiefs, old men, Red Army men, convicts who had been building airfields the day before. They were all waiting for the train to start.

Kasanzev's motley crew drove on until there was no more petrol left in the tank. Yet when the time came and they all climbed out, and had to leave the truck behind, they had come a long way. In front of them, against the pale morning sky, Volkovysk lay burning under thick clouds of smoke.

Nina Mihailovna could not have told how she got through the town. She scarcely realised that many hours had passed and that it was evening once more. She found herself in a cellar, and presently one of Kasanzev's men, Nikita, brought a herring and a piece of bread for her. Everyone in the troop had got that and they had drawn a ration for her, too. A herring and a piece of bread—that seemed more important than the railway station which had turned into a volcano, or the fountains of earth and rubble which had darkened the sun. Nikita, a peasant boy from somewhere near Kursk, with a round, good-natured face, had something else for her—a pair of old down-at-heel army boots, which, for a wonder, weren't too big, and better for marching in than her own.

By now there were about a hundred men under Kasanzev's leadership. They hadn't only been given herrings; every third man had a rifle. Behind them was the burning town, before them the road to Slonim. It was night again, and they turned off the main road to follow a path through the thickly wooded countryside.

Kasanzev's men were one of the many groups marching along the main road or by parallel routes, surrounded on all sides by a boundless stream of beaten men, from the marshes on the Bobr and Narev, from the Bialystock forest, seeping through the woods and moving according to its own elementary laws. A conscious will was already at work to dam this many-branched stream as it flowed east, and divert large parts of it to certain chosen spots. Thus Kasanzev's movement order led by side roads to the old Russian frontier—which was what everyone was trying to reach—but it also led to a little river, the Shchara, to the new defence line, to the new front that was going to be formed with all available troops, including units formed from hastily grouped stragglers. None of them knew of the new defence plan and the new front. Kasanzev knew only that he had to reach an old Polish country house near the Chelvianka river.

Nina Mihailovna kept in step with the rest. She didn't find it hard to get on with the soldiers. They were the same men as had been her neighbours at home in Novgorod—workers and carters, and peasants who brought their produce to town and bargained hard over every cabbage.

At the head of the column Kasanzev said to the sergeant who marched at his side: "Who is this *baba* they have in tow back there?"

"She has been with us almost since we left Bialystock. She's not just a *baba*—she's the wife of a captain."

"Ah, yes, one of those captains who have run away. What did he leave her for?"

The way led out of the wood but ran along its edge. On the left was a hollow which broadened out into a
133

valley falling down towards the Chelvianka. There were continual flashes from that direction, where German parachutists had established themselves and were being taken under fire from both sides of the valley.

"We had better wait and see what's going on," said Kasanzev.

They went on a little and then halted. Nina Mihailovna sat near Kasanzev. He himself had found a comfortable spot for her. Thereafter he paid her little further attention, but looked at her now and again reflectively. The men squatted on the ground or slept. Scarcely one of them had a coat—a soldier's blouse was their only protection against the cold of the night. Kasanzev was talking to a sergeant, an oldish man with spectacles.

"Tank for tank—the Germans were smashed, absolutely smashed," said Kasanzev, and looked at Nina again.

"How are your shoes?" he asked.

"Thank you—fine. My own wouldn't have lasted out."

"No—they would be better for dancing."

"Yes, why not? Do you mean that a Soviet citizen mustn't dance?"

"Just that some people dance and the rest have to look on."

The sergeant tried to change the subject.

"What are we doing here if the Germans were smashed?"

Kasanzev described the fire in the woods and how the petrol tanks and the supply columns had been blown up.

"And next day it was all over. The tanks were immobilised. The men cried like children when they had to get out and blow them up. It wasn't an armoured corps any more."

"What corps are you talking about—the fifth?" asked Nina.

"Yes, the fifth."

"What about the motorised infantry?"

"I was with them."

"So you know 3 Battalion and perhaps Nikolai too—Captain Nikolai Uralov?"

Kasanzev laughed and turned to the sergeant.

"You should have seen him—a red head—like a red rocket! The first time I met him he wanted to shoot me."

134 .

"You know Captain Uralov?"

"Of course I do—and you?"

"My name is Uralova."

Now it was his turn to stare at her.

"You are called Uralova—you are his wife? Well, in that case here's my hand. If you want to, you can come with us to Vladivostock."

"I don't want to go so far as that."

From Kasanzev she also learned that Uralov had led a break-through and later, when everything had gone to pieces, had disappeared into a wood with four men and a heavy machine-gun.

"There are tanks down there," said one of the men.

"They must be ours this time," thought Kasanzev, and went to the edge of the wood. It was now nearly light, and even before he had reached the point where the road began to run down into the valley he could see a house at the far end of the wooded height, about three miles away. It was the old Polish country house where he had to report. Below it two tanks were moving forward— tanks with black crosses. But that was impossible. How could they be here in the rear, right on the old frontier? Where were they coming from? They couldn't have dropped from the skies like the parachutists. But there they were—apparently on reconnaissance. Presently they turned back again, without firing a shot, to disappear in the opposite direction. They evidently weren't alone— they had mates and had probably gone to get them. Kasanzev gave the order to set off again. They must get to the country house as quickly as possible, but not by the shortest path across open country—they must keep to the hill and the cover of the wood which reached down in a gradual curve to the house.

When they reached the house they found weapon pits, slit trenches, gun positions, horse-drawn pieces. Ammunition was being distributed in a dugout, but there were no extra rifles. Each man received a piece of bread and a packet of black tobacco—*mahorka*. There was a liberal supply of vodka.

The journey of Kasanzev's men had come to a sudden end. They lay at the edge of the wood and waited—one of several similar groups which had arrived in the area.

Every third or fourth man had a rifle; others had only cartridges or a bottle filled with petrol to throw at the enemy.

"What are we supposed to do here?" said Anton.

"The battle is already lost," said Kyrill.

"There will be meat."

Captain Kasanzev had looked at the ground. The sickle curve of thin wood led from their halting place to the country house; on the other side a small feature rose gently towards the west.

A German reconnaissance plane circled overhead.

The positions were already spotted.

The sergeant came back to Kasanzev. He had been sent to direct Nina Mihailovna on her way, but had found it impossible. They were still fighting parachutists on the only road to the rear.

"I put her in a hay-stack. Later, when the road is clear, we can try again."

"Wasn't there any room in the house?"

"The staff is there—it's absolute chaos."

"Well, there's nothing else we can do."

As they spoke, Nikita appeared from the direction of the hay-stack which stood on a strip of meadow beside the wood, high above the bowl of the valley. He could scarcely contain himself. With a sly glance he said: "I was having a look at the right flank." A little later he turned to Kyrill and said: "Do you know that my new name is Nikolai?"

"What does that mean?"

Nikita only laughed, and Anton felt like knocking him down.

Kasanzev was discussing the situation with the sergeant. They had been to look at the guns. As far as infantry went, they had seen only a number of badly armed or even unarmed groups.

"The two recce tanks have been having a look—there's a plane up there. What is there left to defend?"

Kasanzev came to the same conclusion as his troop of stragglers: "There will be meat."

* * *

General Narishkin had picked the line of the Chelvianka and the ground stretching east to the Shchara as his

136

defence line. Here he would have his base and from here he would conduct any further operations. Now he was waiting for news from the armies on his flanks—3 Army from Grodno and 4 Army from Brest-Litovsk, although naturally he wouldn't hear from Korobkov any more. He had felt that the blow struck at Korobkov—and it had not been the only one of its kind—had been directed against himself.

He had just received a wireless message from Moscow, the text of which he must read to the senior officers who were already assembled in the cellar of an old ruined monastery between the Chelvianka and the Shchara.

Narishkin's face, with its slightly flattened nose and wide nostrils, looked grey and tired. The artillery commander looked as if he had been up all night, and so did the chief of operations, Semyonov. Narishkin pushed the secret order over to Semyonov.

Silence fell and Semyonov began to read:

Moscow, 25th June.

Order of the Supreme War Soviet.

The Commander-in-Chief of the Byelo-Russian Military District and of the forces on the Western Front, Colonel-General Pavlov, together with the Chief of Staff of the Byelo-Russian Military District and of the forces on the Western Front, Major-General Klimovsky, and the Chief Signals Officer of the Byelo-Russian Military District and the forces on the Western Front, Colonel Grigoriev, have criminally lost contact with their troops and have failed to regain contact. They have been found guilty of treason and condemned to death by shooting.

Further to the above: the sentence was carried out in Minsk.

The officers went from the cellar in silence, with set faces, leaving Narishkin, Semyonov and the artillery commander alone.

First Korobkov, now Pavlov, Klimovsky, and Grigoriev. It was difficult to see why Narishkin and Semyonov, too, weren't lying dead with the rest. Anyway here they were between the Chelvianka and the Shchara, and they were responsible for the lives of ten thousand men, perhaps twenty thousand by now, since men kept arriving and no one could count them. Everyone knew the orders. The artillery had been allotted its tasks. An observation plane was ready.

Time had been short for the preparation of the task. They had not been able to gain as many days as they would have with an orderly withdrawal, and so to a large extent ill-equipped troops had had to be used for the plan. Nor had it been possible to co-ordinate things with the flanking armies. In Brest-Litovsk there was complete confusion after the shooting of Korobkov. Presumably the Army from Grodno was being driven on to the Shchara, so positions had been allotted for these more or less intact formations. The most serious thing from the very beginning—right from Bialystock—had been the almost total lack of information about the enemy. That was the point on which everything threatened to collapse.

Narishkin was just about to drive with the artillery commander to the airfield south of Slonim to take a look round in an old biplane, when Semyonov, who had gone across to his own office, came back in a state of great excitement. This calm man, who usually measured his words so carefully, was incapable of bringing out a single clear sentence. He threw on to the table a handful of messages from the troops on the Chelvianka. From both the northern and southern flanks of the new front the reports were the same. Previously fighting in the rear had been against strong bodies of parachutists. Now the picture had changed. It was no longer a question only of enemy airborne troops but of armoured formations and strong motorised forces attacking from the east.

From the east.

Narishkin brooded over the messages. Others came in saying the same thing. "An enveloping movement—if the enemy forces are strong enough we are in the bag."

Semyonov went to the set—he called up all the formations he could reach. From all of them he had the same information.

"The whole intelligence branch is one big whore-house," stormed Narishkin. "They should be hanged, drawn and quartered. Here we are sitting in the bag—there are no two ways about it. Our task isn't to build up a line here in the west. We must break through—to the east. The direction we're not allowed to go in." He produced the foulest curse in the Russian language. "But there's nothing else for it. A break out to the east—we're still strong enough for it. Roll up your sleeves, Semyonov. Comrade Commander, cancel all orders. Turn your guns round. We'll have the guns in front—then second echelons and the infantry and all the rest of the stuff in the rear." He cursed again. "It must be done. You must do the impossible."

Semyonov and the artillery commander went to work. Narishkin could bear it no longer. He went to and fro merely getting in the way. He couldn't breathe here any more. He was sitting in a tomb and he would be long enough in his grave without that. Yet he couldn't be of any help.

"I'm going to the airfield. We'll meet in hell—or at a hell of a party farther east."

* * *

At this same moment an officer was riding through the suburbs of Slonim. He was muddied from top to toe and on his breast he wore the Order of Lenin and the Order of the Red Star. He pulled up at the broken bridge over the Shchara and drove his jaded nag through the stream. The town seemed dead—houses were burning everywhere; dead soldiers lay in the streets. The weary rider hung over the back of his mount and looked around him, but it was a long time before he saw a human being —an old woman.

"How do I get to the HQ?" he asked.

The old woman looked at him uncomprehendingly.

"You silly old woman, think harder—tell me, where are the soldiers, the officers? A lot of officers?"

The old woman went and fetched a man.

"The Town Major has moved," he said, "to the Party Offices."

"That's right—your Party's offices," the old woman had to add.

"I don't want the Party Offices or the Town Major. Listen. There must be a headquarters here. You know what I mean—high officers, a lot of cars. Have you seen anything like that?"

The man knew nothing.

"Well, where is the Town Major's office?"

The horse was exhausted but it had to break once more into a weary trot. When the rider reached the courtyard of the Party Offices, he caught sight of some trucks. The Town Major was moving. There were a lot of formalities. He had to produce papers and special passes, but finally he learned where to find the HQ he wanted.

The horse by now was at its last gasp. It had to cross the river again and go on along a field path leading to the well-concealed ruins of a monastery.

As the rider dismounted he caught sight of a General about to get into a car.

"Uralov," someone shouted to him.

Uralov recognised General Narishkin.

"Captain Uralov reporting."

"So it's you, Uralov. Well, since it's you, get in. Quick, I must be off."

Uralov sat opposite Narishkin, who had a liaison officer with him. A few men of his personal bodyguard followed in a second car. Uralov opened up his blouse and produced a sweat-soaked document.

"Task completed, Comrade General."

Narishkin unfolded the document and read. He merely nodded and looked in silence out of the window. He could scarcely have expected anything else. Of 3 Army only fragments were left—perhaps biggish fragments. But if he could get in touch with them they might be a considerable reinforcement, and in any case a reasonable reserve.

"I need a courier at once," said Narishkin.

The liaison officer looked at Uralov. He was sitting with his eyes wide open but staring glassily. He was asleep already, with open eyes.

Narishkin reached the airfield and got out. He left behind him the liaison officer and his bodyguard—and Uralov, sitting in the car with his chin sunk on his breast.

* * *

It was heavy gunfire which wakened Uralov from his death-like slumber. Only a score of miles away the same cannonade made Nina Mihailovna start up out of a deep, drugged sleep. After the physical effort and the sleepless nights she, too, had fallen into unconsciousness the moment she lay down.

Now she started up.

"Nikolai," she cried. He must have been there a moment ago. She felt his presence still. Her dress was in disorder and she smoothed it down. The air was stifling, there was straw everywhere. She was lying alone in a hay-stack. The earth was quaking beneath her. She was thirsty. She crept to the entrance of her hiding-place and forgot her thirst again. Fire was raining from the sky and fragments flew everywhere. Where the convulsed earth fell back into place there suddenly lay the broken wheel of a limber. The horses broke loose and galloped over the field. A big grey ran straight at her with wild eyes, distended nostrils and stiff tail erect.

On this reversed front the artillery, which now had their observers in the front instead of in the rear, had come under sudden enemy fire. A few gunners had succeeded in facing about, to the east, and had fired as long as they could over open sights. Then they fell silent. Stillness descended and the smoke of the explosions drifted away. The clear blue sky appeared. And this stillness, which should have caused her the utmost anxiety, made Nina Mihailovna breathe more freely.

It did not last long. The German armour pushed forward with a clatter of tracks, snapping off small trees, hurling bushes and loose turf behind them.

Now the scratch units which had been put together to fight on the new line had to take on the enemy thrusting towards the west. The first wave stormed forward.

*   *   *

A great cry rises into the air from a thousand throats; the cry which will not die until the hearts which lie under its spell have ceased to beat. This is the moment in all eternity which must be grasped with both hands.

Morituri te salutant.

Here the words are *"Za rodinu, za Stalina."*

For the Fatherland, for Stalin.

A grey cloud rises from the ground—a grey wave of soldiers, who have been lost once and have now rallied for the last effort, storms forward against the enemy infantry and the advancing tanks. They have gone hungry

141

for weeks; for years their life has been one long hunger, a hunger they inherited from their fathers, a hunger they have nursed in silence all their lives. Now they have poured vodka into their tortured bellies—not just a drop but whole draughts, half a bottle, a whole bottle; so Kyrill and Nikita and Anton and Matvey run forward. A man falls and Matvey stoops as he runs and takes his rifle. He has a weapon now and is shooting. He doesn't mind what he shoots at, but in front are the green uniforms of the enemy—too far to reach. Nikita falls. Matvey falls. The whole rank falls. *Za rodinu, za Stalina.* A new wave rises—another Nikita, another Matvey. Once more it is vodka and hate for everything and sorrow for a lost life. They run forward, take the rifles of the fallen, run on and are mowed down by automatic weapons. Another wave, arm in arm—great gaps are shot in the chain of men; the broken chain moves on, drunk and roaring and falling.

Shots, bayonet thrusts, butt-strokes. Petrol flasks burst on the enemy tanks and wrap them in a ball of fire. Kyrill rushes with bare hands on his opponent. Anton has forgotten his wife and his three children. On the flickering horizon stand golden towers—the towers of Moscow. A grey tank rolls forward and destroys the illusion. Anton hurls his petrol flask against the fire-breathing monster.

* * *

"We can't do it—there's no end to them."

Lieutenant Vohwinkel signalled back: "A new wave on the edge of the wood. I can't make out what's happening."

"It's like a tidal wave," came back from the other tank.

"HE."

"HE."

They fired high explosive.

"Keep it up—right ahead."

Vohwinkel saw the tracer of the machine-gun bursts from the next tank lash the attacking waves. "Right ahead—right ahead."

New waves rose. The whole field as far as the eye could see was full of men.

142

"We can't kill any more of them." Panic was beginning to break out inside the tank. The loader shouted: "Ammunition running out—only five rounds, four rounds more."

The stubby gun glowed. Melting paint ran from the barrel. The breech-block was white-hot. The lieutenant, the loader, the wireless operator and the gunner cowered half-naked and exhausted in their steel housing.

For four days they had been driving across country, over the Muchavetz, on to Kobrin and then turning south and back over the Muchavetz. Then north-east, far into the heart of the land, tracing curves and loops, leaving Bialystock, with the enemy concentrations reported there untouched, and the roads east from the town uncut. Only four days and they were to become four hundred, and four times four hundred, before the end. But these had been four days without real contact with the enemy —whenever enemy columns appeared they had come and surrendered; and always there had been the same roads, the same villages and the same desolation. The first uneasy feeling of astonishment at the size of the land had crept into their hearts. Now, suddenly and unexpectedly, the wide expanse seemed to vomit forth men. The men caught in the pocket were pushing east in long waves, always the same grey waves like a nightmare, a terrifying phantom in the clear sunlight. A wave broke against the tank. Something tinkled on the steel walls.

"They are throwing bottles."

"Incendiary flasks."

One of them found its mark, bursting on the edge of the slightly open turret. The liquid trickled in. A blue flame shot up. A column of fire stood over the tank. Lieutenant Vohwinkel thrust the turret open and sprang down. The loader and the gunner climbed out. Like blazing torches they rolled on the cool ploughed field— beside Anton and Kyrill, for the flames had leapt to them, too; beside Nikita, whose eyes were already glazed.

Nina Mihailovna heard thin cries — whether from Germans or her own people she did not know. The horizon swam. Dust choked her throat. Dive-bombers roared over the haystack and swooped down into the valley. There was a continual thunder of gunfire. Men in grey and green were falling on each other. They were dying; that she did understand. She was thirsty, with an unbearable longing for a sip of water. And Nikolai had not come. Who had it been, then? She thought he had been with her. Who had it been?

* * *

Narishkin flew over the wide landscape. The Shchara, flowing from the Pripet marshes through Slonim and on to join the Niemen, was a thin, gleaming ribbon cut diagonally by the railway line from Volkovysk to Slonim and Baranovitchy, the line which led on to Minsk and Moscow. According to the latest reports it had been cut at least once. There could be no more talk of a coherent front—the fighting had developed into a series of individual actions.

The only order he could give to those troops of his, fighting without any supply system whatsoever, was for a breakout to the east—whether it was allowed or not.

Save what could still be saved.

Narishkin's slow-flying UT passed over the tops of the trees, sank low over the ryefields and flew like a dragonfly over meadows of ripe grass. Whether the troops had received orders or not, under enemy pressure and because of the direction of his attack, they had turned to face east of their own accord. The infantry among them consisted of 30 Infantry Regiment, which it had been possible to put into action at full strength. It was to move forward in three groups, in three battalions. Of one battalion there was nothing left; of another there was only one man in five on his feet; and the third battalion was breaking out from the edge of the wood and advancing against German machine-gun and mortar fire. The Red Army men recognised the low-flying UT, which dipped its wings in salute to the troops moving forward below it.

"The General is sitting up there. That's Narishkin up there, he's watching us, he's with us."

"*Za rodinu, za Stalina.*"

The shout could not reach Narishkin, but he saw them advance. The UT felt its way along the edge of the bowl where the artillery division lay. The howitzers down there were silent. They had been overrun. The gunners were fighting with carbines. On the southern edge of the wood the scratch formations rose in wave after wave.

Now for 159 Infantry Regiment.

Narishkin wanted to greet this distinguished regiment and then turn back east. Because of the number of enemy fighters the little UT had to stick close to the contours of the ground and almost creep along the earth. When Narishkin reached the position of 159 Infantry Regiment he saw only the dusty trails of German tanks on the march, that was all. After coming in low over the spot a couple of times he knew what had happened. He took off his cap and threw it down. The General's cap sank over the grave of 159 Infantry Regiment. It had been destroyed attacking enemy armour.

During its flight towards Slonim the UT came under machine-gun fire, and turning off towards the south-east disappeared over the forest.

* * *

The column which turned its MGs on Narishkin's UT consisted of the heavily armed vehicles of Lieutenant-General Bomelbuerg's advance guard.

Long, hot, empty days lay behind this division. It wasn't even "second line"—it had been left completely behind. The country in front of it had been combed out by armoured units and motorised formations, and all there was left for the infantry to do was to move north-east along side roads—sometimes marching, sometimes stumbling over grass and plough, fanned out in little detachments. Part of the time it had advanced along a railway line where trains no longer ran.

Bomelbuerg had not been able to stand it at HQ, where so little was going on, so on various occasions he had undertaken sweeps into enemy country with his advance guard on his own initiative. Nothing on a very big scale and nothing to boast about—which Bomelbuerg was far from doing. It was scarcely more than a question of trips into no-man's-land. There had been no contacts with enemy troops, and when a few Russians had appeared— once it was a whole column—they had begun to wave white rags when still a long way off, and their one idea was to be taken prisoner as quickly as possible.

On this day, too, Bomelbuerg was right forward

intending to push on ahead with a patrol. A motorised force was driving an enemy unit before it and had left the little town of Slonim untouched. The advance guard caught sight of the houses of Slonim over the green tips of the standing crops. Then people began to appear on the road—old men with bare heads, carrying white flags. In spite of their venerable aspect they seemed to be in some haste. An old man with a patriarchal air was led up to Bomelbuerg.

"This is the General," someone prompted him.

"Your excellency, Herr General, they have just begun to shoot the political prisoners in the courtyard of the prison. Help us—come quickly into the town with your soldiers. Each minute lost is lost for ever. Each minute our sons and daughters are falling under the bullets of these murderers."

The old man spoke in broken German and Lieutenant Hasse repeated what he said to the General.

Bomelbuerg's first reaction was to say: "Into the town quickly." Then it occurred to him that the situation wasn't at all clear, for according to intelligence reports a Russian army had its HQ in the town. They asked the old man about it.

"They left everything lying, got into their trucks and drove off. There are no more soldiers in Slonim. But a NKVD detachment stayed behind in the prison."

Bomelbuerg had come so close to the old man's face that he saw the long white beard.

"Keep calm, old man, we'll help you—right away."

The advance guard comprised an armoured car, four trucks and a small detachment of infantry from the motor-cycle battalion.

"Which is the forward company?"

"Boblink's."

"All right then—we'll take a platoon with us."

It was Corporal Gnotke's platoon which climbed into the trucks of the advance guard. The column moved forward again, firing with its MGs as it went at a low-flying plane without hitting it. The plane turned away to the south-east. Bomelbuerg told them to ask the old man whether one could expect a rising in Soviet Russia.

"A rising is more than likely," answered the old man,

146

"but there aren't any men to lead it. Here in Byelo-Russia the whole intelligentsia down to the high school students have been arrested. But a lot of them haven't been taken away yet and are still in the prison."

In Slonim there were a lot of burning houses. The people were doing nothing to put out the fires. The dispossessed owners (the soldiers learnt from their White Russian guides) didn't want to do anything to save Soviet property. The town seemed to be dead. The inhabitants squatted in cellars and slit-trenches. Many had feared that they would be arrested at the last moment and had therefore preferred to hide as far away from their homes as possible.

The column halted before a high grey wall. There was an old, rusted iron door, bolted from within. They could hear bursts from machine-pistols. The motor-cyclists stopped under the wall and pulled themselves up. Gnotke's platoon followed in the same way, jumping from the trucks over the wall to round up the dazed NKVD men. Others ran into the building and opened the doors of the cells. Half of them stood open and empty; the prisoners who had been crammed into them lay shot under the wall of the courtyard. As the pile of dead mounted, the last victims had had to drag away the corpses before standing up themselves to receive the bullets. Now the rescued prisoners streamed out of the grey building. The inhabitants of Slonim, so long invisible, came in through the now open iron gate. Women found their husbands again. Others sought their menfolk and found them among the dead.

Gnotke thought of a night in Berlin long ago.

He had made two trips to the cattle-yard and then, overcome with terror, he had run off. Not till days later had Riederheim found him in a pub, sitting alone at a table. Then it had been night; here it had happened in bright sunlight. He caught sight of Corporal Heydebreck and thought of the corporal's cousin, Peter von Heydebreck, the SA Gruppenfuehrer from Pomerania. It was strange that the fate of that one man, whose end he had not seen with his own eyes, touched him more deeply than the fate of a hundred others he had himself helped to arrest.

147

"Long live Germany" had been Peter von Heydebreck's last words.

Germany—that's just it. Here we are in Slonim as liberators. Is that possible when we have such memories —can we come with blood-stained hands and still be liberators?

* * *

The Byelo-Russian railway terminus in Moscow was like a gloomy cave. The few blue veiled lights could not dispel the darkness in the great building. Everywhere there were soldiers leaving for the front; people were talking quietly and good-byes and sobs mingled into a dull murmur. Turuchin had never seen so many weeping women in one place. To his own wife he said: "Go home now—why stay here and suffer?"

"Can't you stay another day?"

"How can I? Hasn't everyone to report to his unit on the outbreak of war?"

"And what will happen to me?—I suppose I will have to go into a munitions factory."

"Things will get better soon—we'll soon push the Germans back. Go away now—we're only tormenting ourselves here. The train will leave soon, anyway."

Quartermaster-Lieutenant Turuchin led his wife to the exit, trying clumsily to dry her weeping eyes. He stood and waved until she had disappeared across the dark square. Then he went back through the murmuring crowd, looked for the train to Minsk and got in. At last the leave-taking was over—sad good-byes to his wife, and before that to his father-in-law and mother-in-law and to the neighbours, with vodka everywhere and tear-stained faces. He felt that the worst was over and that he could face the future calmly. Where would he find his regiment again? "Advancing towards Germany, of course."

"Where did you leave your regiment?"

"Between the Bobr and the Beresovka — on manœuvres."

"Then they are probably near Warsaw by now."

The war was being fought on foreign soil—no one doubted that, least of all the four junior officers sitting together in the compartment on this, the first evening of the war.

The journey to Minsk should have lasted fourteen hours. This time it took three days—days when the station buffets were shut and there was nothing to buy; nothing to eat and nothing to drink. Only on the morning of the fourth day did they come within sight of Minsk.

The train stopped again—for a long time. Doors opened and closed. People were running hurriedly along the corridors. Turuchin turned his face to the wall. The day would be long in any case—particularly since all the food he had brought had been eaten, and he would have to go hungry until he reached his regiment.

"Comrade Lieutenant," a fellow-traveller touched him on the arm. "Wake up—Minsk is being bombed."

It was a bad joke—only a fool or a provocateur could think of such a thing. Yet Turuchin sat up. He groped for his shoes and put his uniform right. By the first grey light of dawn he could read the name of the station. The coach and the corridor were empty. Turuchin climbed down on to the platform; he must see what was going on. The passengers had all collected at the head of the train, by the engine. Farther ahead lay the still shadowy silhouette of Minsk. There was a strange noise in the air—a distant, subdued humming. And you could see something—great, dark drops falling.

"Where are our planes?"

"Where is our Airforce?"

"How can the Germans bomb Minsk at their leisure?"

There was an Airforce General there. They all looked at him as if he could explain everything. Isn't the Soviet Airforce the strongest in the world? Aren't Stalin's falcons fed on chocolate and biscuits? Now there was no more humming—no more black drops fell through the air. Fires began to glow—at the goods station, over the town centre, in Karl Marx Square.

"That thick black smoke is over the centre."

"Are there no anti-aircraft guns?"

"Where are the falcons?"

"There they are at last."

"A bit late, comrade."

Soviet fighters rose, roaring over the horizon.

"At last, at last."

Everyone turned towards the little wood behind which the airfield must lie. Minutes passed and fear crept into their hearts. Only three planes had taken off and no more followed: three machines against the innumerable German planes which dominated the skies over Minsk. What did this mean? This was far behind the front, which must be three hundred, five hundred miles away by now.

The passengers stood about waiting for something to happen, but the train got no signal to proceed. It was four miles to Minsk—they could walk that distance. Turuchin had to change trains in Minsk, anyway. He fetched his cardboard box, containing underwear but nothing to eat, and set off, following a footpath through the woods.

Suitcases, sacks, boxes lay strewn on either side of the path. The only sound was the humming of fat flies over the face of a corpse.

Turuchin was glad to catch sight at last of a soldier walking along in front of him. It was a sergeant—but even he didn't seem to be quite normal. What was one to make of it when a sergeant said that he had belonged to a unit which had been put to flight? A Soviet unit which had been put to flight! Yet this Sergeant Subkov made a good impression in spite of the odd things he said, and since he wanted to go to Minsk, too, they went on together.

The silence was suddenly broken as a new attack began on the town. When they came out of the wood they saw the burning sheds of the goods station before them; and no one seeemd to be trying to put out the flames. The diving Ju's had driven the people into the cellars and slit-trenches. Turuchin and Subkov dived into a trench, too.

Later they went to look for the RTO. Transport officers, majors, colonels were all shouting at a young lieutenant. They were arguing and cursing and one officer ran into a signals cabin to switch the points himself. Another let down a signal and someone else hauled it up again. It was incredible. Turuchin felt he was in a madhouse.

"And what do you want here?" said the lieutenant turning to Turuchin and Subkov.

"We want the RTO."

"The RTO has gone—I am his second-in-command."

"I must get to Bialystock and on to my unit."

"There are no troops there now."

This was odd.

"You must report in Rutchnya."

"In Rutchnya—on the autobahn?"

"Yes, but get off the steps quickly before the Germans see you standing here."

Turuchin and Subkov went.

"Did you hear that?—the Germans might see a fly crawling about on the station, he said."

"Yes, he's very young and he's all in. The RTO has cleared out and left him holding the baby," Subkov remarked.

"But where will we get something to eat?"

"Maybe in Rutchnya."

The food problem, however, solved itself in an unexpected manner. They went down the main street. Here, too, the houses were burning and flames were bursting out of the upper storeys. A heap of ruins where a five-storey house had stood was alive with convicts, condemned to forced labour, digging out people whose cries could still be heard from under the rubble.

Then to his surprise the whole solid order of things collapsed before Turuchin's eyes. It was worse than anything he had experienced that morning. A convict— a dark Uzbek—picked up a stone and suddenly they all had stones in their hands. With stones, spades and helves, they threw themselves upon their guards. Shots were fired but only into the air. The soldiers took to flight and the convicts broke loose, disappearing into the ruins and the surrounding streets.

Turuchin's one idea was to get away from here—but where to? Suddenly he felt himself lost; and then he was tortured by hunger. They stopped in front of a shop. Women had been waiting for hours to get salt, matches and paper for blackouts, and after a long wait the queue had scarcely diminished. How could you go to war without salt, without matches, without a piece of bread? The women's patience was at an end. The window—it was already splintered by the bombs—was pushed in; the crowd burst through the doors and climbed in at the

151

window. Turuchin and Subkov were in the midst of them. They scarcely knew how they had got into the shop.

"Can't we buy anything to eat here?" asked Turuchin. That was a ridiculous remark, but he was like a drowning man clutching at a straw, and it seemed to him as if his words might somehow account for his presence in the crowd of looters.

"You're a fool," Subkov told him.

"Take what you want," said others.

Women, workers and even convicts were emptying the shelves. One was eating a herring, another sweets—others again were grabbing biscuits or sauerkraut or whatever they could lay hands on. Turuchin, too, took whatever he could find. After all, he had been three days without a bite. Afterwards he was angry at the sergeant, as if it was he who had got him into this situation. He found Subkov again sitting in a rowdy group. They were eating herrings and pickled onions and drinking vodka. The bottle went round and round. I can't do anything with him, said Turuchin to himself, I must get rid of him. But they left the shop together.

Their way was blocked by rubble. There were wires lying on the asphalt. Water sprayed high from broken mains. The Stukas dived down almost into the streets and Turuchin and Subkov ran down into a cellar.

It was the cellar of a modern block of flats for engineers and technicians employed on the numerous building schemes in Minsk and the occupied part of Byelo-Russia. Their wives came down into the cellar with their children, and other people ran in from the street. The building shook when a bomb fell near by; plaster fell from the walls; the children screamed.

"And they still say we're fighting the enemy on foreign soil."

"To think that we are so helpless."

"Where are all our airmen?"

"Don't panic, they're all at the front causing the Germans terrible losses."

A woman—or perhaps it was a girl—laughed and seemed unable to stop. Everyone turned towards her.

"What is it like at the front?" Turuchin was asked.

"I've been on leave in Moscow," he answered, and felt

ashamed that he had to admit that he knew nothing about the front. All the while he continued to look at this woman—this girl—who seemed ready to burst out into laughter again at his answer. She was sitting there bolt upright; under her parted black hair her face seemed almost white. A pretty, regular face—but an ugly wound, not quite covered by a strip of plaster, ran down her cheek to her neck. The wound was very recent. She didn't fit in amongst these people—she wasn't from this town; she was a foreigner, perhaps a spy.

Turuchin could not pursue his thoughts. A woman had collapsed. Her little girl screamed and other children joined in. Turuchin and Subkov carried her into the next room whilst others looked after the children. When Turuchin came back and looked round for the girl she was no longer to be seen. The wave of attacks seemed to be over.

Out on the street again Turuchin and Subkov were stopped by a truck-driver.

"Can you tell us the way to Rutchnya?"

"Yes, we're going there ourselves."

"All right, jump up."

Their road led through the centre of the town. Several times they had to drive round obstructions in the street. Then they left the stone buildings behind and came into the suburbs, where the wooden houses on either side of the road were on fire and overhead the flames met like a roof. They drove on into another street, to another and another again—it was the same everywhere. A girl with a gas-mask said she knew another way, through the factory. When they reached it, the courtyard was blocked with machinery being dismantled and made ready for shipment. There was no way through and the truck had to be left. Subkov stayed behind, too. Turuchin was glad to be rid of him. He went on on foot.

* * *

No one in the cellar could have known that the hysterical laughter of the girl with the wound on her cheek was, if not her first sign of life for days, at least her first sign of awareness of what went on around her. She wasn't a spy, as Turuchin had thought, nor a foreigner either, although her clothes had been made by a Polish

153

dressmaker who had worked in Warsaw and even in Paris. She had been dug out of the rubble of her home and then put in a car, but after she had reached the NKVD barrier at the other side of the town she had been forced to continue her journey in a truck with refugees and wounded. She had come through Volkovysk and Slonim, where she was taken into the overcrowded hospital with a high fever. She was the bearer of a remarkable pass—a document which not only requested all possible aid for her from those whom it might concern, but the authenticity of which was vouched for by the number of times it had been stamped. The corridors and the very steps of the hospital were covered with wounded. Each day a piece of bread and four lumps of sugar were distributed. This alone was enough to make the soldiers who had arrived from the Narev, or even further west, unwilling to give up their places. "If you aren't gone by morning, you will be shot," the doctor had had to say to them before they would drag themselves away from the comparative comfort of the hospital and hobble off.

Here Irina Petrovna had lain for days without moving, scarcely heeding what went on around her. Nor had she made any objection when the doctor said to her, too: "We have no room any more—you will be put on the train to Moscow with your pass." The escort she had been given in Bialystock had been in a hurry to get away and had already driven off; now she was left entirely to her own resources. After a few hours the train in which she had been placed steamed into the burning station at Minsk—and here she was, for the time being, stranded. She knew some people in Minsk—she had a friend here, Lena Klimovskaya. They had gone to school together in Moscow and had occasionally seen each other during the last two years.

She walked to the Klimovskys' house and went in.

An extraordinary sight met her eyes. Bits of the General's uniform were scattered about the room. Books torn from the shelves lay on the floor mixed with pictures, letters and files; NKVD men were going through the rooms. Major-General Klimovsky had been shot that morning. His daughter came out—a white mask above a dark dress buttoned up to the neck. Irina was transfixed

—it was as if it was herself she saw standing there. Lena stumbled towards her and fell into her arms.

"Lena—you look ill. It is terrible, everything is so terrible. Where are your father and mother—what is happening to us?" A NKVD officer came up and separated them. Irina was led to the door. Lena remained at the end of the corridor. . .

Irina stood in the street once more. Klimovsky had been shot and she must not speak to Lena. Where was she to go now? Step by step she went on her way, into the unknown, into the void.

She found herself in a cellar. Children were weeping. The women were talking about salt and matches, and someone took it into his head to say that Stalin's proud falcons were fighting the Germans over the front. That was too much for her and she could contain herself no longer. She laughed, and she was not the only one—Lena laughed, her mother Marya Andreyevna laughed, and surely the people who had been burned to death in Volkovysk must have laughed, and the limping wounded in Baranovitschy. Everybody between Bialystock and Minsk, she thought, must have laughed together. It was a relief; the laughter dissolved something, set something flowing in her veins again.

She went down the main street and came to the station again. How was she to find a way out of this trap? After all, she still had her railway ticket to Moscow and the pass which her father had written for her and the army had stamped, thus proving its validity. But no more trains were leaving and there were so many people waiting; people with faces such as she had never seen before— distorted faces, exhausted faces, repellent faces, faces full of affliction and worry. There were thieves and murderers, and there was a mother who would not let her dead child out of her arms. There were looters, and she, too, felt an urge to plunder. She was terribly hungry and ready to help break down the doors of the trucks and run off with a sack of flour; but there were too many hands and the sack tore and all the faces were covered with white.

A train thundered into the station. The quarrelling figures were separated and the flour flew up in clouds

155

of dust once more. A train from Baranovitschy—people hung out of the windows and clung to the steps. No one would get out. The guards stormed and cursed, as others had stormed and cursed before them, but the train stood still.

Irina caught sight of a pair of friendly eyes which seemed to have followed her in the crowd. They looked at her as if they knew everything about her, including the misery, which had brought her near to tears, and her wild desire to crush in her small hands the whole station with its flour and its dirty crowds. This unknown man, who seemed so strangely familiar to her, had kindly blue eyes, a long white beard, and his white hair hung down over the back of his collar. He was an old man, pitifully dressed, his withered body clad in tatters, his feet wrapped in rags, and yet there was a light in his eyes and his whole being was radiant.

Old Shulga stood in the middle of the station. He had reason to be cheerful in the midst of catastrophe. In this delicate girl looking around her with the startled eyes of a deer he saw, in spite of her strange behaviour, not the spy Turuchin had seen—nor, in spite of her foreign clothes, a foreigner. Where, he wondered, could a young girl like that grow up these days? Only in a sheltered family, in a house where the past was not forgotten.

Now the glasshouse where you grew up, far from reality, has been shattered. But I see that you will survive in the open air and it will do you good—you are still flying in uncertain circles over the flood-waters, but your eyes are sharp and you will soon find a twig on which to alight. If you fall, it will be into the hands of God. An old man is looking at you with thankfulness, for in you who have grown up so far removed from reality he has seen the indestructible face of Russia.

That was what old Shulga's eyes said.

Irina Petrovna felt as if a close relative from across the seas had greeted her, and when she moved on and disappeared into the tumult she no longer felt so much alone.

* * *

Bomelbuerg's division moved east by forced marches. On the Shchara it had crossed a deserted battlefield—

a stretch of country covered with tank tracks. There were a lot of dead men in the ryefields, and dead horses, too. Burnt-out German trucks, abandoned Russian guns and limber wheels were scattered through the meadows. Of what had once been a country house there were only the walls left. A Russian divisional HQ was said to have been there.

They left Slonim to the north and advanced towards Baranovitchy. The division was supposed to take up positions east of Baranovitchy and stay there until the surrounded remains of a Russian army had been liquidated.

It was already night when Boblink's company reached its destination—a deserted village, a single long street with many of the houses burnt to the ground. Others had no thatch left on the roofs. Here and there the long arm of a pump pointed to the sky. The men were tired and had lain down to sleep soon after their arrival. Lance-Corporal Heydebreck was writing a letter by the light of a candle. It was almost midnight when he left the hut to crawl in beside the others in the barn which had been allotted as their billet. Once—that is to say, until they were forbidden—he had been a boy scout. He had learned to track and to creep up on his opponents, and to distinguish the noises of nature from each other and from all the accidental noises made by man. He lingered at the door of the barn and listened. The men in the huts behind him were asleep. The wood behind the huts was asleep. The meadow was asleep, too. But from the river came a gurgling noise which after a little while was repeated. What could it be? A ripple? There wasn't a breath of wind. A fish? It might be a fish—or a frog perhaps. He felt his way into the dark barn leaving the door open behind him.

The noise had not come from a frog. A human being had caused it—a man who had worked his way across from the other side on the flat river bed, and then lain in the mud of the bank below the barn. A head had come up—in the light of the stars it looked black, not red as it usually did. "I haven't much time to waste," said the man to himself, and pulled himself up on to the bank; that was what had caused the second noise. "I haven't much time to waste, but if that fellow up there doesn't go away soon I shall have to twist his neck— and I would like to avoid that. I'll wait until I have breathed three more times then I'll do it."

That was the moment when Heydebreck disappeared into the barn.

Uralov slid up the bank like a cat. He felt his way along by the barn and past the huts. At a corner he stopped. So far he was quite satisfied. The Fritzes were going to make things easy for him. The sentry in front of one of the huts—probably a company HQ was there— was standing, not in the shadow of the house, but in the radiance of the starry night, which was not very bright but bright enough for a man to be clearly silhouetted. It never occurred to a patrol to keep to the shady side of the village; the two soldiers were walking along in the middle of the road. Uralov never let them out of his sight. If they stayed on the road and kept on towards the river he would have to deal with them; but if they went round the village and back towards the wood he would let them go. They turned on to the road which led round the village. Fine, have a nice walk— I won't disturb you. There remained the sentry in front of the company HQ. He presented no special difficulties and probably did not notice himself how quickly and noiselessly he was despatched from this life. Once Uralov had pulled the corpse into the shadow of the house the way was clear. Near the HQ he found a wire and snipped it. He held one end in his hand and used it to guide himself. A second, a third, a fourth wire was cut. It was not long before communications to the rear and to the command post of the horsed troop downstream were thoroughly disrupted.

Uralov had not had much time to lose; the task had been timed to a minute and already—although they approached quietly—he could hear the advance party wading through the river, carrying machine-guns and straw soaked in petrol. When they reached the bank they separated and glided along the huts as noiselessly as Uralov had done. But the slight sound of metal touching metal awoke Captain Boblink, who came bare-headed out of his hut and ran a few paces uncertainly. At the

158

pump two hands gripped his neck and squeezed until his knees gave way and he sank lifeless to the ground. Now all was ready and a breathless silence fell on the village. But presently from the other side of the river there came a confused sound, which at first was muffled, then it became the noise of marching feet, the soft beat of hooves on grass, the creaking of wheels mingled with suppressed cries.

Langhoff sat upright and listened. He was surrounded by snoring men. Corporals, sergeants, spotters, signallers —he had eight men in all, his little team, the soul of the whole troop. Could it be the river making that noise? If it were a mountain stream it would rumble along like that and perhaps even roar like thunder. Something was rumbling—what could it be on a dark night like this? Ask Sergeant-Major Lemke. The line to the guns was dead. This was it. Langhoff shook the signaller awake. "Get up, Emil, the line's dead. Get through on RT." The signaller started up. "I called them ten minutes ago. Troop came on the air—they've shut down now for another fifty minutes."

"That's a bloody awful mess. You'll have to run for it—troop is to report if everything is OK."

The signaller looked dispiritedly at his commander, and his mate too hung about reluctantly.

"Can't it wait till first light, sir?"

"Everything's quiet here."

"If anyone has anything to say it will be the troop commander."

An explosion shattered the silence of the night—a rifle shot fired from the other end of the village.

"Get out," yelled Langhoff, and wakened the whole team with his shouting. The signallers had scarcely left when a second shot rang out—quite near this time— followed by another.

A burst of machine-gun fire swept overhead but it was too high and there was only a rain of twigs and leaves. The machine-gunner ran towards his weapon but Langhoff caught him by the arm.

"Stop—we must see what's up first."

The rest were crowding blindly towards the rear.

"Where are you off to?"

"Into the wood."

"Bastards—as long as they are shooting up towards us we're defiladed here. Don't move."

A second burst of fire brought down more twigs and leaves. It was impossible to tell what was really happening and the uncertainty was becoming almost unbearable. Langhoff was still wondering whether a reconnaissance were possible when the scene was suddenly lit as bright as day. Simultaneously there was a murderous burst of fire and the barn across the river broke into flames. Rag-torches were being thrown on to the few remaining straw roofs in the village and the illumination became even brighter.

"There you are, you see—they'll cut and run now. That's all they want. They don't leave themselves time for anything else, and there are too many for us to tackle. As long as they leave us alone we'll sit tight."

Wild figures, lit intermittently by the flames, burst out of the desolate and deserted village square. The well was surrounded by men—shadowy forms with modern weapons who let loose bursts of fire into the barn-doors and burning huts. On the fleeing infantrymen of Boblink's company they used bayonets as well as clubs and bare fists.

The movement began to take shape. The Russian advance guard split in two to form the flank guards for a monstrous snake which squirmed and pushed and forced itself along. Soldiers with and without weapons, civilians, sick and crippled, cattle from the collectives, horses, sheep, more soldiers, guns. New faces continually appeared from the dark waters of the river and crossed the brightly lit scene. It was a break-through—by a whole corps, by an army or part of an army. It seemed as if the pocket had burst and was pouring over this one German company. Men and horses and transport—they all rolled and trampled towards the east.

It was the third operation of the kind General Narishkin had carried out. This time all he had were the remnants of his army and portions of 3 Army from Grodno. They had crossed the stream two hours after midnight in an attempt to get as far east as possible in a forced march, and daybreak found them in a widely scattered leaguer in thick forest. With the exception of the sentries and the patrols, everyone lay in an exhausted sleep.

It was midday before the camp awoke. Ivan, Pyotr and Anton stretched their limbs. Pyotr turned his pocket inside out. Once there had been bacon in it, and mahorka with newspaper for making cigarettes, and bread dried and toasted over the fire. There were still traces of all of them and everything was greasy; otherwise the pocket was empty.

Everyone else's pockets were empty, too. "Such is life —a full belly one day and nothing the next! " said Pyotr philosophically.

"But what's this sheep running about for?"

"That's right—why?"

Ivan, Pyotr and Anton did not waste time. They caught the sheep, cut its throat, skinned it and divided it up neatly. Others did the same.

The leaguer awoke and everywhere beasts were slaughtered. For once there was no one to prevent it, and the officers' only care was to see that the meat was divided equally among the groups. Narishkin, together with those few staff officers he had left, got a haunch of meat which Uralov, who had taken over the depleted defence platoon, roasted over the open fire.

In his tent Narishkin had looked through the reports of the patrols which had come in; he shoved them wearily to one side.

"There's no need for them any more, Pyotr Ivanovitch."

"No, we have reached the end, Alexey Alexandrovitch."

"In these circumstances we have no further orders to give."

A fourth pocket, from which there would be no further escape for organised bodies of troops, loomed ahead. There could be no thought of an organised march to the east any more. They could not do it with their own strength and no help came from without. The time had come to give a last order; the disbandment of such units as still existed. The last hope was to scatter, to trickle through to the east in little groups or as individuals. That was all that could be recommended, but General Narishkin could not give such an order. He had not even had the right to order a retreat and was still tied down by the fiction of an offensive war.

So there was to be no last order and no farewell.

"We still have to eat the roast, Pyotr Ivanovitch."

"I hope Uralov is as good a cook as Anna Pavlovna," said Semyonov.

"Good Anna Pavlovna, I hope she got through safely."

"I think so—when we sent her off the roads were fairly clear still."

"And the sergeant we gave her is a quick-witted chap."

The lack of guidance at the top speedily communicated itself to the other ranks. On this day they ate as they had not eaten for weeks—as perhaps they would not eat again in their lives; and in the evening fires flamed up throughout the wood. No one forbade the Red Army men to do what up to now had been strictly forbidden. Let them slaughter the cattle, let them sit for the last time at a bright camp fire. From next day everyone would be on his own and have to save his own skin as best he might.

Towards morning Narishkin awoke. He heard singing near by; a simple, melancholy voice. Coming out of his tent he saw Uralov sitting near the fire, which had burnt low. He was singing the song of the Golden Capital— Moscow. Narishkin sat beside him and encouraged him to sing more.

"You must know the song of the Wild Peartree, Nikolai."

Uralov sang the song of the Wild Peartree and others, too; he sang his best. In earlier days—Narishkin could remember them—the whole land from the White Sea to the Caucasus had been full of songs, but now they were heard only in the catacombs under Odessa and Kiev, and on the log-rafts of the great waterways.

"The White Whirlwind," said Narishkin.

Uralov sang with a sad voice and thought of Nina. Narishkin thought of Lena—what would become of her? How would she manage to live? As always in these days the thoughts of Semyonov were in the shadow of the great pile of rubble in Bialystock. Poor Maryusa—she was too young to die. Maria was dead but Irina had been saved.

"A snowstorm sweeps along the road
My true love walks behind it;

162

Stand still, my love,
My love, stand still,
Let me look, my love,
And look my fill."

The day came with a new warm light. Narishkin watched his soldiers lying by their fires. Now they were stretching and walking softly away—an unorganised yet conscious movement spread through the camp. He went to the edge of the wood where presently a tank officer came up—it was Colonel Morosov of V Armoured Corps.

"Comrade General, do you see those crowds of Soviet soldiers on the road, moving from east to west?"

"Yes, I see them."

"How do you explain it?"

"You have heard of defeats, Morosov—you have studied military history."

"But has there been such a case in military history?"

"Such great masses have never marched into captivity from a Russian army—nor from any other army."

"Then are these Stalin's captives marching into freedom?"

"That is a difficult question—it is up to the West to answer it."

The crowd on the road below swelled like a torrent. Now it was a great army moving along the road.

"How will they treat this grey mass?" asked Narishkin. "Everything will depend on that. Our future and the future of the West."

"A great gulf has opened—people and government are no longer one in our land." Morosov looked at the endless column marching into captivity. "Is that the way out?"

He received no answer.

"What will you do personally, General Narishkin? Forgive me for asking."

"The nation's soul can arise again."

"Will Russia have a new government then?"

Again Morosov got no answer.

"What will you do, General Narishkin?"

"I will submit to my fate."

There was nothing more to say. Morosov moved off. He had seen his corps victorious, then destroyed, and had come two hundred miles through woods and marshes with a handful of men. During this time there had been no difference in rank, nor any political officers, but in the moment of danger they had obeyed his commands. They couldn't capture us as long as we didn't want to be taken, he said to himself. And if we come of our own accord it is because we wish it. He reached the road and was caught up in the grey mass moving silently towards the west.

An unending column moved towards the west—still without guards but already prisoners of war. There was also a trickle of men towards the east in groups of three or at the most five men. They were trying to reach the inaccessible swamps stretching towards the Beresina.

Narishkin, too, was on the move. With him were Pyotr Ivanovitch Semyonov, Captain Nikolai Uralov and two soldiers.

They had made good progress the first day and could hope that night to sleep peacefully—for the first time for days—in the cover of the swamps. Ahead of them was a cross-roads where they could see a car halted. A Soviet car, that was certain; but it was odd that it should be facing in the opposite direction from the human stream. Apparently the people in the car were uncertain whether to drive on in the direction they were facing, and into the gathering darkness at that. They called to passers by and spoke to them; then suddenly drove on, only to halt right in front of Narishkin's group.

A major jumped out of the car; so did a captain, the driver and two soldiers as well. Narishkin and Semyonov knew what it meant. The major did not need to present himself as an emissary of the Special Branch.

"Alexey Alexandrovitch Narishkin, Pyotr Ivanovitch Semyonov, I come from Moscow to communicate to you an order of the Defence Committee and to carry it out forthwith."

The major was uneasy—almost as if it was he who was being held up on the road to be shot. Lieutenant-General Korobkov, Colonel-General Pavlov, Major-General Klimovsky, Colonel Grigoriev — and now Narishkin and Semyonov; yet the list, he knew, was not nearly complete. He knew, too, that none of them was a traitor; none of them was guilty, but guilt there was and these men had been chosen to bear the responsibility.

The major's voice almost failed him, yet, perhaps because he felt unsure of himself, he added a few unnecessary remarks. He was thinking of his escort—of the captain, the driver and the two soldiers hearing every word, watching every expression on his face.

"Narishkin, you are no longer general. Semyonov, you are no longer colonel."

Then came the formula:

"Colonel-General Alexey Alexandrovitch Narishkin has been found guilty of treason. Following an investigation by the General Staff of the Union of Socialist Republics he has been immediately degraded and removed from his post.

Citizen A. A. Narishkin is condemned to death on the grounds of treason to the Soviet Fatherland. The sentence will be read to the accused and carried out by an officer detailed by the Special Commission of the 7th Bureau. Execution of the sentence will be reported at once to the 7th Bureau."

He repeated the same text, substituting the name of Pyotr Ivanovitch Semyonov.

"Let's smoke a cigarette, Pyotr."

At once, said the order—there was no provision for granting favours. There stood the witnesses; the captain, the driver, the soldiers. The major was almost beside himself with excitement. He stared at Narishkin, who was no longer a Colonel-General but an ordinary citizen, but Narishkin maintained his ascendancy. He had opened his cigarette-case and offered one to Semyonov.

"No," shouted the major, "one between two."

He did not know how he came to utter something which was not part of the ritual. He should have refused to allow even one cigarette. But it sounded well, and one cigarette instead of two was quicker. It was getting darker and the area was being infiltrated by Germans.

"One between two—all right, Pyotr."

Narishkin gave Semyonov a light. After the first draw Semyonov returned the cigarette.

"You know, Pyotr, in Nikolayevsk—the old man and the apples—that was good—we won them."

The major's face was ashen.

"Maria Andreyevna—she looked wonderful at the last reception, in a yellow silk dress—or wasn't it yellow?"

"She never had a yellow dress." But Semyonov smiled at Alexey's brotherly efforts; he looked completely relaxed.

"It has all been thrown away, Pyotr. Of eight hundred thousand not more than a hundred thousand have got away."

Alexey Alexandrovitch looked up at the pines. The sky was a flaming red—not with fires this time but with the gold of the setting sun.

"The Beresina—that's where it will stiffen up, and again, maybe for good, on the Dnieper. We knew that five years ago, but now, after all that lies behind us, we wouldn't have fitted in any more, Pyotr. You know that with a spoonful of tar you can spoil a whole hive."

What, he wondered, was wrong with Uralov, who looked as if he might burst into tears. He had put him up for a decoration which he would not now get, but he could bequeath him his own star—it would be a memento, too. . . No, never mind — perhaps there's nothing to boast about in an order from the hands of a traitor.

Semyonov was thinking of Maryusa and Irina. How like her mother Irina was—born in Moscow and yet a Cossack girl with the radiance of the Sea of Azov on her brow.

"A cigarette takes too long—the end tastes bitter," said Alexey Alexandrovitch.

* * *

"*Nu, vot,*" exclaimed the major with relief. "Well, that's that."

"*Nu, vot,*" he said again as they drove off.

Someone must bear the guilt, and since it is great it must be borne by many. Semyonov was a cultured man, a good character, a man who could manage figures, a careful father. Narishkin was a first-class commander, a born leader and—as they say—not stupid. He drank but he was never drunk—*nu, vot.*

One man remained—Nikolai Uralov. The night within him was darker than that which sank upon him from above.

* * *

Irina Petrovna fired. Her dress was rent open from top to bottom but she did not know it. "Quick"—a young boy refilled the magazine and she tore the machine pistol from his hand and fired again. Whether she fired on Russians, on White Russians, on German parachutists, on NKVD men or on their victims she did not know. It had come over her suddenly; something had burst—a terrible explosion in her head. She must kill. Kill. The bullets sprayed against a long goods train with its doors boarded up. The splintered wood had caught fire. Had the trucks been set alight or had the German incendiaries put them on fire? Who could tell?

There were fifty people in each waggon and seventy waggons coupled together. The NKVD men had taken their prisoners out of the cells and shot them in the courtyard of the Ministry of the Interior. When there was no more room in the courtyard they shot them in the cells. Other prisoners from the great camp for state construction work had been collected along with workers, technicians and engineers, and shot behind the wall of the Park for Rest and Culture.

The people in the train, who had been selected as particularly useful for certain investigations in hand, had been brought to the station to be carried off further east, but it was no longer possible to get transport out of Minsk station. Nor was there any time to herd them in groups to the Park for Rest and Culture. New orders could not be obtained; there was no way of getting through to a higher command. The NKVD men who had been detailed as guards were at a loss to know what to do, and when the white light of the German flares showed them up as clearly as on a brightly-lit stage, they left their posts and disappeared.

Irina Petrovna threw away the machine-pistol. But the firing went on. No one knew friend from foe.

Kasanzev caught sight of the Party Secretary from Grodno. He had lost touch with his convoy and was looking for. . . Kasanzev never learned what he was looking for or whom; he was torn aside by the whirling mob. Subkov appeared for a moment in the crowd, so did Quartermaster-Lieutenant Turuchin, and Anton and Kyrill from the Shchara; the one with a thick bandage round his head and the other walking with a stick.

They were all hurrying somewhere—but where? They were all yelling, too, for the silence which had so suddenly fallen from the skies now that the bombs had stopped falling was scarcely bearable and each one felt he must explode, become a roaring animal. The howling from the burning wagons drowned them all; but by a miracle the fire died away and many of those seemingly marked for death escaped. They broke open their charred boxes with their fists, and fled—to the west, towards the approaching Germans.

Old Shulga saw the singed ghosts rise from their graves. The intuition which had led him to Minsk was near to its fulfilment. A wave of dry leaves rustled past and he watched them disappear into the night. Was Ponomarenko there, was Lena there? Only if God brought her to him would he see her again. But God brought Irina Petrovna to old Shulga in time to snatch her from the sudden fate which hung over her.

Lieutenant-Quartermaster Turuchin had caught hold of Irina. In her he seemed to see the cause of the confusion, the panic and his personal frustrations. In her he thought to avenge all his suffering and misfortunes. He had caught sight of her with her dress torn open, the sticking plaster on her cheek and her eyes glinting wildly. The spy would not escape him this time.

He caught her by the wrist and dragged her before the tribunal. It consisted of a haphazard collection of people —a cinema operator from Moscow who had been waiting for days for a railway ticket, actors from the Jewish theatre, girl students from a factory canteen, dealers and pick-pockets from the bazaar, workers from the railway depot.

"A spy—she was distributing leaflets."

"And she was making speeches and causing panic in the cellars."

A limping paymaster was prosecutor. The girl was pale —and her eyes were the eyes of a traitress, you could see.

"Let go of her—you're hurting her wrist," said one of the railway workers.

But in the last couple of days Turuchin, who had a carbine now and a pocketful of ammunition, had himself been held up as a spy a dozen times. He had walked until his feet were blistered and had suffered from the wiles of serpents like this woman here. He went straight for the worker.

"What do you mean? Who are you anyway? Are you protecting a spy? Let's see your documents—don't show them to me—show them to these people here, honest Soviet citizens."

The railway workers muttered. The cinema operator and the actors deferred to the man in uniform. The thieves from the bazaar were beginning to lay hands on the girl.

Suddenly an old man stood there as if he had sprung from the ground, white haired, clad in rags. He at least wore the badge of the patriot, of the poorest of the poor —you could see that. "My daughter," said the old man. "Of all my sons and daughters only this one has been left to me. God has preserved her and led me to her and no one shall take her from me."

"It is his daughter," confirmed a sergeant.

Attracted by the noisy gathering, Sergeant Subkov had caught sight of old Shulga and of Turuchin—the man with whom he had walked into Minsk two days ago. They had ended up in a cellar together and Turuchin had said wild things about this strange girl.

"I'll knock your teeth in if you don't clear out," said Subkov, turning to Turuchin. To the others he said: "I know him, he's been hanging about here for days casting suspicion on honest people." The feeling of the crowd veered and turned against Turuchin. He could count himself lucky to get away without being beaten up. No one had any objection to Shulga's taking the girl away.

It was the night of the hundred lamps—the white lamps which the Germans had hung over Minsk. The harsh white light lay on the burnt-out concrete flats in the centre of the city, on the undamaged Palace of Pioneers, on the heaps of ruins in the main street, on the huge deserted block of the Ministry of the Interior and on the death masks in its courtyards; it fell on the jumbled piles of corpses in the Park for Rest and Culture, and on the houses in the suburbs, burnt down to their foundations. In this shadowless light, which showed up with unnatural

169

clarity even a mouse crossing the street, Shulga and Irina walked towards the bazaar, where Shulga had his lair.

From his hands Irina took a piece of bread—bread and salt. That was almost symbolic. It was also almost the first meal she had had since Bialystock—certainly since the slice of bread and the four lumps of sugar in the hospital in Baranovitchy.

The white light penetrated into the cellar; it was quiet there and quiet over the wide expanse of ruins. The old man contented himself with what little she told him of her story; he nodded in agreement and seemed to know it already. In the white light and the great silence his words echoed like those of a giant, a good spirit of other days; and to the sound of his voice Irina fell asleep, breathing peacefully.

The people of Minsk slept, too, after a week of terror.

The Party and the Government had fled. The defeated Soviet troops, drifting through the streets, dissolved like smoke. Finally the special troops and the NKVD withdrew, leaving a no-man's land. The Germans were outside the town.

They came next morning on wheeled and tracked vehicles. Motorised infantry on troop-carriers went through the streets, tractor-drawn artillery and finally tanks, covered with mud and dust.

"The Germans, the Germans." The news ran through the cellars. But the people stayed where they were. The rumours—not only those spread by Radio Moscow, but what eye-witnesses had to report of massacres by the SS in the Jewish quarters—warned the population to be cautious. The German troops seemed to be entering a dead town.

"There is no fighting—the Soviet troops have all withdrawn. The Germans are marching peacefully through the town." Gradually people came out of their hiding places. By the time the tanks went down the main street there were a lot of people about already.

"Have the Germans only got officers?" asked a woman. "You don't see any soldiers?"

"They have long hair and decent uniforms."

"Sweating they are—you can smell it a mile away."

The tanks rolled past. Sweat, oil and dust. The crews

170

had a thick crust of dust on their faces; some were sitting on the outside of the turrets; others had stayed below—they had had a good deal of experience and were ready for surprises. When driving through their first big town—so the regimental commander had ordered—the crews were under all circumstances to be ready for action. The non-committal attitude of the population seemed to show that he was right. There was a smell of burnt houses, of fire and corpses. At first there was hardly a soul to be seen; one or two people hung about the corners and peered at them; but gradually more came: housewives, office workers, workmen, convicts in miserable rags, Red Army men in civilian clothes they had snatched up, girl students from the factory canteen. The German soldiers waved and the girls waved back.

Lieutenant-Colonel Vilshofen stood in the open turret of his tank. He looked up at the high concrete buildings and down again at the inhabitants of the town of Minsk. Russians, Siberians, Asiatics—a dozen peoples seemed to be represented in the Byelo-Russian capital. Many were dressed like town dwellers; others were covered with rags. Contrasts in their clothes, great differences in their faces. A strange land, an incomprehensible people. In the swamps of the Bobr they had abandoned their 50-ton tanks and disappeared into the woods. On the Chelvianka they had thrown themselves with bare fists and bottles of petrol against the tanks and come on so thick that the automatic weapons could not mow them down. A few hours ago as the tanks drove through a wretched village they had come with bread and salt and offered strawberries and milk; old men threw themselves at their feet and the girls rejoiced and threw flowers.

A face in the crowd caught Vilshofen's eye. A girl with parted dark hair; pale, almost a child still. She wasn't rejoicing nor yet did she show any sign of hate. Her glance pierced to the heart and posed a question, the old question, which the old men had stirred in him as they lay at his feet. He heard it again but could not answer it. Could it be answered at all by troops pushing further and further into this land and shedding the blood of its people as they passed?

* * *

171

Anna Pavlovna no longer needed any further explanation of Narishkin's answer that in war men get killed one way or another. On her way east she had learned all the answers. Her way had led her along dusty roads, past dry ponds and under the bombs of the dive-bombers. It had led her through a holding force of German tanks. Further east still, in an open field, she had come under rifle-fire. "Keep below the slope—if you go further over the crest you'll go to heaven before you want to, *babushka*," the Red Army men had called to her.

Well, at forty she wasn't a *babushka* yet, but otherwise the advice was well meant. If she was no longer the General's cook, she was still a person people respected; perhaps it was owing to her friendly disposition to all men that no one wished her ill. To the Red Army men she seemed merely a neat and friendly housewife, almost like their neighbours at home in their village, and the German crews let her pass good-humouredly—a Russian peasant woman, no longer young but neat and plain in her dress. As far as the NKVD road-blocks went, she had her document from the Army to open all barriers to the east, and it often procured her a ride for a part of the way. Admittedly at the first of these road-blocks she had lost the sergeant Narishkin had given her as escort, for the NKVD men had sent him back west while she was allowed to go on. Each time she thought she had passed the worst, and that the battle-field lay behind her, only to discover that nothing had altered and the wave of hounded and famished men flowed on eastwards with her.

In Borissov she regained hope. Here, too, there was the shriek of Stukas and bombs were falling; from the autobahn she looked down on burning houses, and the smell of fire and charred wood was in the air. But squads of Soviet soldiers were busy trying to control the fires and to clear the streets. For the first time she saw columns marching to the front in good order and with rifles— among them companies of the Proletarian Division from Moscow, of which it had been said at Narishkin's HQ that its fresh troops would bring the enemy to a halt. So at last she was beginning to leave the operational zone and come to a place where there was some order in things.

The autobahn bridge over the Beresina was down.

Everyone had to get down off the road and follow a diversion which led over a wooden bridge, on the worn and splintered planks of which the crowds of refugees were overtaken by a convoy. Women with bundles and with children, old and wounded soldiers were pressed to one side. There was still sufficient light over the river for the remarkable nature of the convoy not to go unremarked. There were great trucks and staff-cars with six seats, and the passengers were such high officers that they went right through the road blocks at either end of the bridge without being stopped.

The refugees stood at the road-block to show their passes. The cars and trucks drove on to a patch of wood and took cover under the trees. By the time the first batch of refugees reached the spot the men had climbed out of the cars and were standing or sitting about in groups. They were clean and well-dressed; many wore leather jackets. Each had a brace of pistols within easy reach. But even more striking than their dress and their display of weapons was the general aspect of these men: boorish faces, heavy necks, ponderous bodies—compared with the refugees and the fleeing Red Army men standing round they seemed to be of a different race, to belong to a better nourished and more heavily built breed.

A wounded sergeant picked up a cigarette one of them had thrown away. It was no ordinary one—it smelt nice and when he examined it later and unrolled the tip he found a little perfumed filter in it. So that was the kind of cigarette they smoked. Where did they come from and where had anyone even seen so many well-dressed people, so many Colonels and Generals together? There were a hundred and fifty or maybe two hundred standing about. Perhaps it was the staff of the legendary Proletarian Division. They certainly came from Moscow—perhaps even from the Kremlin; and they were very powerful— you could tell that by looking at them.

No one was able to look very long at these unusual specimens of Soviet society, or exchange ideas about their rank or where they came from. The drivers of the convoy drove the refugees away and didn't spare their language as they did so. Anna Pavlovna was challenged by an officer: "What are you standing about for? Where have you come from and what are you doing?"

"I am on my way to Gzhatsk—I live there."

"Have you papers? Show them."

Anna Pavlovna showed the officer—he was a Major-General—her pass and Narishkin's letter. The Major-General in the leather coat gave her back her pass. He had broad heavy hands like Narishkin's but not browned with the sun; these were white as if they had never come in contact with the earth or the rays of the sun.

"So you were cook to the Army Commander."

"To General Narishkin."

He looked at her again, more closely this time.

"I can't offer you a job as cook. But come with me, you can make yourself useful on the journey. You'll get along that way." A simple woman, not bad-looking, clean at least, he thought. Perhaps there will be a chance on the road—it wouldn't be a bad thing on this deadly journey.

"Come along—I'll show you where the quartermaster is."

He took her to the field kitchen where a meal was being prepared. Anna Pavlovna was to help to fill thermos flasks with cocoa, chocolate and coffee. Sandwiches, cold meat, roast pigeons were laid out on plates and taken round to the groups of officers. An important HQ—but it couldn't be that either, she thought. They carried too many guns and carried them too ostentatiously to be staff officers, and none of them reminded Anna Pavlovna of Narishkin—though he was a heavily built man too—or of Utkin or Semyonov either. The officers on her staff had been different, and they had looked people in the face; these fellows never looked at you. But she was to be allowed to travel with them, and when the convoy moved off after nightfall she was sitting on one of the trucks.

Progress on the autobahn from Minsk to Smolensk was slow. There was a halt every mile or so, often after they had gone only a hundred yards. Bombed tanks lay on the road, a dead horse, a broken-down truck, the scattered load of a supply column. On the other side of the road columns of infantry, armour and guns moved west towards the front. Anna Pavlovna's hope seemed to be fulfilled—with each mile she was moving farther and farther into the rear area.

Many hours later when the night had passed, they turned off the autobahn on to a side road. To right and left were thick woods. After a little while the vehicles halted at a group of wooden houses hidden under the trees—it was the site of a constructional project.

* * *

Constructional Project 057—a huge organisation with buildings above and below ground—was carried on with immense expense of manpower and a correspondingly high wastage of human life. In the Five Year Plan, Project 057 ranked as high as the White Sea Canal had once done. All the peoples of the immense Soviet empire—in particular those from the distant territories, the Far North, the Far East and especially Central Asia—had to pay it a large tribute in human lives. The Project came administratively under the Moscow-Minsk autobahn, begun in 1935, with its head office in Moscow and its operational HQ in Vyasma. Besides the buildings visible and invisible, the project controlled the railway station of Krupki on the other side of the autobahn, the old town of Krupka north of the autobahn and a huge dump of oil and petrol.

Of the Moscow-Minsk autobahn and its importance, Anna Pavlovna knew only as much as any Soviet citizen could learn from the newspapers of the great constructional efforts of the State; of the secret HQ of Project 057, which was to make an indelible impression on her, she could know nothing. She saw only what she could make out in the pale light—neat wooden houses, gravel paths, little gardens in front of the houses, flower beds in the gardens. In front of the administrative block a five-pointed star was laid out, lined with flowers; in the middle was a bust of Stalin. Behind the houses rose tall trees and a fragrant breeze came from the woods; you could almost imagine you were in a convalescent home for engineers—and for the moment there was peace even in the sky.

Day was breaking already and the trucks took cover under the trees. The passengers scarcely stirred; they had fallen asleep. Only a few got out; one of them, a man in civilian clothes, tall and thin as a rake, went across to

175

the five-pointed star and into the administrative block behind it.

In the duty officer's room a lieutenant was sitting at the telephone. He was speaking to another lieutenant at the big petrol and fuel dump on the other side of the autobahn. Some airmen had come, the other was saying; airforce personnel with trucks; they had demanded petrol to allow them to go on with their journey. He had refused it in accordance with orders; but they had threatened the guards and were attempting to fill up their tanks by force.

"All right, Golubzinev," the lieutenant shouted into the telephone. "I'm sending help—I'll ring the officer in command of the road block on the autobahn, he'll get there quicker than I will. What's wrong, Golubzinev—throw him out—what's wrong?"

The sound of a shot came over the wire. Had Lieutenant Golubzinev fired or had someone else?

"Golubzinev, Golubzinev. . ."

Lieutenant Golubzinev did not answer; he had been shot down by the airmen to whom he had refused petrol.

The officer at the table, Lieutenant Yudanov, had a lock of black hair hanging over his brow. He paid no attention to the tall thin civilian who had made his way into the office. He dialled a number.

"Road-block, road-block—give me Major Permyakov . . ."

The tall man came up to the table. "I need petrol."

"I hear that a hundred times a day—clear out. Major Permyakov——"

Over the telephone the commander of the NKVD detachment of the autobahn replied; Yudanov reported to him briefly what had happened at the petrol dump. Only then did he look at the document which the tall civilian held under his nose. A red pass—a pass with the five-pointed star and the hammer and sickle and the engraved portraits of Lenin and Stalin. The civilian opened it so that Yudanov could read the personal data; suddenly he realised that this was the Byelo-Russian Minister of Justice. Yudanov sprang up.

"I beg your pardon, I did not know. But I still cannot give you any petrol. Orders from Moscow—petrol will be given only to transport going towards the front, not to transport coming from the front."

The Minister of Justice put his pass away again. He did not say a word but went out slamming the door behind him. It was not long before he was back. This time he had someone with him—a Colonel-General who came in like a wild boar and looked as if he were going to charge the table.

"What's the idea—are you fed up with life? Stand up, you swine, and get us petrol at once!"

Lieutenant Yudanov was already on his feet.

The Colonel-General went on: "First, you will tank up the whole convoy. Then I need a reserve tanker. Third, I need an escort. I have money with me, gold, valuables and important papers. I do not wish to be held up."

The room filled with heavily-armed figures. They were all colonels and generals—although that did not need to impress an officer of Yudanov's branch unduly so long as he was on duty. Petrol, petrol—Yudanov stood and defended his petrol against this cursing mob of top-ranking officers. It seemed as if their lives depended on the stuff—well, they could drink it. Drink themselves to death on it. The Minister of Justice of Byelo-Russia—who would be next? Another pass was shoved under his nose, and when he had deciphered the name and rank Yudanov suddenly remembered Lieutenant Golubzinev who had been shot down in the office of the petrol dump a few minutes before because he was bound by an order—this same order as he, Yudanov, had to defend against no less a person than the Byelo-Russian Minister of the Interior. This was the supreme chief of the Byelo-Russian NKVD, in whose eyes even Yudanov, with all his special powers, was only a mortal man, a speck of dust to be blown away.

The Minister of the Interior was demanding petrol and waiting for an answer, and the angry men—the Major-Generals, Lieutenant-Generals, all ready to shoot him down—were waiting for an answer, too. Lieutenant Yudanov was as white as the wall behind him but he said: "Comrade Minister, I can give you no petrol. It is an order from Moscow from the War Council. Petrol will be given only to transport travelling towards the front, not to transport coming from the front. Please examine the contents of the order yourself, Comrade Minister."

The Minister waved it away with his hand. He did not need to read the order: he knew it already.

"I can refer the matter to the head of the constructional staff, Major-General Lebyotkin, or, if you should wish, Comrade Minister, I can put you through personally to Major-General Lebyotkin."

"Let's have him, then."

Lieutenant Yudanov put through the call. The officers put their pistols back and began to look round for chairs to sit on. Major-General Lebyotkin was told how things stood by Yudanov and then put through to the Minister. The latter got everything he wanted, and since it was broad daylight outside he accepted an invitation from Lebyotkin to stay on until darkness fell again. The Colonel-General had all his tanks filled for the journey; he got not only one but two tankers as a reserve and an escort of a hundred men into the bargain.

But when he had got over his perilous encounter Yudanov asked himself: What can things have been like in Minsk, when the Minister of the Interior arrives with an empty petrol tank and hasn't even been able to collect an escort?

Well, that was Minsk—here things were different. Here everything would remain as it was, although Order Number 00317, concerning the removal of political prisoners with long sentences on the outbreak of war, had been carried out only in part, for how could the important subterranean work go on if these indispensable specialists were sent off east? The line on the Beresina would hold, and Project 057 would go on working, that was what all the information and orders from Moscow said. The front would hold; reinforcements were continually passing along the autobahn. For instance, the Moscow Proletarian Division had arrived and gone into action. Lieutenant Yudanov knew more than he should have known—but if you kept your eyes open and had an office on the important autobahn from Moscow to Minsk, you had a chance to learn something of the general situation over and above your own job. The Germans will come up against a strong line—he said to himself —and there will be an end to the treason which has spread through the west.

There had been so many cases of it—Korobkov, Narishkin, Pavlov, Klimovsky and Grigoriev. It reached up to the very top. Well, little Lieutenant Vorobyev would fit quite well into the list of traitors to the Fatherland. That was it—they would have to get up a file showing him guilty of treason. But what a fool Budin was. Why did he do things like that?—get himself into a position where a man who was out for promotion like Vorobyev could hold a knife to his throat? He would have to see him right away; the matter couldn't be put off, and Vorobyev's report couldn't just be thrown into the waste-paper basket. Yudanov rang a number. The censor's office came on to the line and he asked for Captain Budin.

"Hallo—is that you, Mihail Vassilyevitch?—thank you, yes, thank you. Listen, I have something to discuss with you—something important. You must come over right away."

"Won't it keep until tomorrow or till this evening?" said Budin.

"No, Captain Budin, the matter cannot keep until tomorrow nor till this evening either. I expect you in my office at once."

It seemed to be something more important than just the latest gossip, so Budin set off at once for Yudanov's office. Yudanov was expecting to be relieved in half an hour and he had to discuss the affair with Budin before then. When Budin came in he had Lieutenant Vorobyev's report in front of him as well as the photographs which went with it.

"Well, what's all the hurry about?"

"Sit down first, Mischa, you'll need a chair."

Yudanov took the photostat of a letter in his hand. "My dear Mischa," it began.

"Do you know the writing, Budin?"

"Of course, it's my wife's. She wrote the other day."

"Well, read on—this bit here."

Budin came from a collective farm and would keep

179

everyone in fits of laughter with comic stories about his village. Now, however, he was really shaken and his round smug face looked quite stupefied. He ran his finger along the portion of the text which the censor—his subordinate Vorobyev—had underlined.

"Life is steadily getting more unbearable," said his wife's letter. "There is no bread to be had and even if you have the money you can't buy anything with it. It is just the same as where you are—just the sort of thing you told me in your last letter. But here I think it is even worse."

"The sort of thing you told me in your last letter" —that passage Vorobyev had underlined twice.

"Do you know what that can cost you?"

Budin slumped in his chair.

"It can cost your head."

"What a swine he is, Vorobyev."

"You may get away with twenty-five years. You idiot, you have a wife at home, you have children—the third one just arrived. How can you do such a thing?"

"I wish I knew—I didn't think."

"Write to your wife right away and tell her not to be so silly again."

"Yes, I'll do that—but what then?"

Budin looked at the photostat.

"I can't throw these away—nor Vorobyev's report either, you know that," said Yudanov.

"Yes, I know."

"I always warned you that he wanted to get on."

"I should have got rid of him—I could have done it any time."

"We must arrange something so that people won't believe him."

"But how, Kostya, how?"

"You're still the boss—you see to it that some papers disappear from his office. Important ones, of course."

"All right, I can do it to-night. Right away."

"Good—do that and I'll have a check-up in the censorship office tomorrow morning. If Vorobyev has papers missing he'll be arrested on the spot."

"Kostya, Kostyusha. . ."

"Even then you aren't in the clear. But I can do the

180

rest. I think I know how things will go. I have work to do now—I must bring the file on the work in my shift up to date. They'll be coming with samples from the laboratory any minute now."

Captain Budin stood up. They parted without shaking hands—there was no need. No dog ever looked at its master more faithfully than Budin at Yudanov.

Lieutenant Yudanov opened his file on the progress of the various schemes: A high-tension transformer on the station at Krupki ready for shipment beyond the Urals. Norms in the asphalt and cement plants overfulfilled 240 per cent., in the underground construction works 260 per cent., horse transport 220 per cent., motor transport 280 per cent.

In Project 057 the system of incentives was so well organised and so ruthlessly exploited that unfulfilled norms were unknown and only overfulfilled ones had to be recorded. Yudanov put his name to the report. The laboratory assistants came with samples in little sacks; he sealed and registered them and laid them aside.

It was twelve o'clock; his tour of duty had lasted from twelve midnight to midday. He was relieved and could go into the dining-room to take his midday meal. He did not enjoy it particularly; perhaps the food was too good. On the Project there were general's rations even for a lieutenant, and if he belonged, like Yudanov, to Section 3, he had not only more points, but better ones, than the others with which he could get anything he liked from the "special canteen". After the meal Yudanov went to his room in the billet for unmarried officers where he smoked a cigarette as he undressed, and lay down on the bed. Things would be all right—he knew already what he had to do about Budin's case. He had to take the matter up openly with Colonel Syemzev. It was either a question of losing two officers—Lieutenant Vorobyev and Captain Budin—or of saving one of them. Given the shortage of dependable officers, that was not unimportant. In that case the choice must fall on Budin, who was more experienced and at the same time more sociable. If Vorobyev's report, the photostat and the negative of the photostat were to vanish along with Vorobyev himself, then the Colonel could write off the whole business and

181

let Budin off with a black eye, so to speak. Vorobyev must be dealt with; his head was as good as lost already.

Yudanov fell asleep with a clear conscience.

* * *

Project 057 went on working as usual.

The prisoners broke stones, mixed cement, boiled asphalt, made roads or carted earth, gravel and sand. Fifty thousand slaves worked with implements and methods such as the builders of the Pyramids had used in Egypt under the Pharaohs. A large contingent of political prisoners serving long sentences and certain technical specialists worked underground. They were brought in by night from the outlying camps and sent down to the underground workings; after ten shifts they were taken out, again by night; for none of them must be allowed to know where he was employed. Over and above that, ten thousand collective farmers had been mobilised with their carts and ponies to fetch and carry stones, earth, gravel, cement, timber or whatever needed to be transported. These "free" workers had to feed and and clothe themselves and, as far as that went, were worse off than the prisoners. Their billets were worse, too. They could not go back to their distant villages every night, so they slept on the edge of the wood in earth huts and shelters which they had put together from branches and bark.

The panic spread by the visit of the Minister of the Interior had so far affected only the heads of the Project; it had still not penetrated to the lower grades and had as yet had no effect on daily routine. The Minister had not concealed the seriousness of the situation from General Lebyotkin, nor from Yudanov's chief, Colonel Syemzev. The Minister did not believe in the Beresina line; in his opinion it could hold at best only for some days. The evacuation of valuable equipment must therefore be speeded up. Fewer trucks for the evacuation of families —more trucks for the transport of machines and installations was the instruction he left behind him. He had also dealt with the question of the convicts. In the event of unexpected developments the guards were to withdraw and leave the convicts to their fate. If there were time, the prisoners were to be set in march without escort. An escort was to be provided only for the political prisoners serving long sentences, and for those with important special skills. A further important point was the huge stores of rations which, in accordance with the general policy of leaving the populace under German occupation to starve, were to be destroyed.

These were the views which Matveyev, the Minister for the Interior, expounded in conversation with General Lebyotkin and Colonel Syemzev; and which, when the next shift took over, were already lying on Yudanov's desk in the form of general directives. When Yudanov came on duty at midnight, General Lebyotkin with his staff had already left for Tambov near the Urals; the only superior officer left above Yudanov was Colonel Syemzev.

Lieutenant Yudanov studied the percentages of the preceding shift on the blackboard. He sat down at his desk and looked over the new directives and the orders which went with them. Then he made some telephone calls. The new ten-day shift of underground workers had begun work, and the evacuation of the previous shift had been completed. The number of men on the new shift was correct; the number of the old shift was two short—they had died at work. The telephone rang. A construction site was on the line; supplies of materials were coming to a halt. Yudanov rang the MT office and discovered that a number of trucks had been diverted for the evacuation of technicians' families. He had the evacuation postponed; the trucks went back to their transport units. Another urgent matter was the machinery standing on the station at Krupki ready to be moved—there was electrical equipment from Siemens and valuable machinery from Krupp among it. Yudanov tried to get on to the station master but could not get through. He therefore decided to drive to the station and see that the move was carried out urgently. On the way to the station he had to cross the autobahn, so he decided to drive along it for a bit to have a chat with Major Permyakov, the commander of the NKVD road-block. He had to make his way forward through refugees, collective farmers, deserters, and cattle.

"I don't know what's going on any more," said the major. "Troops are being shoved about all over the place.

183

The line on the Beresina may or may not hold—at any rate I am holding this line against deserters. But it's getting more and more difficult—I haven't many people left. How long can it last?"

The original holding force on the road-block had been of regimental strength, but large detachments from it were now on their way to carry out other duties. Permyakov had just had to send off a force of battalion strength to deal with German parachutists who had landed farther east on the railway line.

"The bodies of troops which arrive here are getting bigger and bigger. They break through by force of arms —they did that a few hours ago. They are all mad—where do they want to get to? To the Dnieper, to Moscow and farther east still! There are stragglers from Borissov and from Lepel even."

"Yes, they all come along the autobahn. Of course there is bombing, but it's quicker."

"Have a look at that. . ."

The major pointed to a row of corpses stretched out on the ground.

"These are all newly mobilised men. The military commissariat in Tolotshino was to have called up forty thousand of them, but the swine didn't come forward. They could only scrape together something like ten thousand. They cut their hair and sent them off, but when they got to their destination there were only about two thousand left, and here they are now—some of them."

"And if the line breaks and comes back as far as this, what will happen to us? What will the Germans do to us?"

"They kill all prisoners," replied Permyakov. "At any rate, we'll stay here as long as possible and do what we can. But it is getting more and more difficult. No more rations are coming through."

"Don't worry about that, Permyakov. Send a truck or two over to us and we'll help you out."

Yudanov drove on, pondering what he had learned at the road-block. It was by no means too early, he said to himself, to think of evacuating. Large quantities of equipment had already been sent off to Tambov. Now he had to see that they got a move on and put the important equipment at the station on its way.

At the station he found complete chaos. Even in the dark, the air was still warm with humanity and its odours; people stood in the waiting-room and on the platforms up to the ankles in refuse and litter. With difficulty and only with the help of his escort, who had to clear a way for him, Yudanov succeeded in pushing his way through to the RTO.

"Machinery, machinery," shouted the RTO, "of course machinery is important. But human lives are important, too. Look at things here. Forty to fifty thousand people—civilians, soldiers, children, all mixed up here on this little station. Where am I to pack them all? And then that lunatic colonel; he has let down the signals himself and is trying to drive off. How far does he think he will get?"

Forty thousand human beings fought for the points—with fists and sticks at first, but at any moment shooting might start on all sides. Each transport wanted to get on to the main line first. Yet, as Yudanov knew from Permyakov, German parachutists were reported only fifteen miles away and would have to be driven off before the line could be operated.

"There isn't another station like this anywhere," groaned the RTO, but he was wrong—at this moment every station from Riga to Odessa looked like this.

In the first grey light of dawn the Stukas came back again, and the crash of exploding bombs mingled with the roar of the half-demented crowd. Yudanov found the trucks with the machinery on a siding. There seemed to be no more chance of getting them away, so he determined to get a squad of engineers and have the whole train prepared for demolition.

It was broad daylight when he returned to the Project. Captain Budin was already waiting for him in his office and handed over the stolen papers. He had asked for the negative of the photostatted letter from the photography section and that, too, had been delivered.

"That's fine," said Yudanov. "I'll be over at eight. I shall make a general check beginning with your office."

Yudanov made each of the construction sites report on the progress of the work and took notes; then he checked in accordance with the system laid down. So eight o'clock came round and he went to the main office to carry out a surprise check. In Lieutenant Vorobyev's room important papers were missing. Vorobyev was beside himself—he turned out all the drawers of his desk and all his cupboards and then began all over again.

"I don't understand it, they were lying here. It's quite incomprehensible how these papers can have disappeared." After all, he was a conscientious officer and anyone— particularly Captain Budin—would bear him out. There must be an explanation—he had always kept his things properly and had stayed too long in his office rather than the reverse. . .

"Don't bother defending yourself—produce the papers, that's all I ask, Lieutenant Vorobyev."

"I'm going to—but where from? I don't understand it. You can see for yourself, Comrade Lieutenant."

"Yes, I see and I can smell, too—to me it smells of espionage, Lieutenant Vorobyev."

"Where can the papers be?"

"That's enough play-acting—you are under arrest. Hand over your pistol, Lieutenant Vorobyev."

Lieutenant Vorobyev was led off.

* * *

An hour later Colonel Syemzev was ready to leave. He handed over command of the Project and the camp to Yudanov. As he did so he said quietly: "By the way, I have looked into Budin's case. There is nothing against him."

In the space of forty-eight hours the command of the Project had passed from a General to a colonel and from a colonel to a lieutenant. Now twenty-two-year-old Yudanov had to take over the responsibility for the blowing up of something like forty to fifty million roubles' worth of plant and material. For doing so he might get the Order of Lenin or a bullet through the head. First of all he had to get together the demolition squads—there was a company of engineers ready for the job—decide on what was to be blown up and have the charges prepared. The verdict passed on his work would depend on the timing of his orders, which must be neither too late nor too soon.

After Syemzev's departure the discipline of the convicts

and their guards, as well as the zeal of the officials, began to suffer. Yudanov had to take the ignition keys and work-tickets away from the drivers to keep them from driving off on their own. He should have had dozens of convicts, who were either mutinous or not working, shot, but he did not do so.

The bridge over the little river Bobr was reported destroyed—whether by bombs or by parachutists was not clear. Deserters from the nearby front, both officers and men, were wandering about in masses on the site looking for a vehicle or food, or merely for a few hours' rest for their worn feet. German tanks were supposed to have crossed the Beresina south of Borissov, and Borissov itself was said to be already surrounded. According to another rumour the Proletarian Division had been cut to pieces, and farther north all the Soviet tanks had been knocked out in a tank battle and only some of the crews had been able to escape over the Beresina.

For the first time since the organisation came into existence productivity did not reach the norm. When the Stukas came and roared low overhead no one stayed at his work. Not only the convicts but officers, officials and soldiers—Budin and Yudanov, too—ran into the camp. It was safe behind the barbed wire, for experience showed that the camps were not touched by the German airmen.

Budin was supervising the preparations for the demolitions and Yudanov up to now had not had a spare minute. He had not even time to take Vorobyev, who was still sitting in his cell, over to be dealt with by Permyakov at the road-block. Well, he would do it next day.

But next morning he had other things to worry about. The convicts from his own and the nearby camps had arrived for work as usual. But those from the big camps at Natsha—there were from twenty to thirty thousand of them there—had not arrived. Yudanov tried to get through to the NKVD detachment on the Natsha by phone but there was no answer although the line was live. At last he sent Budin with a platoon of the guards to find out what was going on.

Budin came back and reported in great excitement:

"Thousands, tens of thousands of them are wandering about quite free on the roads. There are no more guards

—there's no one in the billets, no one in the offices. There are no sentries on the watch-towers. They all went off during the night."

Yudanov did not have to wait long for confirmation. Major Permyakov rang up from the autobahn.

"What is going on at your place—have you gone off your heads? Your prisoners are arriving at the road-block without escort. I had the first lot shot down but I can't shoot tens of thousands."

"What are you going to do yourself, Comrade Permyakov?"

"I am staying here on the autobahn. I have no orders to withdraw!"

Neither had Yudanov any order to withdraw, yet clearly demolition and withdrawal was the only course open. He got through by radio to Gulag—the head office for concentration camps—in Moscow, and reported that something like thirty thousand convicts were wandering about without guards, and that the NKVD detachment had vanished without saying a word. In Moscow, was the reply, there had been no order issued for the withdrawal of NKVD troops. Sabotage was the only explanation Moscow could suggest.

Yudanov called the headquarters of the NKVD to ask for directives for his future action. The headquarters did not answer. But Gulag came on the air again and asked whether instruction 00317/65 had been carried out.

"Yes," replied Yudanov.

The instruction dealt with the long-term political prisoners and their evacuation to the east on the outbreak of war. In actual fact it had been carried out only partially, for these prisoners were irreplaceable as specialists in the underground installations. Yudanov turned to Budin:

"Get on with it then, Budin. The long-termers must be got away without exception. Never mind about the work underground. They must get off tonight."

It was already too late. Discipline had broken down to such an extent that the underground workers had come up into the daylight by themselves and were mixing with the other workers. An important State secret had thus been violated, and the responsibility was Yudanov's. He called Moscow—called Gulag, but he could get no direct order for the demolitions. He had to decide himself.

"What shall we do?"

"You won't get the prisoners back into camp," said Budin.

"There's no question of that."

"We still have half the battalion of guards—the rest are preparing the demolitions."

"What shall we do?"

"Blow everything," said Budin.

"Blow everything—but not too soon. If only we knew the situation on the Beresina."

"There's a captain out there from the political branch —a Captain Kasanzev—he was commanding a scratch battalion. You can ask him about the Beresina line."

"Good, bring him in."

"Then there's a Lieutenant Odinzov from the Proletarian Division—he was in a tank battle at Lepel. You can ask him, too."

"But will they speak?"

"I'll see to that. I'll drink a bottle of vodka with them. They'll soon speak after a few glasses. They won't be afraid of the devil himself after that."

"The food dump must be blown up—is everything ready?"

"Yes, as far as the stuff goes."

"What do you mean?"

"We have plenty of fuse-cord and enough explosive to blow up Smolensk, but there aren't enough detonators. There are only enough for the main installations."

Yudanov was uneasy. He became military.

"For what installations, Captain Budin?"

Budin counted them off—the electric plant in the asphalt and cement works, the petrol dump, the ration dump, the underground hangars and installations.

"And the houses?"

"They will be set alight."

"Good, then get hold of those two—Kasanzev and Odinzov."

Budin was already at the door when something occurred to Yudanov.

"What about Vorobyev? I haven't been able yet to

189

take him over to the road-block?"

"There's no need. I have put a charge under the cells."

"Is that an important installation?"

"Very." Budin was ready for a joke again but Yudanov was not in the mood. He went back to the signals office, but the sets were silent. Moscow was not listening or no longer wished to hear from Project 057. Yudanov looked through the window. The convicts from the Natsha had arrived, not in columns as usual; they flooded over the site in a grey tossing sea. Having won back their freedom they had not known what to do with it other than go to their work as usual. Even the shots at the road-block had not been able to keep them back. There were women and long-term politicals among them; they hurried timidly past the administration block. How long would they continue to have a wholesome respect for the guard battalion's two tanks drawn up there and for the gun muzzles staring them in the face?

"Moscow—Moscow—Moscow."

It was like the SOS of a sinking ship. The headquarters of the NKVD did not answer. Gulag did not answer. The defence commissariat did not answer.

"No more work, no more work." The chant of the prisoners rang out insolently.

"Citizens," one of them roared.

"Freedom, freedom—we have our freedom. What we need is something to eat and we know where to find it."

Yudanov could have given the order for the demolitions now, but he was waiting for the reports of Captain Kasanzev and Lieutenant Odinzov.

* * *

On the first day of her stay in Krupki Anna Pavlovna had helped to wait on the guests with whom she had arrived. General Lebyotkin had insisted on inviting them to dinner, and had collected three or four dozen of the more distinguished around him at a horse-shoe table. General Lebyotkin sat in the middle, on his right the Byelo-Russian Minister for the Interior and on his left the Minister of Justice.

A number of waiters and waitresses were busy bringing in the food—among them Anna Pavlovna, who never ceased to be surprised at what she heard and saw. On

Narishkin's staff they had eaten and drunk well, too, but there things were done more simply. Take the hors-d'œuvres alone here—as well as the various pâtés, some twenty kinds of fish were brought in, but only here and there did a guest sample them. The dishes had to be carried back almost untouched, and it was the same when the main courses were served. To begin with they drank spirits, then came the various wines and then Caucasian champagne.

A band played during the meal. This was something Anna Pavlovna found hard to understand, for during her escape she had heard the whistle of bullets and had waited at the road-blocks in front of which lay shot deserters. In the kitchen a head chef in a white coat, like a doctor, watched the preparation of the food and sampled each dish as it was carried out. Great attention was paid to correct service, and once when Anna Pavlovna offered pâté de foie gras from the wrong side her mistake was at once pointed out to her.

The big heavy hands, the signet rings on the fingers, the polished finger-nails frightened her. All the men spoke with loud, coarse voices. Speeches were made—in honour of the "wise father of his people"—the Minister for the Interior, Matveyev—and in honour of their host.

The Minister for the Interior did not speak. He looked grievously ill and sweat stood on his brow. The lamps were burning low already. Cheese and butter were cleared away. Black coffee, cognac, black cigars, perfumed cigarettes followed—blue clouds of smoke rose to the ceiling and drifted to the window. It was time to leave, but first he must speak to Lebyotkin and Syemzev. Matveyev rose, and his companions got hurriedly to their feet. He left them standing at the table and disappeared with Lebyotkin and Syemzev into a nearby office. Behind locked doors he told them of the general situation, about the threat to the Project, and recommended certain indispensable measures which should be carried out forthwith.

When he came back the convoy was ready to leave. He got into his car and the long column of trucks and limousines, reinforced this time by a heavily-armed escort, disappeared down the forest road they had arrived by at first light that day.

Anna Pavlovna stayed behind. She could stay for a night or two with the book-keeper, Maria Arkadyevna, who had also been brought in to serve the guests. Some rest would do her good and she wasn't alone here. Perhaps there would be the chance of a lift; she had learned that a big convoy was being made up to go to Tambov. It would have to go by way of Moscow and so must pass through Gzhatsk, which was where she wanted to get to.

On the first evening both women were too excited to think of sleeping at once. The banquet, the number of courses, what the courses had been, the conversation at the table and the faces of the diners gave them a lot to talk about still. Anna Pavlovna enjoyed being able to stretch out her legs and rest her feet. And again and again she expressed her astonishment at finding such a pleasant place to work in, at the clean rooms, the new timbered billets, the gravel paths, the flowers in the gardens.

"It's like a sanatorium—that was my first impression when I arrived."

"You wait a day or two and have a good look around, Anna Pavlovna."

"Such an old wood—I've hardly ever seen such high pines and I do so like the birches growing among them."

"Well, you have plenty of time—go around a bit. There is a footpath here outside the window. If you go along it you will see something worth seeing."

Anna Pavlovna was in a proper bed again—in a bed far behind the front. She scarcely heard the bombers which flew over the wood towards morning. It was almost as if she were sleeping at the Narishkins' in Moscow and the roar of the traffic was rising and falling in the distance.

* * *

When she awoke the sun was shining in at the window. Beside her bed stood a glass of milk and a slice of bread and butter that Maria Arkadyevna had left for her. She took time to dress and have breakfast; then stepped out of the house and remembered the footpath which Maria Arkadyevna had suggested to her for a walk. The noise of the work on the construction sites was soon left behind her. The wood took her to itself; a pleasant coolness fell from the trees.

Reaching a clearing, she caught sight of something which made her stand stock still for a moment. In terror she drew back under the trees—it was a high barbed wire fence and behind it miserable convict huts. Why had Maria Arkadyevna sent her here? Had she said too much in praise of the nice houses, the gardens and the flowers? But the camp was not the only thing she was to discover. She followed another footpath, and this time reached the camp graveyard where thousands of untended graves stretched over a huge square. In the spring the fresh grave mounds had sunk in over the corpses, adding a further touch of desolation. Even on this hot summer day Maria Pavlovna began to shiver. She wandered on without knowing where she was going, but her experiences were not yet over. Her encounters with the living, with the labouring convicts and the dishevelled collective farm peasants were even more terrible than what had gone before.

When she came back Maria Arkadyevna was waiting for her.

"What's wrong with you? Are you ill? You must lie down at once."

She let herself be put to bed without resisting. When she woke up again she felt as if she had had a bad dream. Maria Arkadyevna was sitting on the edge of the bed.

"I was there—in the clearing and at the edge of the wood where the peasants have their bark huts and sleep on damp leaves."

"Never mind—we mustn't speak about that. You know that when I took on the job here I had to sign a document that I would not speak of anything I saw or heard."

But later Maria Arkadyevna came back to the subject herself once more.

"I think your journey from Volkovysk was just as bad."

"No—this was worse."

"Never mind—let's have a cup of tea."

They were sitting drinking their tea, when a siren screamed. The Stukas were there—an attack on the station, the fuel depot and the administrative buildings.

"Come on, leave everything." Maria Arkadyevna took

the other by the hand and ran out with her along the footpath. Technicians, soldiers, peasants, officers, prisoners were running towards the camp in confusion; the prison door stood wide open and anyone could go in. The sentries at the machine-guns on the watchtowers were used by now to this recurrent invasion: the camp was an oasis of safety amidst the shooting pillars of flame; the petrol tanks whirling in the air; the collapsing houses. The German fliers left the camp alone although they often came in low and signalled by dipping their wings.

Anna Pavlovna had not yet awakened from her bad dream—indeed, she became more and more involved in it. These people, this smell of unwashed, lousy human beings fed on pig-swill, the coarse language, seemed to have no connection with reality; it was unfamiliar, distorted, befouled. The convicts laughed at the sight of the officers and troops seeking shelter among them, and the women—their own camp was farther off but in the general confusion they went wherever they liked—heaped bitter taunts on their oppressors and said shameless things to them.

"Come here, commandant, come here, my little man."

"Don't go away—we'll start a family. Right away. Come on, don't be so bashful."

"You're not usually like this. You know how to go about it. The planes won't hurt us, they'll just watch."

It was a former cashier from the Bolshoi Theatre in Moscow who spoke. One day the accounts had been wrong and now she was here. A woman from a collective farm had gleaned wheat in the fields and had been condemned for theft of public property. There was an actor, a film producer, a sewer cleaner from Odessa, a professor from Moscow and another professor from the language institute in Tashkent, and all of them were wrapped in the same stinking rags; in all their faces there was the same cast of hopeless misery. There were engineers, too, and Orthodox priests, but the great mass consisted of peasants and collective farm workers; of these, Cossacks, Uzbeks, Turkmenians, Kirghizes and Mongols made up the majority.

An air battle raged over the wood, but the Soviet fighters were hopelessly inferior in numbers, fire-power and manœuvrability. A Rata glided in flames towards the horizon; a second lurched over the tree-tops, sought to regain height and crashed into the camp burying prisoners beneath it.

A howl of rage went through the camp against the Soviet airmen. "They're useless. They should give up. They've tortured us for years and now they're still killing us."

Yudanov, Budin and others decided that it was best to leave the camp. A few troops remained behind and faced the storm only to disappear later into the woods with some of the women. There was nothing more that could be done; discipline would never be restored.

Next morning Anna Pavlovna awoke to the noise of an invading sea of humanity. Screaming hordes went to and fro on the road through the camp headquarters. The prisoners from the big camp on the Natsha had arrived and were coming right up to the houses. They prowled round Maria Arkadyevna's billet, too. A face was pressed against the window pane, a squashed nose and black hungry eyes. Anna Pavlovna retreated to the other end of the room and the face at the window disappeared again. The crowds passed on, bawling: "No more work, no more work."

Only in front of the administrative block was there a clear space. In the office Captain Budin, Captain Kasanzev and Lieutenant Odinzov sat facing the commanding officer, Lieutenant Yudanov.

Kasanzev's report was quite simple and clear. He had been commanding a battalion on the Beresina. The troops had been made up partly of newly-mobilised men from the Orel military district, partly of the remains of units destroyed west of Minsk. From the first their equipment was inadequate; there had been no artillery at all. The new recruits had never heard a shot fired and did not know what a shell-burst sounded like. When the first German shells fell they had climbed out of the trenches and rushed off headlong in panic.

"Just like a herd of cattle," said Kasanzev, "and it wasn't only my battalion that ran, it was the whole division. We didn't see a single man of them again. The others behaved better until the German armour came;

then it was all over. There was nothing you could do —we had nothing to face the tanks with."

The story told by Lieutenant Odinzov of the Proletarian Division was less notable for its clarity. Perhaps Budin had plied him with too much alcohol, or else he hadn't stood up to it as well as Kasanzev. He went into great detail and was immensely proud of his élite division which apparently, however, no longer existed.

A fortnight before—that was to say, just before war broke out—they had set off from Moscow.

"14 Armoured Division, 16 Armoured Division and the Proletarian Division."

"A whole corps, then?"

"Yes, VIII Corps under Lieutenant-General Vinogradov."

The operations of VIII Corps had lasted two days. Beaten on the first day it had re-grouped during the night to go into the attack on the following day. The second attack ended in a complete catastrophe.

"We were pushed up against the Beresina. The bridges were down and we were cut off. All the armour was left on the other bank. The men got back over the Beresina by themselves or in little groups without weapons, and often even without rifles. After that I had only seventeen men left in my company. Of all our division only one regiment is left."

Yudanov knew as much as he needed to know. The time had come—the moment for blowing up Project 057. He went over to the signallers once more. They called Moscow. But if once there had been a confusion of orders and instructions, now the offices in Moscow were completely silent. Yudanov collected such officers as were left and read out the document which had to be signed before the demolitions could take place.

We, the undersigned, acting for Major-General Lebyotkin and Colonel Syemzev, have decided on the basis of a general appreciation of the situation to blow up the installations under our command in accordance with the orders of J. V. Stalin.

Installations A33, 34 and 35 will be blown up.

The second series of demolitions will include all generating plant and electrical equipment and the ration dump.

The third series of demolitions will cover all underground installations.

The fourth series will consist of the petrol and oil dump.

All offices, workshops and billets will be set on fire. Prisoners have been instructed that they must make their way east.

Signed: Lieutenant Yudanov.
Captain Budin.
Major Permyakov.

Appendix: Major Permyakov did not sign this document personally since he could not leave his duties at the road-block on the autobahn. He was informed by telephone and agreed that the demolitions should take place.

Yudanov tried to send the text of the document through to Moscow. The sets were constantly on the air, but no reply came through. The day was wearing on; darkness was creeping out from the woods. The space they had so far kept clear in front of the administrative block shrank more and more; the island in the midst of the grey flood of humanity crumbled away; neither the tanks drawn up in front of the main gate nor the muzzles of their guns made an impression on the convicts any more. The guards ordering the prisoners to keep back were answered with mocking laughter. In the prisoners' kitchens they had overturned the great coppers of thin soup and broken up the equipment. Ten thousand people had gone without food that day.

Yudanov looked through the window. Budin stood at his side. There was murder in those eyes out there—there was a fisherman from Archangel, a Yakut from the snow-clad tundra, a murderer from Saratov, a Kurdish shaman. The primitive faces of Russia gathered from all parts of the empire. Primitive faces, animal faces.

"They are possessed by the devil."

"They're out to kill."

Budin had been out more than Yudanov in these last days; he had seen more of the convicts and had kept his eyes and ears open.

"You should be glad that the shaman is there—and the priests, too. They have extraordinary influence on them and put all sorts of ideas into their heads—but they keep them from killing."

The fisher from Archangel—a giant of a man although he was nothing now but skin and bone—had come up alongside the first tank. He turned to the side and spat on it. His grey eyes looked up and sought the window where Yudanov stood. What was he wanting? Yudanov had once had him put in the punishment cells for four weeks.

"Spit on it, Ivan, spit on the window—spit on that man behind it," cried the murderer from Saratov.

Should he give the command to open fire? Ivan from Archangel was still the only one who had come inside the ring of guards. The shells of the tank guns would tear great gaps in the crowd as it pressed nearer; but if any shots were fired now no shaman or priest would be able to help any more. Forty thousand raging men would take their revenge on Yudanov and Budin for having been turned into caged beasts.

Meanwhile Moscow did not answer. Would not answer. That was clear by now. The operators should have got through hours ago.

"Pass on the order for the first demolitions, Budin."

Budin had the telephone already in his hand.

Ivan stood in front of the window in his greasy, crumpled jacket and his boots made from old tyres. He was nothing but skin and bone; his long arms reached down to his knees. There was a cold gleam of joy on his face; he was relishing his triumph. The sentries from the defence battalion left him alone, for without a direct order no one would go near him; but the direct order never came. The others who had come with him still held back from the gun-muzzles.

"And the second series, Budin."

The second order, too, was at once passed on.

What did Ivan want? How far would he go?

He never got to the point of making clear his intentions. An explosion rent the air. Others followed—in a chain of explosions the asphalt and cement works went up in the air. A moment later the second series followed, overlapping with the first, running along the edge of the woods and through the ration dumps—so much food that it

198

would have lasted three million men for several months.

The earth shook under the first heavy explosions; the last were so close at hand that all the doors and windows of the administrative block were blown in and half the roof flew off. Ivan suddenly found himself on the edge of a whirlwind in a thick rain of splinters and tiles. There was no need for the shaman to intervene; followed by his mates, Ivan trudged off. When the dust had settled and Yudanov looked out of the empty window frame Ivan had disappeared as if he had been an apparition.

The demolitions had begun without warning. They had not been carried out without dead and wounded—but that was of no consequence; every normal shift had had its victims. The shouts of the liberated convicts were due to something else. The rations! The explosive charges had not been able to destroy the food-stuffs—only to scatter them, hurl them over the whole area. Up to now no one had known that food was stacked in the dugouts at the edge of the wood, and in the long dumps covered with tarpaulins. But now with the workshops in flames, with houses burning and petrol tanks on fire, hordes of prisoners moved about on the edge of the wood in the red glow of the flames. They ran, threw themselves down, stood up and ran again. Faster than the chain of explosions the rumour had spread through the woods and on to the autobahn, and men already on their way east, dreaming that they might perhaps reach their homes in Bokhara, Fergana or Tien-Shan on the distant Chinese frontier, turned back again and ran. Their eyes gleamed greedily when they reached the spot and found the others already at their meal.

There was everything there. The little slit-eyed Turkmenian from Tien-Shan bent down for a Caspian herring, bit into it, saw a fatter one, threw the first away and hastened to snatch the other from under the next man's hand. Then he saw that herring lay all over the forest floor—ten barrels or perhaps a hundred barrels had gone up here. But why eat herring? The yellow lumps hanging on the next tree were butter, half a hundredweight of it. And why eat butter?—there was chocolate, sweets, caviare, delicacies such as he had never seen before. Rice, flour, sugar, anchovies, cigarettes and vodka—ten thousand bottles of it. Most of them had burst open on the trees and fallen in splinters but others had remained intact and lay on the soft moss—and not only bottles of vodka but cognac, wine and champagne. Then there were great, round, twenty-five-litre flasks of alcohol, sixty-nine per cent. proof. Bogdanov, the Moscow professor, Chiang from Tien-Shan, Ivan from Archangel, Nikita from Saratov, the endless multitude of convicts, and with them ten thousand collective farm peasants, sampled everything. To begin with they took unmanageable clots of salvaged butter, whole great lumps of sugar, great pieces of Moscow sausage and ate it all together. Their table stretched for miles along the edge of the wood and it was lit by the torch-light of the burning houses.

The demolitions were almost finished—only the biggest of them all, the huge petrol and oil dump on the other side of the autobahn, had still to be carried out. Before that Yudanov wanted to get started with his convoy; he had had eighty trucks loaded. He took another look at the edge of the wood where an immense orgy was in progress. They were all stuffing themselves—many of them shovelled the food into their mouths indiscriminately; others lay on their backs with distended bellies.

"Just look at the peasants," said Budin.

They were there, too—the collective farm peasants, bearded and tattered, with their little carts and unkempt ponies. Usually they were cautious but now they were moving about in great excitement.

"The lazy beasts have never worked like this before."

"Yes, they're over-fulfilling their norm a thousand per cent."

The *kolkhozniki* were stuffing themselves like the rest —but they were thinking ahead, thinking of the morrow. They laboured until the sweat ran off them, carrying rice, flour, herring, sugar, cases of tinned food, flasks of alcohol, loading their little carts in which up to now they had moved only stones and sand. They had aroused the disapproval of the others, who thought in their greed that there might not be enough left for them, so that they had to drive a way for themselves and their ponies through the half-demented crowd with their fists, with stakes and bits of wood. But they had piled so much on their carts that the ponies could not pull the load over the bad patches of road, and bits of their long caravan were left at a dozen points—where the woodland road was deep in mud or on sandy stretches. Part of the stuff had to be unloaded. The carts and the ponies were collective property, so everyone now wanted to decide what should be left behind and what should stay on the carts. They had all drunk freely; there was a confused shouting and blows were exchanged, but at last there was nothing for it but to make their peace—they had everything they needed in the way of food and drink. They lay where they were by the muddy puddles or the patches of sand, and so the scattered remnants of the great feast were spread throughout the camp.

Yudanov drove off towards Smolensk with the defence battalion and the eighty trucks, leaving Budin behind with a detachment of sappers.

Smoke stood over Smolensk—a thick black cloud drifted over the river. The bridge on the autobahn was destroyed and everything had to turn off to the south and cross the Dnieper by ferry at Solovyovo. All the roads were packed with refugees from Minsk, from Bialystock, from Vilna, from Riga. Jews, women, deserters and Party officials crammed the woods and roads. It was a bottle-neck, for the ferry was the only means of reaching the other bank and the road to Moscow. There were carts, horses and trucks, cattle from the collectives, saloon cars, tens of thousands of men and women, all jostling one another on the bare strip of sand which offered no protection from the cruel sun and no cover from the bombs. To get across you had to produce a pass stamped by a Party or Government office. Yudanov had good, indeed exceptional documents, yet it took many hours before his trucks were ferried over to the other side.

But there he had to turn back once more. Moscow had come up on the air and he had received a command to return to Project 057 from Colonel Syemzev, who had got out at Moscow on his way to Tambov. The colonel had got—or so he said—about fifty trucks ready in Krupki to be loaded with whatever equipment and rations could be salvaged from the ruins. There was still time for that. The German advance had come to a halt; it would be days before they had their supply system functioning properly. Until then the situation on the front was stable. The Beresina was being held.

Yudanov drove back. With his convoy he left only a few men from the defence battalion; the rest he took with him and two days later reached the deserted site again. The trucks had already arrived—not fifty but close on a hundred of them. Little Budin was full of his own importance; he was boss now—the commander of a land of Cockayne. His twenty-thousand remaining subjects had not been sober for three days and nights.

"You should have seen them. Some idiot let Vorobyev out of the cells before the demolition. They saw him right away. 'That's the one who kept back our letters and got us a couple of years more. He has no uniform any more and no badges of rank.' That was what they said, and they chased him right through the wood—with the dogs after him, too—and killed him off. Then they ate some more—too much of it and everything mixed up. The priests tried to stop them from eating. They paid no attention but stuffed themselves full and lay down and died. Next to them others were lying with the women. If only they had stayed in the woods—but they spread out into the open. And the peasants were always moving about with their carts; the movement was spotted and we had planes on to us—firing into it all with MGs."

"An interesting spectacle," said Yudanov ironically. He had taken over command again. Budin had to come back to reality.

"And how have the demolitions been carried out? Is the plant at Krupki station blown?"

"You can't get near the station any more. You have no idea what it's like—the RTO was shot by officers and all the officials have gone. So have all the railway workers."

"Has the petrol dump been blown?"

"We didn't manage the first time, and then we had no more detonators left."

"But that's impossible—we'll lose our heads for that."

"Don't worry—it has been seen to. The Germans did it for us. Look. . ."

On the other side of the autobahn rose a heavy black

mushroom of smoke. So that was all right.

"All right—now get on with it. A hundred trucks have to be loaded at once with whatever equipment is left. But get the rations above all."

It was soon evident that Yudanov required all the soldiers he had brought with him to keep the looters from the food which lay around. Caviare, shoes, sweets, uniforms—everything was loaded on to the trucks. Meanwhile, the eating and the drinking, the fornication and the dying went on; the hordes which had arrived two or three days before had long since filled themselves to repletion and now lay about like dying flies. But others came—Red Army men from the units routed on the Beresina—and they all had the same hunger and the same desires.

Professor Bogdanov from Moscow and Ivan from Archangel were among the sensible ones. After the first excesses, which they had barely survived, they had recovered their sense of proportion and were trying to keep back the rest from self-destruction. Professor Bogdanov had once worn glasses, which had long since been lost, but where the frame of the glasses had pressed into the flesh there were circles eaten away by lice, which did not heal but merely formed scabs which, in a curious way, gave to his face the look of a man of culture. He wanted to get to Moscow. The noise of the nearby front told him that the feast must soon come to an end, and he had gathered some people round him and saw to it that only hard food was packed as rations for the journey.

There could be no question of the front on the Beresina holding. The noise of fighting in the west told Lieutenant Yudanov that he must hurry. A truck with wounded airmen from an airfield half-way to Borissov appeared on the road through the wood. Another truck was loaded with wounded tank crews. A red-headed captain with a bandaged head, on a motor-bicycle, was looking for the HQ of an armoured regiment which was supposed to be on the site of the camp.

Budin and Yudanov learned from him that new forces —including even a regiment with T34s and a whole air division—had been put in against the German bridgehead on the Beresina.

"The Germans had terrible losses but it didn't help. They held the bridgehead, made a counter-attack even and broke through our line with armour."

The red-headed captain on the motor-cycle tore off again. It was time to finish things off here. Yudanov turned to Bogdanov and Ivan, who formed a sort of illegal staff and had far-reaching authority over the convicts. All prisoners were free, he explained superfluously; they could move about without guards and go wherever they wanted. They could stay here, too, but it would be better if they set out towards the east. Bogdanov and Ivan should see that they did.

"Where to?" asked Ivan.

"To Tambov." Yudanov could not tell them where they would get rations on the way; that they would discover for themselves.

The convoy was moving already; Yudanov and Budin drove behind. They looked around them for the last time. "Everything is to be destroyed and nothing left to the enemy"—that was what Stalin's order said. But a lot had been left lying which they had been unable to blow up. The biggest and most worrying omission concerned the long-term prisoners, the underground workers on secret installations, who were now at liberty and scattered over the whole countryside.

As darkness was falling Yudanov arrived at the road-block. He greeted Major Permyakov but hardly recognised him. Permyakov's face had fallen in; he had great rolling eyes in a lean skull. He wore a steel helmet and all his troops had helmets, too—no more caps with blue tops and raspberry edgings. Permyakov had received no orders to withdraw.

At first the job at the road-block had been easy and he had been able to see what was going on. If a car arrived it was stopped. The major or colonel was taken out of it; his girl-friend (often there were a couple of them) had to jump out and could go on foot to the station at Krupki and try to get on from there. The others —the people who had run away—were collected and escorted back to the front. If they became cheeky there was a shorter way with them; they were taken aside and got a bullet each. But when the situation became more

204

acute and the throng in front of the road-block greater, there could be no more of this humane and individual treatment. They had to be dealt with as they came, in packets. But even at this twelfth hour there was no question of dropping everything and clearing out—no question for Major Permyakov, nor for the troops under him. He had got his whole regiment together again; he had armour and dogs and automatic weapons. They would let whatever was coming get within range and see what happened then.

The staff from Project 057 had always been on good terms with Permyakov, and now that Yudanov discussed the question of the released convicts with him he was ready to make concessions.

"There are thousands of them without escort and I haven't been able to give each one a document," said Yudanov.

"All right—they can come through for an hour—till nine-thirty," answered Permyakov. "At nine-thirty the road-block will be closed to everyone, and anyone who isn't through by then. . ."

The matter was arranged. Yudanov sent some men back. They were to find Bogdanov and Ivan and tell them the time limit. They, in turn, would have to see that departure was speeded up accordingly.

Budin and Yudanov passed the block. They followed a diversion and found the autobahn again on the other side of the blown bridge. An hour passed. Yudanov was just thinking that Permyakov need not have carried out his orders quite so literally and that he could have taken up a better defensive position on this side of the blown bridge, when a Stuka attack went in behind him. The bombardment lasted five minutes; the bomb-splinters came whizzing over the river. Immediately on top of it a wild burst of firing broke out at the block.

Permyakov's hour had come.

* * *

When Yudanov was saying good-bye to Major Permyakov, the commander of the reinforced German advance guard, Lieutenant-Colonel Vilshofen, was getting his orders in Borissov. He was to advance on Tolotshino, which was far beyond Krupki, east of the Bobr even.

He drove past broken-down Russian tanks which were still smoking—Christie-suspensions, long-barrelled guns, T34s. This was the second time Vilshofen had seen them and again the German tank guns had been unable to do anything with them; the airforce had had to put them out of action. The burnt-out tanks were left behind. His own drove into the falling night. Fleeing Soviet troops were overtaken, shot down or dispersed into the woods. There was a bombed petrol dump in the way, a station over-flowing with people. On the other side of the road the wood was alive with strange figures. The beam of his searchlights tore the darkness apart; they were all unarmed.

Guns flashed ahead. This fire from light field-guns, anti-tank guns and MGs was not unexpected—it came from a blocking position which the airforce had reported, some three or four miles long, straddling the autobahn. Vilshofen looked at his watch. He had two minutes to wait until the dive-bomber attack began on the positions ahead. Seven minutes later he drove on. But though these troops had been dive-bombed with heavy casualties, they would not give in. Machine guns hammered, explosive charges were thrown, machine pistols rang out. Each man had to be dealt with in turn; not one put up his hands. Seriously wounded men lay behind piles of corpses and emptied the magazines of their automatics. And it was not only men who sprang out of the darkness at the infantry but great dogs as well.

It was some hours before the tanks could drive on. They slid down into the steep valley of the Bobr, went round the blown bridge, clambered up the other side and got back on to the autobahn. Again bodies of ragged unarmed men appeared in quilted jackets with wadding hanging down in lumps. On their feet they wore clumsy shoes made from motor-tyres.

The tanks drove men, cattle and horse-drawn vehicles before them. They crushed together terrified creatures running for their lives and at last cleared a lane as they drove ahead. Great God, this mass of cattle and men and splintered carts must come to an end! The tank-tracks must soon get the solid cement of the road under them again. The soft vulnerable mass was unending but there was no stopping, no turning back. The tracks of the tanks ground on like wheels caught in thick mud, on a substance that might have been snow, or might have been water, or might have been a herd of buffaloes; but was men.

Get on, get through—the objective was Tolotshino. Get on and get through—but these were men. Chiang from Tien-Shan drifting past in the wheeling crowd was like Balthasar from the adoration of the Magi. The bearded head of the Evangelist and all the figures from the high altar at Blaubeuren went down one by one; the tracks went over the Holy Virgin and her Child. An old man from a village they had passed through came into Vilshofen's mind—and the face of the girl in the streets of Minsk. The old man had sat on his chair in front of his burnt house, and when Vilshofen had asked "Was that your house?" the old man had answered: "It was my house, but I will have lost it gladly if you free us from our tormentors."

Get on and get through—is this what the path of liberation looks like?

Shut down the turret and close your ears—all the saints of the calendar are weeping outside.

Tolotshino is the objective.

The advance guard crossed the Natsha and went on a few miles. It did not reach Tolotshino until next day.

* * *

Lieutenant Yudanov had the crossing of the Natsha behind him. At his back there was a roar like an approaching wave, and there was the noise of firing. He came to a fork, turned off the autobahn and drove on through Tolotshino, where a smell of burning timber and smoke was in the early morning air. That same day he reached Smolensk.

The station square, surrounded by low wooden houses, had been transformed into a great army camp with soldiers standing about, rolling cigarettes, smoking, talking or listening. They had come from Rzhev, from Ryazan, even from Voronesh on the Don. One train after another ran into the station and convoys poured into the town. Yudanov had to look a long time to find a place to park his trucks, of which he had only thirty left—the rest had been caught between the Bobr and the Natsha.

He tried to get into touch with Colonel Syemzev, or some other members of the construction staff in Moscow or Tambov. At the Town Major's it was impossible to get in; all the other offices were being evacuated; the Party offices were deserted—one person having been left as an observer. There were long marching columns everywhere; the air was full of the smell of sweat and horses. Civilian life had come to a stand-still. Abandoned trams with no current to drive them stood about on the lines.

Yudanov went over the stone bridge to the old town and came to the great cathedral. For the first time since it was opened, the "godless museum" in one half of the church was empty; in the other half, which was left for the believers, was a silent kneeling mass. It was not only old women—Yudanov saw young faces, Red Army men and even officers, among those praying. To his astonishment he found an acquaintance here—that Captain Kasanzev who a week before had been in his office in Krupki. The man had been political commissar in his unit, yet here he was on his knees. Yudanov waited until he stood up and took up a position so that the other must pass in front of him.

Kasanzev, it was clear, did not like to be seen here. "Such a famous catheral," he said, "you can't just go past—you have to have a look at it—and at the things at the other end, too."

Together with Yudanov he turned to the "godless" end and the waxworks on show there.

"There they are—that's what they looked like—those damned parasites."

There were models of a kulak, a village policeman, a tavern-keeper, a priest, and a capitalist with a dusty top hat on his head. The red of his blood-stained hands had faded a little.

"They are lice on the body of the people."

Yudanov looked at him with his black eyes, his glance one of mockery and contempt. Kasanzev did not know what to do or say. At the other end of the church the people knelt in prayer; their silence filled the great cathedral and enveloped him. He had become one with it and had rested in it, a moment since.

"I wanted to see something else, not just the autobahn . . ." he tried to defend himself. The two men went to the door and out on to the street.

"The autobahn, the Stukas—you can't talk about bombs and corpses all the time—you've got to get your mind off them somehow." He walked along beside Yudanov as if he were under escort. Yudanov said nothing; the ironical smile never left his face. Kasanzev tried again.

"Between Orsha and Smolensk a lot of guns got left behind," he said. "The petrol ran out, so they took out the breech-blocks and there they are—guns and tractors. And all the woods are full of deserters."

"And what are you, Captain Kasanzev?"

That was what Kasanzev had been afraid of. He looked round him like a trapped animal searching for a way of escape.

"Get out before I change my mind and hand you over to where you belong," Yudanov shouted at him.

Kasanzev did not need to be told twice. He quickened his pace and disappeared round the next street corner.

The people of Smolensk were not all sitting in the cathedral. Yudanov met looters dragging sacks of sugar and tobacco, shoes and clothing and even pieces of furniture from the deserted houses of the Party officials. But most people had been formed into civilian labour battalions and women's brigades. Long grey columns with shovels were going to the west side of the town, across the old town wall to make earth-works, anti-tank ditches and anti-tank obstacles on which the Germans would be finally brought to a halt.

Yudanov left Smolensk behind him and returned for the second time to the Dnieper ferry at Solovyovo. When last he was here thousands had stood on the bare strip of sand; many now lay dead on it but the crowd had not diminished. The convoys on the road from Smolensk and from the autobahn were unending. The AA fired without a pause and when the Stukas put one troop out of action another drove up and went on firing. Day and night the Stukas swooped over the ferry like vultures. Important government convoys, evacuated equipment from factories and the cattle driven off from the collective farms, were given priority. Soldiers, officers, and workers who had not been specifically detailed as specialists to look after equipment, were sent to a troop-collecting point. Communists and Young Communists were turned away; for them the order was to stay where they were and wait for instructions. Everyone wanted to cross, and those who were turned back wanted at least to see that their families were sent over. The shouting and lamenting were unending. Many tried to force their way on to the ferry and were shot down; others threw themselves into the water and tried to swim to the other side, either drowning or working their way over with the help of driftwood.

Yudanov struggled forward to the ferry followed by his convoy. A sergeant stopped him.

"What do you think you are doing—who gave you orders to come here?"

"I did," answered Yudanov.

"I'm in charge here."

"And I'm in charge of this convoy."

"Get out then—show your papers."

Yudanov produced his papers with irritating slowness. He kept his identity card and his special pass in his hand and presented only his movement order made out for a journey to Tambov. The sergeant was blazing already.

"You know what you can do with that," he roared.

The soldiers, who had been looking at this strange convoy with its mixed load of rations, came running up when they heard the sergeant's roar of anger and were preparing to haul Budin and Yudanov out of their car. But the sergeant had glanced again at Yudanov's papers and was beginning to have second thoughts. After all, the lieutenant, like himself, came under the Ministry of the Interior, and the papers he had presented were good ones—suspiciously good, in fact, much too complete.

He did not adopt a friendlier tone but became correct in his behaviour: "Come this way, please, and prove that your papers are genuine."

Yudanov was led to the officer on duty and then taken across to the other side. This was not a road-block like Permyakov's—he saw that right away. This was a big NKVD force under the command of a Lieutenant-

210

General, and Yudanov was passed on from one person to another with his unusual documents. At last he was sitting outside the General's office.

"Excellent, excellent—Mihailov has been killed and we got rid of Sossinov. We have no one to fill their posts. We'll keep this man Yudanov here," said the General.

Yudanov accepted the offer and was attached to a Colonel Akulov for special duties. Budin, too, remained with the NKVD troops.

*   *   *

The next few days brought little change on the Dnieper front. The German infantry had just reached the Beresina and the Dnieper had been crossed by their armoured divisions and motorised units; but the Russians still controlled the autobahn to Smolensk. Farther east, it was true, Vitebsk had fallen into German hands, or had been given up to them through cowardice or treason.

The NKVD staff to which Yudanov belonged lay east of the Soloyovo ferry on the road to Dorogobush. All roads led to Smolensk and on to the ferry. Red Army men who had lost their units, platoon commanders, company commanders—these were not cases for the staff to deal with; they were kept together and handled on the spot. A hint or a threat of punishment, a punch on the nose when that didn't work, a blow or two—there were sterner measures in reserve—usually sufficed to bring them back to their senses, and send them on their way to the straggler-collecting-points and so back to the front. The collecting-points were bursting with men—stragglers, deserters, refugees, convicts—small fry; they were used for the defence of Smolensk, and huge batches were sent down to the great troop concentration under Marshal Timoshenko in the south.

Nina Mihailovna, Anna Pavlovna, Anton who had been wounded on the Shchara, Professor Bogdanov—were all small fry. Forty of them went to a truck, and Captain Budin took over ten such truck-loads—four hundred in all. He had to sign for them and see that they stayed together. He took them north-east of Smolensk where the newly-mobilised troops were digging earth-works. Anna Pavlovna had a good document, it was true, and the stamp on it was genuine; but the name of the Army

Commander on it was no use any more. Budin, being good-natured, advised her that it would be better not to keep on producing a letter with that signature on it. Nina Mihailovna, who also came to him, looked pale and Budin would willingly have let her go; but the only document she could produce was her Young Communist card, and with that she should have already reported in Minsk or Smolensk for employment. "The country is in great danger—every pair of hands is needed," he said to her, and Nina Mihailovna understood. She no longer thought that she had to get to Moscow on an important mission.

Company commanders, platoon commanders, officers' wives, sick soldiers, convicts—they were all small fry and were not allowed to pass the outposts of the blocking force. The staff and the special departments where Yudanov had his office dealt with other cases.

The front round Vitebsk collapsed. Whole divisions went to pieces—among them an armoured division. They had been fighting for a long time without armour, with nothing but rifles; the troops had run away and many had been taken prisoner. The commander was wandering about in the woods behind the front with some of his staff. Word had come in saying roughly where he was to be found, and Colonel Akulov himself took over the job of finding him and took Yudanov with him on the journey.

They found the commander forty miles behind the front in a wood with a little group of people—four men and four women. They had bivouacked under the trees and had food and bottles and glasses spread out around them. Colonel Akulov stopped the car and went over. A major came to meet him. There was another major there, too, and the head of the divisional Special Branch.

The major from the operational staff stuttered and could hardly pronounce the word 'tovarish'. "Tovarish Colonel, we withdrew here—we are studying the situation and trying to form a picture of what is going on."

The colonel turned to the divisional commander.

"Where are your regiments?"

The commander had vacant eyes. He seized a map and ran his finger along it saying in a sing-song voice:

"1 Regiment is here—2 Regiment here—and 3, yes,

there—that's where they are."

"No, they're not. They've gone over to the Germans."

The commander became angry.

"How do you know—what business is it of yours? Go away—don't worry about it."

"What have you to say?" the colonel asked the head of the Special Branch.

"The whole HQ is always drunk. He's the worst. He never commands anything—he's usually after women. I wanted to shoot him several times and that's why I came here after him."

"Do it now."

The commander sat on an outspread blanket and stared at his erstwhile drinking companion with bewilderment. The other drew his pistol and shot him between the eyes.

For a moment Colonel Akulov looked at the man with the smoking pistol in his hand; then he uttered the single syllable:

"Fire! "

They left eight corpses lying there.

* * *

The earth-works thrown up west of Smolensk had not been able to hold up 29 Motorised Infantry Division; they had overrun them in the course of their advance and penetrated into the town. Now earth-works were being constructed north-east of Smolensk, a task which was being carried out by the system of norms and percentages. It was the same as on a big State construction site, and engineers from technical staffs which no longer existed were put in charge of the operations. Captain Budin from the NKVD HQ at Solovyovo controlled the engineers and work brigades and was responsible for the progress of the work.

For Bogdanov and the convicts, nothing had altered. It was the same as it had been at Krupki, or before that when they were building the autobahn. Norms, and plans to be fulfilled, and sleep in the open, cabbage-soup and four hundred grammes of bread twice a day—except that here the soup and bread did not often turn up. But for Anna Pavlovna, Nina Mihailovna and the civilians—the telegraph clerks, office workers, factory workers, students and housewives from Smolensk—life was not the same. They had been reduced to the lowest level of Soviet life, that of the collective farm peasant and the forced labourer; the big phrases about defence of the Socialist homeland could not disguise this fact.

They had to fulfil the norms by heavy work, and at the same time feed themselves and provide their own blankets, working clothes and—if possible—their own shovels. They fed themselves in the same way as millions of Red Army men supplemented their rations in these days. From the fields of the collectives they got cabbages, unripe ears of rye, cucumbers and little immature potatoes. In a short time the fields for a considerable distance round were stripped bare. The conscript labourer toiled and hungered, lived on the substance of his emaciated body—lived, as the normal Soviet citizen had for years, on the abundant energy inherited from his grandparents. The best chance of surviving the building of these gigantic earth walls was to become brigade leader, or somehow to get into the closed circle of overseers, book-keepers and supervisors of the grey mass.

With her Young Communist card, her training for trade union work and the propaganda courses she had taken, Nina Mihailovna had all the qualifications to attain such a post, but she no longer had the necessary physical strength. She had a shovel in her hand, but its metal was soft and the blade crumpled up like paper. Her neighbour's tools were the same; yet she could not comfort herself with wild cursing, to which even the cultured Anna Pavlovna was reduced. She worked and things went black before her eyes. And so it was with others, but her weariness had another, deeper cause.

The day seemed unending; the sun was burning hot and there was no shade such as there had been here and there on the autobahn. The rags on her body had once been a dress; she had worked on it with the Polish countess, and Nikolai had loved to see her in it. How far away the days in Bialystock seemed! She was cut off from them by the road to Minsk and the autobahn. Burnt-out tanks, discarded bedding, prams, bicycles, clouds of steam and dust; a smell of hot concrete, of tar, oil and putrid corpses. Bombs were falling and horses reared. On and on and on to the ferry—that terrible ferry. And all the woods were full of deserters. Nikolai surely couldn't be one of them. Where was Nikolai? If only she could see him here with a shovel in his hand.

From the top of the earth wall she could look down on the town of Smolensk. Over the city great columns of smoke were rising. There was fighting in the streets. People said that the Germans held the southern part, and that the Red Army had crossed the river and was defending the northern half. And up here the earth rose and rose; a wall was thrown up bit by bit, with another behind it and another behind that again.

"*Davai—davai*—get on—get on."

She was not keeping up with the norm. For every shovelful she failed to throw, her neighbour, an Uzbek girl, threw one for her without saying a word. And Anna Pavlovna would help her out with a shovelful from time to time.

"You are too delicate for this kind of work," she said.

What was wrong with her? Once more she had to hold on to the shaft of her shovel.

"*Davai—davai*—get on with it—get on." The words came through thick clouds.

"What is wrong with you, little dove?"

She clung to the shaft of the shovel and was sick. It was not the first time it had happened that morning. The Uzbek girl exchanged glances with Anna Pavlovna.

"What's wrong with you—what month are you in?" asked Anna Pavlovna.

Nina Mihailovna had not thought of that before. She counted the weeks which had gone past and remembered a haystack—horses tearing over a field—burning men leaping out of a tank. What had happened? Who had been with her then? Her glance fell on the Army boots on her feet and at last she knew. The sky was suddenly pitch black; her knees gave way and she slid to the ground. The Uzbek girl and Anna Pavlovna were about to carry her away, but she straightened herself up again.

"It's over now—I was only feeling weak."

She gripped her shovel which had fallen from her hand and took her place again in the row.

Three people had been mobilised on the earth-works

215

—a girl from Uzbekistan, a woman from Gzhatsk, and they helped the third to fulfil her norm. Down in the town there were three bodies of troops fighting side by side: a regiment from Voronesh and a regiment from Rybinsk, but neither needed to help the third unit which consisted largely of convicts. The convicts fought like devils, and when the regiments on their flanks—the regiments from Voronesh and Rybinsk—had withdrawn, they were still out in front fighting a hand-to-hand battle. Only when German uniforms appeared in the neighbouring streets did they fall back.

The troops from Voronesh and Rybinsk had had to evacuate the left bank of the river and the whole of the old town. During the night the old bridge went up. In the morning the troops, looking across the river, which had no bridges left, to the portion of the town they had given up and the old town walls rising from the foaming Dnieper with the high, proud towers Boris Goudunov had built, felt their defeat more bitter still—as if they were being judged before the tribunal of history. But they could not hold on even to the north bank. The Germans had come upon the town like swarms of flies, and had been killed like flies. Cossacks crossed the Dnieper and cut the German supply lines; but German reinforcements got through—first of all a motorised infantry division with troop-carriers, then an armoured division, and then another. They overwhelmed the north bank with their artillery and dive-bombers, then pushed over the Dnieper on assault boats. The first wave was thrown into the river; others pressed on behind. The Germans seemed determined to die, but they won the north bank of the Dnieper.

The regiments from Rybinsk and Voronesh and the convicts had their backs to the dwindling northern quarter of the town with its factories and workers' houses. Their losses were terrible. Once more the convicts were the last to withdraw, giving up their barricades of trucks and tram-lines and cobbles and sand only when their flanks were no longer covered.

3 Battalion was involved in bloody hand-to-hand fighting. Its commander, Captain Uralov, was ordered to report to the lieutenant-colonel. The order reached

him, not in his headquarters in a leather factory, but with the forward company whose commander had been brought to the rear severely wounded. The company had to hold an important cross-roads and was on the point of losing it; if it were given up, that would cut off the retreat of half the battalion. Captain Uralov could not comply with the lieutenant-colonel's order; his appearance forward with the troops was required to stiffen their morale. This scratch unit made up of Ivan from Archangel, Chiang from Tien-Shan, Pyotr from Saratov—fifty convicts made into Red Army men—restored the situation, cut off a detachment of Germans and chased them up a blind alley.

They fought pitilessly, taking no prisoners, killing all they could lay hands on. In the midst of the massacre they were taken by surprise—a German tank appeared at the end of the street. Now they themselves were in a trap, with the surviving infantry on one side of them and tank-borne infantry on the other. No shots were fired: they fought with knives and fists.

The regiment withdrew, falling back to the tank obstacles on the edge of the town, and made contact on its flanks with the regiments from Voronesh and Rybinsk. For forty-eight hours it held out on the outskirts of the town, during which time Uralov and two soldiers, who were cut off, sat hiding under the tiles of a roof. On the second night they ventured out on to the street, working their way forward bit by bit over factory yards and along the backs of store-houses. On the morning of the third day they reached their own lines at the moment when the Germans resumed their attack and broke through the defences on the edge of the town. Uralov and his companions succeeded in making contact with their own unit in the midst of the fighting and retreated along with the others.

The whole sector on the outskirts of Smolensk began to move back, withdrawing north-east under concentrated fire to the earth-works. But these, too, lay under enemy artillery fire, and when the troops who had fallen back from the town reached them they found workers killed by shell-fire, and large numbers of women who had died at their work beside their shovels and barrows. The rest had fled to the east, to the ferry at Solovyovo.

Uralov found himself with a unit which had newly arrived at the front. On their way to Minsk—where they had been told they were going—they had been suddenly detrained and had taken up positions during the night behind the earth-works. They did not know what to make of the enemy shells falling into their positions in the early morning; according to them the front was hundreds of miles farther west. They could not believe that the retreating troops, the men who had been beaten back from the edge of the town, and now came panting along to take cover behind the earth-works—strange figures, hungry, ragged, thirsty, cast up by death—were their own comrades.

Planes appeared in the sky.

"They're ours."

They were Stukas, dive-bombing. Fountains of earth rose into the air. There were casualties, but the newcomers still did not seem to understand.

"This is the front line, you fools."

Uralov went on again, shaking his head. He was looking for his own regiment. He reached another force and reported to the commander on the spot, gave the number of his regiment and explained that he had been cut off for two days and was looking for his own unit. The commander sent him to the commissar.

"What is your name?"

"Uralov."

"Yes, the matter has already been reported. You did not comply with an order from your regimental commander. You went over to the Germans. It's a bad affair —you are under arrest. Surrender your weapons."

Uralov was led back to Division who had him taken back to the security unit in the rear. The mere suspicion that he had had contact with the enemy would have been sufficient to have him shot. It was only his Order of the Red Star and his Order of Lenin that Uralov had to thank that he got as far as the prison cell of the NKVD HQ at Solovyovo.

The earth-works north-east of Smolensk, the Dnieper to the bend in the river below Solovyovo, and the railway line to Roslavl now formed the front line. There was a second defence line, with strong artillery positions, twenty to twenty-five miles farther east between Dorogobush and Yelnya.

July passed into August; hot days of dust and the noise of battle. In the cell where Uralov lay it was still hotter, and even at night no breath of fresh air entered. The guards brought him a loaf of black bread and water which was warm by the time it arrived. After two days he had eaten his loaf but he did not get another until four days had passed.

The day came when he heard other noises besides the explosion of bombs. It was the thunder of heavy guns. The dilapidated house where he lay shook to its foundations; plaster fell from the roof; the narrow room filled with thick dust which stopped up his nose and clogged his mouth. He tried to decide the direction of the firing. They were Russian guns and it must mean an attack—a counter-offensive towards Smolensk.

The attack lasted three days.

On the evening of the third day Uralov was taken out of his cell and along with some others driven east in a column. They passed through Dorogobush and the second defence line which would be the front line in a few days, following in the wake of a long convoy of trucks; the NKVD HQ was moving from the ferry at Solovyovo to a spot on the road from Dorogobush to Vyasma.

After another two days Uralov was brought before a young officer. Lieutenant Yudanov recognised the man at once as the red-headed captain on the motor-bicycle who had been looking for his HQ on the building site at Krupki. He told Uralov to sit down.

"My first question," said Yudanov, "is concerned with non-compliance with an order. Why did you not comply with the orders of your regimental commander? Why did you not report to his HQ when instructed to do so?"

"I could not leave my battalion."

Uralov gave an account of the situation which had kept him with the forward company.

"That's all right—that agrees with what other people have reported. The regimental commander confirms what you say."

Uralov would have liked to know who the others were and who of his unit were still alive; but he suppressed a question on the subject.

"Now for the main question—what task were you assigned by the Germans?"

Uralov did not know what to make of this question. What answer could he give to it?

"What were you doing for two days over there? We know everything—we know that, too, but we want to have it from your mouth. We want your confession."

Yudanov had not yet got to the state in which Permyakov had been but he was suffering from the same consuming sickness. A lot of faces had appeared at his table and disappeared again for ever. He was overwrought and impatient.

"Are you going to tell me, or aren't you?" he shouted and banged on the table with the butt of his revolver. Uralov was unaffected. He reported how he had spent the forty-eight hours with two soldiers in the roof of a house; there had been nothing else there but hunger, thirst and lumber. He gave an account of their escape by night through the factory yards and said in conclusion: "I only saw the Germans in the distance. I could not possibly speak to them—in fact, I have never even spoken to a prisoner. What kind of assignment could I have got under these circumstances? I am being kept here unjustly —let me go."

"Think it over well—you haven't done anything very serious yet. You haven't had time for that. If you own up we will put you back in the line—otherwise you will have to appear before the revolutionary tribunal."

That was only a manner of speaking—the tribunal was already in session, at that very table, and it depended on Yudanov and a scratch of his pen whether the man before him was liquidated or not.

"I have nothing to confess," answered Uralov.

He was taken away again, but now he got a ration of bread every day and soup and mahorka. After another twelve days had gone by, he was brought before the lieutenant again.

"Well, Uralov," Yudanov greeted him this time, "we have put a call through to your district and got a satisfactory reply. We have decided to send you back to your regiment with a warning."

"Why a warning? Shouldn't I do everything I can another time to avoid being taken prisoner?"

"Don't start that again, Uralov. We can't let you go without a warning. You will get your personal belongings and pistol back. You are free."

Uralov had an order movement for his regiment in his pocket. Above him he had the blue sky once more; a white cloud hung motionless over a reaped field. It was August and the hot summer had reached its zenith. He had been given rations for the journey and something to smoke as well. On the way, at the edge of a wood or at a village well, he would sit down with bivouacking soldiers, give them some of his tobacco and they would roll cigarettes and talk about the war. There had been dramatic changes on the front; Smolensk now lay almost forty miles behind it. In the elbow of the Dnieper between Smolensk and the Solovyovo ferry a huge body of troops —people spoke of fifteen divisions and several armoured corps—had been cut off.

Uralov looked over the stubble fields and up at the warm sky. Wisps of clouds drifted through the clear air.

"It won't always be summer," he said; "winter will come."

It struck him as odd that the soldiers he met could sit undisturbed here behind the front for a day or two, roll their cigarettes and smoke and talk in peace. Throughout the whole campaign he had never seen anything like it. The front had always been pierced by armoured spearheads and rapid manœuvres and everywhere there had been uncertainty, alarm and fear. But here they sat and smoked mahorka and chewed sunflower seeds and looked idly up into the sky. It meant that there was a front and a rear. That was the new element which had emerged during the days he had been away from things.

Uralov got back to his regiment and reported to HQ. "I'm glad you're back," said the commander. "I have to get things into shape here. I am just about to hand over the command of the regiment and expect to be relieved at any time now. You, of course, will get your old battalion back."

The regiment had pulled out of the front line and was resting fifteen miles or so to the rear. As a matter of fact one could hardly talk of a regiment or battalions; the division existed only in name and had dwindled to a few remnants. Of his own battalion Uralov found only thirty-seven men. He came across them on the edge of a wood, where they were getting political instruction. A commissar was lecturing them on the situation. The soldiers sat there, smoking, asking no questions, taking no part in what was going on. They were all glad to see their old battalion commander again. When the commissar had gone, they complained that they had no field kitchen and had not had any rations for the last ten days. They had got potatoes from the fields and eaten the hearts of the cabbages. They went to the villages round about and bought milk with their own money, begged or even stole, according to circumstances —and the officers were just as hungry and pretended not to see what was going on.

Such was the situation when Uralov came back. Things were like this not only in his battalion and in his regiment —the situation was the same with many of the infantry formations on the whole front.

Next day the commander called Uralov to the rear. "We have to re-form the regiment, and I want you to give me a hand with it," he said.

Men were coming in from the straggler-collecting points. Uniforms had to be procured. In order to get rations Uralov had to fight the quartermaster. He had his hands full. The stuff he got from the quartermaster was not much good; the uniforms he brought back from Division were worn, and often in the same condition in which they had been stripped from the dead, and there were not enough to go round. After a few weeks he had equipment only for forty-five per cent. of the troops and then only personal arms—World War rifles dating from 1917-18; there were no machine guns at all.

On the front the fighting went on. Often when the wind came from that direction the artillery fire on the bend of the Dnieper could be heard in the camp in the woods. But there were no important changes—at least, not on

222

this sector of the front. The German advance on Moscow had been held up or had come to a standstill; the only changes were in the southern sector where Kiev and large tracts of the Ukraine had been lost and the German armoured spearheads were aiming at Orel and Kharkov.

September came to an end. The nights were cold already; in the mornings there was hoar-frost on the ground. Uralov's regiment received orders to move up to the front. They marched westward, in the direction of the Desna.

PART III

"And all the fowls were filled with their flesh."

Revelations.

In front of the railway station in Smolensk things looked much as they had done ten weeks before, when Lieutenant Yudanov had been unable to find room for his thirty trucks. But German was spoken now, not Russian, and cigarettes were smoked instead of the home-made twists of black tobacco, and trains came into the station one after another and more quickly. Otherwise it was just the same—the same confused mass of men and vehicles. The square in front of the station had become larger; fire had eaten great gaps in the rows of wooden houses round the sides. The square and the gaps in the houses were packed with MT; there were piles of packs and helmets; soldiers were standing about talking or gazing at troops coming back from the front—dirty, ragged, unshaven. On the edge of the crowd Russians were bartering mahorka, sunflower seeds, bread, old clothes and bent nails. In the midst of this immense mart a lane was kept clear through which a continual line of ambulances drove to the station. Their load was pitiful; a sharp smell of carbolic reached the onlookers who caught an occasional glimpse of grey faces and muddied, blood-caked rags. In the opposite direction drove armoured vehicles, field kitchens, troop-carriers and ammunition trucks.

Every ten minutes a train came in; from north-west, west and south—Russian wagons and German wagons too, for one track had been altered to the German gauge as far as Smolensk. From the north-west came units of Hoepner's armoured group—from Lake Ilmen came the 3rd Motorised Infantry Division, the S.S. Death's Head Division and Lieb's Brigade. From the west, along the narrow gauge railway, came a battalion of reinforcements, and another immediately behind it. Regiments of 5 Armoured Division, which had been equipped for the African desert, came from the west with their tanks painted brown and the soldiers in tropical uniforms. Equipment was being unloaded everywhere. Tanks and trucks rolled over the ramps, moved off and bored their

227

way through the jammed streets. They moved east to the temporary bridge at Solovyovo, to the autobahn and south-east towards Roslavl.

"It looks like a big offensive," Heydebreck said to Emil Feierfeil. Both had been wounded, and after a period in hospital in Germany had arrived in Smolensk with a reinforcement battalion. They had to join a convoy but still had time to look round before leaving.

"The road surface is bad," Feierfeil remarked. "There are tram lines but no trams running."

"Typical oriental democracy," said Heydebreck, and meant by that everything he found strange—the cobbles, the ruined churches with the onion spires, the throng on the black market, the wretched stuff that was offered for sale there, the smell from the wide open doors of the houses.

"It's a good job we've got away from those new boys in the reinforcement battalion."

"Yes, remember that little fat one last night—he started to get the jitters right back in Borissov."

"There's a lot going on here."

"There's an offensive coming."

*   *   *

Vilshofen walked through the streets of Smolensk past the ruined houses. The town had a pleasant situation in a valley surrounded by gentle, cultivated slopes. It could be a pretty town.

He reached the Dnieper, where a temporary bridge had been put up alongside the remains of the old stone bridge, which had been blown up, and waited for his battalion. It arrived as darkness was falling. They drove across the river to the old town, and slowly on through narrow streets full of transport to the outskirts where they passed piled-up heaps of abandoned Russian equipment. Outside the town they followed a good tarred road —the main road to Roslavl—but before Roslavl they turned off into a wood and reached their rest area and the village where they had been billeted.

After a brief sleep the tank crews left their cramped quarters in the peasant huts. It was a cold morning with hoar-frost on the ground. The village, almost undamaged, was surrounded by woods and on a hill, standing somewhat apart, stood a shell-torn church. Maintenance and roll-calls filled in the days; the arrival of post from home broke the routine. New maps were issued for the operation which lay before them—all roads led to Moscow.

Church parade was on orders for Sunday—the regiment's first during the campaign in the east. Vilshofen had no idea what he was starting when he laid down that the service was to be held in the ruined church on the hill.

Sunday came. No bell was tolled, but a military band had taken up position on the hill and a chorale rang out over the land and greeted the men as they came up the slope. Something like six hundred soldiers collected in the towerless, windowless nave—and they were not the only ones present. The news had gone round among the inhabitants that a service was to be held in the church—the old pilgrims' shrine; so they had come not only from the surrounding villages but from even farther off, on foot and in their small carts. Thousands gathered on the little plateau, with a wall of carts round them and the blue autumn sky above. The soldiers in the nave and those outside made one congregation and prayed to the same God.

There was no organ in the deserted church, only a choir of young voices supported by the muted band. The singing swelled through the fallen doors and the empty windows, over the heads of the great assembly to the edge of the plateau, to the carts and the horses peacefully chewing the freshly-scattered hay. The men and women outside held their children by the hand and fell on their knees.

"Heaven is my throne, and earth is my footstool: what house will ye build me? saith the Lord: or what is the place of my rest?" was the padre's text.

Even during the sermon the crowd outside the church did not stand up, but remained kneeling, praying in their own tongue. The word of God was no longer banished from the land.

In the evening there was a special announcement on the wireless:

"Deep penetration of the Russian positions at Orel and Yelnya. Fluid advance along the whole front."

Next morning into the midst of the repairs and maintenance work burst the order: "The regiment is moving forward for further employment." Two hours later they drove off into a keen east wind towards Roslavl.

A young lieutenant, the new area commandant, moved into Vilshofen's old HQ, a stone house in the middle of the village. One of his first official actions was the publication of an order concerning the preservation of the collective farm system. The new *prikas* was stuck up on the same blackboard in front of the village Soviet on which the target figures set up by the Soviet authorities, and the amounts to be delivered from the cottage gardens and collectives, had once been published. The people gathered round the notice, read it through and shook their heads. An illiterate old man had it read out to him. He wanted to hear it all, word for word, and so that he would lose nothing he ran his finger along the lines of the text. The people went away and came back to read it through again. They could not get this *prikas* into their heads.

"What will happen to my cow now—the brown one I gave to the *Kolkhoz* eight years ago?" asked one. For him it wasn't only a question of this one cow—he knew all the calves she had dropped, and in the meantime they had become cows, too.

"Read it—everything stays as it was."

That seemed unbelievable.

The people went away again and stood about in the middle of the village street. The old man who had had the text read out to him shook his head: "We are always being trampled under someone's feet—we don't need foreigners for that. It might as well be our own people who walk over us."

Heydebreck and Feierfeil had got back to their old unit. They had come as far as Roslavl in a truck from another formation, and from there an officer from 14 Company had taken them on in a peasant cart. So 14 Company is horsed—that was the first impression they had of the changes in the division since they went away. 14 Company, the supply company, had been fully motorised before the Russian campaign began, but the MT was gone; the roads had swallowed it up. The Russian roads—the infantry could tell a tale about them.

But the supply company had got to know them from another point of view—these roads which went up and down, which had no foundations and a surface like powder, which turned into roaring riverbeds in the rain, and into a howling wilderness when the sandstorms came. It had begun with broken springs, broken axles and damaged radiators, cylinders ground away by the dust. The workshop lorries were continually on the move to repair trucks which had got stuck—an unpleasant job, particularly in the woods at night when the whole place was swarming with snipers. No spare parts had come forward, nor were they likely to, since most of the trucks were of French make anyway. One day two trucks had broken down, three the next day and then five all at once. The supply company commander could have found his way back to the frontier by his abandoned trucks with the notice on them: "Do not cannibalise—being recovered." After a few months on Russian roads things had reached a point where the whole supply company had had to be converted to horse transport.

So after their convalescent leave Heydebreck and Feierfeil rode on a peasant cart into the heavily-damaged village west of the Desna, where their company lay in position in earth bunkers. There were a lot of new faces —young chaps, reinforcements from Saxony, Bohemia and the Sudetenland. But there were also some old friends for Heydebreck and Feierfeil to greet—first and foremost, Corporal August Gnotke.

"Well, how was Berlin?"

"Fine, of course—but we weren't there long enough."

"The journey back wasn't so good—forty men in a truck."

"Were you in Klein-Stepnitz?" asked Gnotke.

"Yes," said Feierfeil, "I was there."

"Well—what else?"

"Pauline isn't there any more."

"Where is she, then?"

"In Berlin—Hans Riederheim got her there. I must say that she's very thick with Riederheim. She expects a letter from him every day."

"Is that so? You wouldn't think he needed her. He was after every skirt in Mogilev, in Propoisk—every place

231

where we have been billeted. Well, that's their business."

Gnotke made a gesture as if he were cancelling something out; he did not look particularly happy as he did so.

"You two will be with me, of course."

Gnotke was no longer at Company HQ. His platoon had been put in the advance guard. Riederheim was there, too, and so was Langhoff's horsed troop.

"You can settle in here right away—there are two spare bunks. Both left yesterday. One with dysentery, the other. . ."

He made another gesture with his hand.

Heydebreck looked round him. A couple of young chaps were sitting about; an older man had pulled off his shirt, turned it inside out, and was now inspecting it.

"What's he doing?"

"You'll soon be doing it, too. An hour's delousing is part of the daily routine. You find fifty to a hundred every day. This is trench warfare."

Trench warfare. The division had been halted for weeks already. The front ran north and south for most of the divisional area, and then turned east. In front lay thinly held positions, but there was often a flare-up in the north where there was a good deal of artillery, including some heavy stuff. One morning a fortnight before—half of the village had still been standing then—Langhoff had been sitting over coffee; his whole troop HQ was round about him and a section of sappers was laying mines and running in and out of the house. There were shells falling round about in the village, but that wasn't unusual. Suddenly Langhoff jumped up and shouted: "Listen! Get forward into the bunkers at once." His own troop went, but the sappers said, "He's off his head" and stayed where they were. The bunkers lay about fifteen yards to one side—there was a trench to them from the house. When they came back half an hour later three direct hits from a 155-mm howitzer had landed on the house—one at the door, one on the end wall and one behind the house. The sappers had seven dead and four badly wounded.

"Langhoff has a sort of sixth sense—there have been a lot of cases like that," said the elderly soldier pulling on his shirt.

"That's what they all say—but he has another version."

"How does he explain it?" asked Heydebreck.

"He says he didn't realise it consciously, but that from among all the odd bursts he had picked out a heavy gun ranging on the house. 'After all, these are all sense perceptions', he says, 'and you can trust your senses.' I'm only telling you this so that you'll keep a look-out. Most of the chaps who get killed are new or have been away a while."

Lice, dysentery, shell-fire, wind and often rain, supplies coming through with difficulty—that was how Heydebreck and Feierfeil found things at their company.

"There are often other jobs for the advance guard, too," said Gnotke. "We're moving off east towards Desna tonight—the artillery is staying here for a while. You can both report to Lieutenant Hasse."

"Isn't he with the General any more?"

"The General doesn't need him now—the climate here suits him so well that he manages with his adjutant. Hasse has got command of our lot here with the advance guard."

*　　*　　*

To cross the Desna, take up position, dig in and wait for the Germans who, according to reconnaissance reports, were still fifteen miles from the Desna—these were the orders of Uralov's regiment.

The night was pitch dark. The regiment moved in the order 1 Battalion, followed by 2, and then 3. At the head of 3 Battalion was Uralov on a horse which one of his men had caught: a Kirghiz horse, not very well broken in, which he called Mahomet. Once when they had tried to put it in a stable it had kicked everything to pieces, but in the open it was a good horse. It found its way on a pitch dark night; in a snowstorm you could simply let go of the reins and shut your eyes and it would bring you to a house and men.

But things had not come to that pass yet. It was only October; an October night with heavy clouds and the darkness like a wall. The regiment marched in close order. The commander, who was a very sick man, had stayed behind in the last village—in a hut with a couple of

233

runners and signallers. Until the lines had been laid to the rear Uralov was in command of the regiment. Cross the Desna, dig in, make a bridgehead—he would do it with 1 and 2 Battalions, and keep 3 Battalion on the other side of the Desna as a reserve. There were very few officers left in the regiment. In his own battalion there was one lieutenant. Ivan, from Archangel, who had got ten years for killing the captain and boatswain of his fishing boat, he had made his adjutant, and the chieftain of the Saratov thieves, Nikita, he had promoted to platoon commander. Neither of them was any worse than any other lieutenant and knew far better how to manage the troops.

Nikita and his platoon belonged to 3 Battalion, but they were marching ahead of 1 Battalion as advance guard. The platoon had crossed the bridge, followed by 1 and 2 Battalions. 3 Battalion under Lieutenant Pokrov remained behind. Uralov himself had reached the bridge with Ivan, and Mahomet's hooves were clattering on the tree-trunks, when suddenly firing broke out—unexpected and murderous fire on both banks and from all sides. The two battalions had walked into a trap.

Everything had happened so quickly that Uralov had not been able to give a single order. Those who escaped the cross-fire retreated in disorder across the bridge. According to reconnaissance reports the Germans were supposed to be still fifteen miles away, so the battalions had been surprised marching in close order. He collected his battalion on the edge of the wood. Some more men from the other battalions joined them—fifty-six men from 1 Battalion and thirty-seven men from 2 Battalion; that was all. Of the officers only the lieutenant from 2 Battalion came back, and from the advance guard Nikita alone.

Uralov ordered his men to take up firing positions on the edge of the wood, and at first light mustered one hundred and forty-six men over and above his own battalion strength. He observed the Germans through his glasses; there were very few—at most a platoon—but they were excellently equipped and had a lot of heavy infantry weapons. They were forming a bridgehead on the east bank, and Uralov thought of a plan to cross the river and take them from the rear. At this point the

Desna was eight feet deep, and the fifteen men of his battalion who could not swim he intended to leave behind on the edge of the wood with the survivors of the other battalions.

The plan came to nothing. The soldiers grumbled and wanted something to eat first. He would get nowhere by simply issuing an order. On the second night he slept uneasily: several times he got up and wandered about in the woods listening to what the soldiers were saying to each other. "What sort of a battalion commander is that?" "We have been moving up to the front for seven days and all that time there has been no soup—nothing but a bit of black bread. Then he sends us over a bridge right into the German fire. When a commander is no good he should get a bullet through the head. How can we cross the river and fight the Germans? Look at them —well fed and healthy. Only a company of them and we have lost a whole regiment. And look at their supply wagons—they're huge and you should see what's in them. . . "

In the course of the night four German field guns had taken up position. But the German gunners were careless and their guns were badly camouflaged; you could observe everything they did. It must still be possible to cross the river higher up and take them from the rear in the night. Uralov had split the regiment into battalions again; Lieutenant Kasakov led 2 Battalion, and for 1 Battalion a new second lieutenant had arrived from the rear. But once again his plan came to nothing. The order was received to dig in on the spot and the battalions were allotted sectors laid down on the map. The Germans opened up from their bridgehead with heavy infantry weapons and then with the four field guns—but this time without causing many casualties. The forward troops were well camouflaged and work was not disturbed. Further back in the wood Uralov had a bunker built and fitted out as his HQ; from there he had lines laid back to the village and to the battalions. The troops were sparing with their fire, as the supply columns had not yet arrived and ammunition was scarce. But the most serious problem was the lack of food.

Something must be done about the rations. Uralov

decided to ride back to the rear himself. He found the regimental commander in the last stages of consumption. The old couple, on whom he was billeted, looked after him as if he were their own son, and they had fetched a woman doctor who had taken refuge in the village from the bombing of Roslavl. The battalion could expect no help from him, so Uralov telephoned to Division, but Division did not sound very promising. He rode on another six miles, reached Division and refused to leave the ration stores until he had received an issue for his men—no noodles and no bread, only herring, a whole wagon-load of them. He was given the wagon as well but horses were scarce, so he harnessed Mahomet. The beast had never been in harness and was about to smash the wagon to pieces when a couple of soldiers ran to him, grasped the reins and held him fast. One of them —he was a Kirghiz—knew something about horses, and in the end Uralov was given the soldier as well. Even then the journey was rough going, but at last they reached the village and arrived in front of the cottage which housed the regimental HQ.

Uralov gave the signallers sitting in the passage some herring, and went into the regimental commander who lay on the bed as before, barely conscious of what went on around him. The refugee doctor from Roslavl was with him. "There is no question of the Lieutenant-Colonel carrying out his duties," she said, "he has just had a severe haemorrhage."

There was no other officer at Division who could take over the regimental command; they were willing to send a captain to help him out—that was all that Uralov could get out of them. He went out to find the soldier, whose name was Chiang, and they continued their journey to the battalion positions. By the time they reached the bunker and had distributed the herrings it was after midnight.

At exactly half an hour after midnight murderous artillery fire began from the other side of the river. Not only were the four field guns firing, but shells of all calibres were falling on the Russian positions. It was clear that the Germans were preparing to attack, and when, half an hour later, the heavy firing was still going on, there

236

could no longer be any doubt about it.

At this moment the commander rang through.

"Listen, Uralov. The captain from HQ hasn't arrived. Come right away, I need help." The position did not allow Uralov to leave the battalion, yet was there nothing else for it. Remembering Smolensk and the unpleasant consequences which non-compliance with a similar order had had for him, he mounted his horse and set off again, with Chiang running at his side.

Nothing had changed at regimental HQ. The signallers still squatted in the passageway. The commander, whose condition had obviously deteriorated in the last few hours, still lay on the bed. He had been waiting to be relieved for weeks and now the help promised by Division had not arrived.

"Report the artillery fire to Division," he whispered as Uralov came to his bedside.

"Yes, Comrade Lieutenant-Colonel."

Division knew all about it already—they had heard the noise of the firing themselves. Uralov asked for orders to withdraw the battalions from the edge of the wood to a better line farther back.

"No, the regiment will remain on the line indicated on the map. Wait for further orders. The captain who is going to help the regimental commander is on his way already."

Uralov ordered Lieutenant Pokrov to take over 3 Battalion. Ivan and Nikita, who undoubtedly enjoyed great authority with the troops, remained as his adjutants.

The commander coughed so much that Uralov was frightened that a new fit of bleeding would come on. Time went by and the captain from HQ did not arrive. Every ten minutes Uralov got a signal from the battalions on the situation; the artillery fire showed no signs of stopping, and now Stukas were attacking in wave after wave. Bombs were falling in the village, too. The owners of the cottage came in and the wife prepared a bed for Uralov with a clean white quilt. Then the two old people retired; they had dug a hole for themselves in the garden, big enough and deep enough to be splinter-proof.

Ivan came through from 3 Battalion:

"The lieutenant has been killed. Our losses are terrible.

237

There is no one in command any longer. Can the battalion commander come back?"

"Did you hear, Comrade Lieutenant-Colonel? I must go to my battalion at once."

"You can't leave here."

Uralov ordered Lieutenant Kasakov to name a second in command for his own weak battalion, and to take over 3 Battalion, which was still the strongest. More bombs fell in the village and the house shook.

Four o'clock came—then five.

There was no more word from the battalions. Soldiers began to arrive from the front and said that 2 and 3 Battalions had been cut to pieces. Enemy tanks had come and driven to and fro over the trenches.

The German artillery lifted its fire farther to the rear. Shells began to land in the village—quite near the house. The windows were blown in. Earth came flying into the room. The commander tried to sit up but fell back again. His face had changed and his voice was thinner. "Leave me—I order you to go to your battalion."

Uralov got on his horse and galloped forward. A cold wet morning was creeping over the fields. The battalion was coming to meet him in utter rout. Kasakov could scarcely hide his relief; Uralov was back—now there was someone to take the responsibility off his shoulders.

"Where are 1 and 2 Battalions?" asked the lieutenant. Uralov did not want to discourage him further and replied:

"The two battalions have had orders from me to withdraw and dig in five miles to the east and make a new defence line there."

But it was impossible to restore discipline. The fleeing troops even forgot to take cover and strove madly to get clear of the enemy fire. Bursts of machine-gun fire raked them. They reached the village but it was in flames; the house in which the commander had been left had disappeared.

The Germans kept on the heels of the fleeing men. It was still six miles to the new positions. But under the ruins of the house where the commander lay buried there was still plenty of rifle ammunition and some machine-gun belts, and from there the road, which rose slightly, could easily be commanded; this was the place for a short stand. On the other side of the street stood the village church with the graveyard round it.

There was no means of collecting a rear-guard, for no one paid any attention to orders. But Ivan and Nikita managed to scrape a few men together. Nikita jumped into the hole in the garden beside the old couple, taking with him his ancient Maxim, which he had rescued, and Ivan lay behind the ruins of the house with a handful of men.

The main body moved on along the road to the east. On these six miles of road Uralov had to try to get control of the panicking, fleeing mob while Ivan and Nikita held off the enemy. The scattered troops reached the new positions, if not in battle order at least not in a wild flight, and an hour later Ivan arrived. Nikita had remained behind. "He was firing like mad," said Ivan, "and he still had lots of ammunition."

* * *

Hasse and his men had held the bridgehead until Zecke's regiment moved up.

An Order of the Day was distributed to the troops: "Soldiers of the eastern front—today the last battle begins. . . "

While Zecke's regiment was marching over the bridge, the advance guard went forward in extended order over the positions at the edge of the wood, which had been bombed from the air and broken up by the artillery.

Heydebreck and Feierfeil went into an enemy bunker. Three men were sitting at a roughly-made table of branches. There were herrings lying on the table. One of the men had a herring in his mouth, the second had one in his hand and the third stared at the door with open eyes. All three were dead. There were dead in the trench outside, too, and there were herrings scattered everywhere. It was to be a long time before Heydebreck could forget the scene.

The advance continued. The enemy was thrown back and the first line pierced. It was good to be able to move and get warm. The nights spent under the open sky or in cold, damp, scantily-covered holes in the sand had been bitter. Riederheim had said one evening that they should

239

all write home and ask for winter clothing. Winter in Russia—that was a terrible thought. The only way it could be avoided was by a rapid advance and a quick end to the battle.

The sun struggled through the low-lying cloud and gilded the autumn woods. The units which had been combing the woods came into the open, formed up and marched on along the road. There were dead lying in the ditches. Russians came to meet the advancing troops with their hands above their heads. Grey masses; the rags on their bodies worn and frayed.

The oldish soldier, whom Heydebreck had noticed the first evening when he rejoined the battalion, sacrificed his field dressing and gave first aid to a wounded Russian; then he took away the Russian's ground-sheet. "He doesn't need it any more," he said, "and I was bloody cold last night."

Suddenly the order came to halt. The point section had been fired on. They had got as far as the village without meeting resistance and had passed the first houses; but there was one spot no one got past alive. The advance guard and another company were held up on the outskirts of the village. Thus the whole regiment, whose axis of advance lay through the village, was brought to a halt.

Zecke, the regimental commander, came forward in a staff car to see what was wrong. It was quite unexpected—a road-block which must be cleared away as soon as possible so that the advance could continue. They had to hurry because the flanking regiments were already far on ahead. He drove up a slight rise and had barely reached the top when a burst of machine-gun fire went over his head. Fortunately it was aimed too high. The driver pulled the wheel round and landed with the colonel in the graveyard at the side of the road.

"Well, we won't get any further like this," Zecke admitted. He looked around him. There were dead troops on the road and the charred body of a woman in the graveyard. The wooden houses were burning and smoke was rising everywhere; amidst the flames and smoke it was impossible to tell where the resistance was coming from.

"Bring up the heavy weapons."

The advance guard brought up mortars; a gun was moved up from the horsed troop and house by house the village street was taken under direct fire. But it didn't make any difference; anyone who went up the rise in the road was hit and fell. The resistance was not coming from the houses—that became clear when they had collapsed one after another. There must be a trench in one of the gardens with a hidden machine-gun nest in it. So there was. When the firing stopped a man was found in a hole with an old Maxim in his hands; he had fired his last belt of cartridges. An elderly civilian and a white-haired woman were sitting beside him. The Red Army man and the two old people climbed out of the hole. Sergeant Riederheim pushed the machine-gunner and the two old people back again, pulled the pins from a couple of hand-grenades and threw them in.

The road was clear, but even now the regiment could not get on. Zecke was called to the phone. The General wanted to know what was wrong with him—he was falling behind—the other two regiments had gone ahead. Now it was too late; the whole division must stand waiting, because now he had to get off the road and leave it free for a cavalry division which was pushing forward to the enemy positions six miles ahead, on the edge of a wood.

The sun was shining, so the troops had no objection to resting a bit longer. They wandered about the village and massacred the hens they put up from among the charred ruins. They bivouacked in the gardens, eating and drinking, and ransacking the bee-hives.

The few inhabitants who were left had inscrutable faces; it was hard to say what they thought. The days were past when the villagers came to meet the leading troops with bread and salt and the village girls brought milk and strawberries. Heydebreck still remembered those days. He had just come through Poland with the reinforcement battalion and had seen the hungry people and the children begging for a piece of bread at the stations. So this is going to be like Poland, too, he thought. It looks as if we are going to let the Poles and the Russians starve—it's one way of doing things, but where does it get us? An old man caught his eye; there was no doubt about it— he had a striking and unusual appearance; lively eyes in

241

a centenarian's face. Heydebreck could not decide whether their expression was mocking, or sad, or both together. He was so struck that it was only when the old man had turned away that he noticed his miserable shoes and the tattered condition of his clothing, and the fact that he had a girl or a young woman with him. She herself was worth looking at—it was obvious that she did not belong to the village; she, too, was dressed in rags and looked as if she had been sleeping in the open. The pair —yet they could hardly belong together—produced an extraordinary effect.

Heydebreck asked a German-speaking woman doctor from Roslavl who they were.

"They are strangers here—they come from over that way." She pointed towards the swamps in the north, but would say no more.

* * *

Uralov lay with the remnants of his regiment on the edge of a wood six miles from the village. He was trying desperately to make contact with the units on his flanks and with the rear. He needed ammunition and rifles. A lot of the men had thrown theirs away; the only thing they always saved in any situation was the gas-mask container, which took the place of a knapsack and in which there was generally a piece of bread or an onion or a beetroot, or whatever they had managed to pick up. That they always brought with them. The first thing his men demanded of him once more was food. He found a cable, connected his field telephone, got through to Division after several attempts and received the astonishing order to fall back another six miles and wait for reinforcements.

But before they could reach the new defence line fate overtook them in the shape of German cavalry—an SS Division—and now they were over-run, ridden down and cut to pieces. They were helpless in the face of the snorting, stamping, sabre-swinging cavalry, and it would have been the end of them all had the wood not broken the attack and provided a certain amount of shelter.

The night came and was more merciful than the horsemen; for they made no prisoners. Yet the cries of the wounded and the death rattle of the dying could still be heard. Then the darkness was torn apart; flares sank down out of the sky and every leaf, every twig, became transparent. Each fold in the ground and even the thickest undergrowth was laid bare in the harsh white light. Bombs fell and shattered the wood. Everywhere there were dead and wounded and blood. Many were struck down by the falling trees.

The cries of the abandoned men grew weaker. The rest got out into the open; but here their case was little better. Bursts of tracer swept over the ground and pursued the broken troops until at last they found safety in a morass. In the morning only twenty men rose out of the marsh along with Uralov.

These were all that remained of a regiment—these and Mahomet. Chiang fetched the horse from a reed-grown pond and brought it to him, and a little troop led by a captain on an unkempt Kirghiz horse set off blindly towards the east, without a compass. East—towards the new day. The horizon behind them was bright with the light of burning villages. They could move only by night; by day they lay in the marshes or in the thick undergrowth. They dared not show themselves; the air was full of the roar of planes, which fired on everything—even on a single man. To the east; there was no room for any other thought in their tortured heads.

In actual fact, Uralov's group was moving not east but north-east; following a water-course they turned farther towards the north and came out on the Smolensk-Moscow autobahn. Here, on the main withdrawal route towards Moscow, they were drawn into the stream of retreating troops. Artillery, armour, infantry — all retreating; supply columns, headquarters staffs, constructional staffs, the ruins of nine whole armies—of 105 Armoured Division, of 204 Motorised Division, a torrent moving east, armies of ghosts that moved by night.

On the second day after they arrived at the autobahn, the Stukas came over—not many compared with the masses exposed to their bombs; fifty or sixty of them, perhaps. The great disordered mob burst apart, fleeing in all directions through woods which had suddenly been thinned by the bombs. The diving Stukas killed horses, cows and men—everything that came under their fire.

Once it was Guernica, now it was the autobahn between the upper Dnieper and the Vyasma river, one hundred and fifty miles from Moscow, twelve miles from the town of Vyasma: Napoleon's last staging place on his advance to Moscow. The target was an army which had been over-run on the Shchara, the Beresina and the Dnieper, a leaderless army beaten by hunger, panic and superior weapons.

* * *

Captain Uralov passed through Vyasma and looked about him for a proper formation, a defence line, into which to fit his dwindling force. It was no laughing matter to be taken for a deserter, which could only have one end—a bullet.

There were empty streets; all the windows were boarded up. Suddenly a crowd of young boys surrounded him.

"Tovarish Captain, have you time to spare?"

"Any amount—what do you want?"

"Show us how to throw hand grenades."

Uralov got down from his horse and went to one side with the boys. He pulled the safety pin from a couple of hand grenades.

"Watch that you don't hold them too long in your hand when you have pulled out the pin."

The grenades exploded against the wall of a shed.

"What are you going to do with them?"

"When the Germans come we are going to throw them in at the windows where they are sleeping."

Uralov went on to look for the town commandant. He came across a group of Militia busy digging in across the road. It was the local Militia, the town police; a little squad under a sergeant.

"Hello, comrades, what are you doing here?"

"We have orders to man a defence line."

"But where are our troops?"

"The town commandant has left. There are no troops here. But here is *Pravda*, dropped to us from a plane. It is the today's issue."

Uralov looked at the first page. He read:

"Our troops have relinquished Vyasma after heavy and heroic fighting."

"What's this—what does this mean?"

"There is no fighting here and no troops, either."

Uralov looked at the sergeant and the sergeant looked at Uralov. They understood each other without need for further words.

Uralov still thought he might be able to find the town commandant. He asked an old woman who showed him the house. The windows were boarded up and on the door was pinned a piece of paper which read: "The town commandant has moved to Gzhatsk. All troops passing through must report to him there."

So they went on thirty-five miles to Gzhatsk—not on the autobahn but by side roads. The little troop had got still smaller, and now Uralov had only two men with him —Ivan from Archangel and Chiang from Tien-Shan.

Snow began to fall, the first snow. It weighed down the twigs of the trees until the lowest branches touched the ground. Next day it thawed; and now the roads became soft and there was no bottom to them. The horse sank into the mud up to its fetlocks, but it pulled its hooves out again and went forward step by step. So Uralov rode into Gzhatsk with Chiang on one side and Ivan on the other. It had been raining, and the naked telephone poles and the onion domes of neglected churches were mirrored in the puddles.

Not all of the windows of the little wooden houses had been nailed up or curtained over.

* * *

"You should see this man on the horse, dear."

"I've seen too many men on horseback—far too many."

Men on horse and on foot and in trucks, from Bialystock to Smolensk and from Smolensk to Gzhatsk. It was good to be able to lie stretched out and not have to look at anything except the low, smoke-stained ceiling.

Anna Pavlovna, who had come home to Gzhatsk, was standing at the window, and near her on the couch lay Nina Mihailovna. All Nina Mihailovna wanted to do was to lie there until she had to move, on the next day or the day after, for the terrible suspicion which had come over her on the earth-works at Smolensk had proved to be well founded. She was pregnant—almost in her fourth month.

"Look at that tired, bedraggled horse, and see how the

rain has made the man's blouse cling to him," said Anna Pavlovna. "He's still wearing summer uniform—the whole army looks just the same. Tired and soaked with rain—but he's still proud. The patrol has stopped him. They are telling him to get down from his horse but he sits where he is. He doesn't comply with the order. He must wear some high decorations."

Someone was blowing a whistle now.

Nina Mihailovna heard the shrill sound of the whistle. She was tired and shut her eyes.

*　　*　　*

Uralov had been stopped by an NKVD patrol. The two NKVD men were well dressed and wearing winter clothing already; white furs and white caps with flaps over the ears. They ordered him to dismount, but he did not do so. On his worn blouse he had the Order of the Red Star and the Order of Lenin.

One of the NKVD men whistled for help. A sergeant came along, but he could not make Uralov get off his horse for he had to respect the Orders he wore. He seized the horse by the reins and led its rider to the commander of the NKVD detachment. Behind came Chiang and Ivan, escorted by NKVD men.

They were all taken to a two-storied stone house where Uralov dismounted. Chiang and Ivan were led away and Uralov was escorted into the house by the sergeant.

In the entrance hall sat an officer.

"Surrender your weapons."

Uralov laid his pistol on the table—it was a Soviet make. He had another, a German one, in his trouser pocket but he did not give it up.

"Have you any more weapons?"

"No."

"All right—first floor."

There were a lot of soldiers standing there and a lot of officers, too—a colonel, a lieutenant, a lieutenant-colonel, gunners, tank crews; the whole landing was full. The process was quick and the interrogations short, yet it was three or four hours before it was Uralov's turn. He was shown into a room where a colonel sat behind a desk.

"What is your formation?"

"V Armoured Corps."

"Where is your regiment?"

"I do not know where my regiment is. It was cut to pieces—the last unit I was with was on the Desna."

The colonel wrote something.

"What have I to do now?"

"You'll soon be told—get out."

Outside, he had to wait until fifty officers had been collected. Guarded by NKVD men with machine pistols they were led downstairs. A gate opened and a wide courtyard, once the courtyard of a factory, received them. It was scarcely possible to get in, so great was the throng standing there—seven or eight thousand of them, troops and officers mixed. The NKVD men kept a lane open so that they could get through. Well, they have taken our weapons from us, thought Uralov, something will happen. Perhaps we will all be shot down. He looked round, searching the wall to see if there was a machine gun in position somewhere. A young lieutenant, who had found a piece of wood to sit on, looked at him, stood up and offered him his place. Uralov felt so wretched that he accepted the seat thankfully and sat down.

"What do you think, captain?" said the lieutenant after a while.

"There is a lot to think about."

Uralov was hungry, his thin blouse was soaked and he was frozen to the marrow, but he did not seem to care. He had a lot to think about, here and now, sitting on this piece of wood. There had been no time before. Narishkin, that wonderful commander—his death might have set him thinking. But in the woods south of Minsk he had had to concentrate on getting through, and later his job had caught him up again. He had always had to be two things at once—a fighting officer and his own quartermaster; the progress of the battle had demanded his whole attention but at the same time he had had to see to ammunition, uniforms and rations. It was in the NKVD cell at Solovyovo that he had first begun to think things over; yet in that case he had really suffered no injustice. Security was necessary, and the NKVD, after all, was the organisation for it; but the things that were happening here, not only to individuals, but to tens of thousands, had nothing to do with security any more.

247

"We fought and held on as long as possible, and when it wasn't possible any more we broke out; but now. . ." Walls all round, the soil trampled into mud by thousands of feet—it was like a sheep-pen.

"They are herding us like cattle."

"*Nitchevo*—keep your head up," said the lieutenant.

Uralov stood up—there was no feeling left in his feet and legs. He had no coat. He had lost it in the first battle, on the Bobr.

The lieutenant had half a litre of vodka in his pocket. "Have a drop—it will warm you."

"I haven't slept for a long time and we had nothing to eat," said Uralov to explain his wretched state. He took a sip of vodka and then another. The lieutenant, he learned, was called Skryl and came from a military school in Minsk. At Dorogobush he had been posted as Number 2 to an observation officer with the heavy artillery. When overnight the rear line became the front he had been drawn into the general flood. He had not so long a road behind him as Uralov—only the retreat from Dorogobush to Gzhatsk; but that was enough for him to have his own thoughts.

"It wasn't a retreat—it was a collapse such as history has never seen," he said. This twenty-year old boy had grasped that at least. He seemed to have his own ideas about the reasons for it, too, but they weren't the sort of thing one could say out loud. Nor were the thoughts Uralov was thinking. This factory yard with its ten thousand troops was a cattle-pen. Was not the whole land like this? And who had made it so—who were the cattle-drovers? You didn't have to look far afield for them. The NKVD sentries up on the wall watch-tower were well fed—they had always had something to eat, they were sheltered from cold and wet, and wore furs and caps which covered their ears. And who was the lord and master of all this great herd? Who was the man who had taken the whole responsibility upon himself, and now must shoulder the blame for this immense catastrophe?

That was the point Uralov had got to in the course of a few hours of silent reflection—Uralov, the most faithful of Soviet citizens. Perhaps for the first time in his life he delved into his memory, and from the depths a face rose before him, the furrowed, bearded face of a Russian peasant with ice-grey eyes—no other eyes had ever looked at Uralov like those. Was it possible—could it be his father, could he have any memory of him? He had been scarcely more than four at the time. The face disappeared again. With Nina it was the same, her face, too, was intangible and he saw it as through a veil of water.

Ivan and Chiang turned up again. They had wormed their way through the throng seeking Uralov and brought a scrap of roofing with them, so now Skryl also could sit down.

An NKVD officer mounted the watch-tower and took up position beside the sentry. Something was going to happen.

"Attention, everyone," shouted the officer. "Form up in fives. Form up regardless of rank—officers and men in one column."

They all stood up and formed fives. The great door opened and the column marched out along the broad, muddy street, through puddles, past darkened houses, until it reached the main road; then after a couple of miles it turned off into a wood. Here there were earth bunkers, quite well constructed, and one could see that troops had been quartered here. Twenty men were put into each bunker and found they could sleep quite comfortably. There were no blankets, naturally, but there were pine twigs instead. The lieutenant had remained with Uralov, and Chiang and Ivan were there, too.

"I have the feeling that we will form some sort of unit here," said Uralov to Skryl.

"Yes, it looks like that."

"But I don't want to take over a unit of people I know nothing about."

"No, that's no use—no good ever comes of it."

"Let's have a sleep first."

They lay down, and after reveille and roll-call they were both still asleep. It was still early in the morning when they got up and went to the bunker where the HQ was. Rations had been given out in the meantime; each man had got three raw potatoes, and now, since there were no cooking utensils, they were roasting them at open fires.

In the HQ bunker sat a major.

"Excuse me—I am ill—I have a temperature," said Uralov, and this was true. "I could not report here at the proper time. This lieutenant helped me a great deal."

"So that's it—no doubt it was the same when you were with your other units. Well, we'll soon show you what active service is like."

Uralov looked contemptuously at the man, but said nothing. It would be courting death to speak his thoughts aloud.

"I can only post you to the officers' pool," said the major. Uralov was quite agreeable—it was exactly what he wanted. The rest of the day he spent resting, for they were not going to move off until nightfall. But before that they had all to parade once more. The whole of the newly-formed regiment marched into a clearing and drew up in a horse-shoe, round a newly-dug trench. An eerie silence fell over the ranks. The guard commander drove along before him four men, bare-foot and clad only in their under-pants, with their hands bound behind their backs, to the edge of the trench; twelve NKVD men with machine-pistols followed and, a little to one side, two plenipotentiaries of the NKVD.

One of the latter had a sheet of paper in his hand and he read out:

"In the name of the Union of Soviet Socialist Republics, Ilyin, a lieutenant in the tank corps, who deserted in the field and abandoned his troops, is condemned to death. His family will be deported to Siberia."

The second prisoner was an infantry captain—he, too, had the death sentence read out to him.

The third man was a major in the artillery.

"My God, Koslov," murmured Skryl. He had stood beside Koslov using the bifocal telescope at Dorogobush. And when the Germans broke through the front line and suddenly appeared in front of the reserve positions, Koslov had served a gun himself, firing over open sights at the attackers.

Skryl wanted to jump out of the ranks and bear witness for Koslov; but discipline rooted him to the spot. The sentence on Koslov and his family was read out. Suddenly Koslov, whose hands were tied behind him, turned, leapt into the bushes and ran on. He managed to reach the wood but was caught again. While he was being brought back the others were made to kneel. They then received a bullet in the nape of the neck from the NKVD plenipotentiary and were thrown into the trench. Uralov had only heard the shots; he did not want to look. Skryl —who stood at his side—had suddenly the face of an old man.

"If the whole army is running away, one man can't stay on alone," he said when they were dismissed. "No one is guilty—they could have shot each one of us like that. How can they kill off their own people like that?"

Immediately after the executions the column set out for Borodino. They marched through the night. In the morning they reached a bare heath, where they found regular troops under the command of a tank corps Lieutenant-General already in position in the undergrowth and among the clumps of trees. Uralov's impression was that something was going to happen, that a battle was impending. Once more he had to take over a battalion—the lieutenant who had brought it to Borodino was no longer to be found; he had disappeared. Uralov mustered his new unit. Of his old comrades he had brought Ivan and Chiang; Skryl, too, had stayed with him. The troops' first question was: "Is there anything to eat?" Well, that was nothing new—it always began like that.

There were no rifles. Uralov telephoned to Division and demanded weapons and rations. Towards evening a truck arrived bringing rifles and ammunition; it was a simple matter to calculate that thirty to forty per cent. of the battalion would remain unarmed. No rations had come; Uralov could not help having the impression that they were all being eaten in the rear areas. If he had had Mahomet, he would have been more mobile and would have been able to ride to Division; instead, he decided to look around in the country in front of the battalion position. He took Ivan and Chiang with him and they soon found a little *kolkhoz*, a dairy farm with some cows. Nothing mattered any more. Chiang and Ivan caught a cow. Uralov went into the farm office, where the collective chairman, a woman, was sitting, and scribbled a document for her according to which his battalion had received two hundred and eighty pounds of flesh from

251

the Kirov *Kolkhoz*. The collective chairman was extremely angry, but she took the paper and the three men went off with the cow. They came back to the battalion; the cow was shot and cut up with bayonets.

Next day an NKVD officer arrived.

"Are you a member of the Supreme Soviet?" was his first question.

"No, I am not."

"What right have you to take a cow?"

"I have taken a cow today," Uralov answered, "but tomorrow the Germans will come and take all the cows. How are my men to fight and hold the village if they have nothing to eat?"

The NKVD officer drew up a statement and Uralov signed it.

"You will hear more of this," were the officer's last words.

They were to be the last that the Soviet State had to say to Uralov.

It had been quiet for a long time on this sector of the front. Farther south, round about Borodino and a few miles farther along the autobahn, lay infantry units from the armoured division—all this was second line stuff. The tanks and motorised units were farther ahead and formed the first line of defence. On Uralov's immediate front, in a little wood, was a company of sharpshooters.

It began with the sharpshooters. Ten German planes appeared over the little wood and laid it flat. None of the hundred and twenty men seemed to have escaped the fury of the attack which raked every square yard of ground. At the same time an artillery bombardment began beyond Borodino and the autobahn; the sky was aflame. Hours later, when the firing on the left flank had died down, it became clear that something decisive had happened. Uralov had no direct communication with his rear but an officer came forward from Regiment, and from him he learned that the Germans had succeeded in breaking through, but the Proletarian Division would restore the situation. The Proletarian Division—they had heard that one before. The real explanation for the lull in the fighting to the south, over the field of Borodino, was a deep penetration by the Germans in the direction of Mozhaisk. The flank of the front, which was now cut off, began to collapse, too. At first light on a grey, frosty morning, the fleeing troops streamed towards the battalion position from the direction of the dairy farm. They were infantry, running as hard as they could on the soft wet plough and leaving wounded and dead behind them. Bursts of machine-gun fire raked their ranks.

Uralov's battalion had not a single casualty, but it dissolved. The whole line dissolved. The fleeing troops swept everything with them like an avalanche, spreading out on all sides.

Skryl and Ivan, Chiang and half a dozen others stayed with Uralov. They fell back into the thick woods, collected branches and dry leaves, burnt them, spread out the ash and camped on the burnt patch, waiting for the night. The Germans had broken through and were in their rear. Should they fight their way through to their own troops? No—not again. Surrender? Not that, either. Everyone knew what happened to captured commissars and there was a story, too, that the Germans hanged all Soviet officers. What was there left for them to do?

"Let's stay in the woods for a day or two and think it over," Uralov proposed.

*   *   *

It was snowing. One night a couple of inches fell—the next, a few more. In the daytime it rained. There was snow, rain and sunshine, and all the woods were dipped in bright golden yellow. There was snow, rain and an east wind, and the sky towards Moscow was lead-grey and heavy.

There were cold nights in cramped billets. The bridges were blocked but the blocks were cleared and the advance continued. There were defects in the fuel systems. Trucks were abandoned. But the Germans pushed on against the enemy's soft resistance. Whole armies—the remnants of all the armies between Smolensk and Moscow—were surrounded. Perhaps two hundred thousand men with horses and transport—no one had counted them—were caught in the Vyasma pocket.

On the south flank of the pocket, with one squadron up, the battalion advanced in a long column. Tank after tank had to be got across a stretch of swamp. The little village on the left was reported to be free of enemy; ahead was a little wood with a road leading into it. It was late afternoon, and everything was dusted with a thin layer of snow, when the battalion commander, Vilshofen, drove down the column with his adjutant in an unarmed command tank. He had the feeling that they were running into a prepared position. A plane dropped a smoke signal over the wood—purple smoke which meant: "Watch out —tanks!" Enemy anti-tank guns were firing already.

The battalion commander made for the open. He chose the way to the right, across country, and drove on over the thin layer of snow. The squadron commander driving behind could see the mines going up on either side of him. But the mines could not do much damage to the tanks—at the most a track came off and the tank was brought to a halt. The leading squadron answered the enemy fire and silenced it, but not before one of the tanks had been hit and half the turret torn away. The leading squadron halted near the village from which no further sound came.

Then something happened.

From the woods, out of the village, from all directions they came towards the tanks—hundreds upon hundreds of Russians with their hands above their heads. They came towards the tanks, hesitantly and timorously at first, waving, emptying their pockets and distributing presents— a pocket knife, a packet of mahorka, a leather strap. Commissars handed over their leather cases, an officer his map case. They kept coming in, by the thousand, and settled down in a square marked off by tanks.

Dusk was falling already and the squadron had to find a leaguer for the night. The squadron commander sent a lieutenant with his gunner and wireless operator into the village to have a look round. They came back having suddenly come under fire on the village street, but bringing thirty Russians with them, who had come over of their own accord. All the way back bullets had whistled overhead but no one had been hit.

There was no end to the constant trickle of Russians from the village and the woods; already there were five thousand of them gathered round the tanks, and still they came. The dusk was full of faces. Night fell and the

Russians squatted in an immense square; a huge multitude of them. At the four corners stood tanks with their great headlights switched on.

The squadron had taken precautions, yet no surprises were likely from the Russians. They squatted side by side, peaceful, exhausted, tired of fighting. The tank crews wondered about these weary men, sitting peacefully amongst them, and what their fate would be. What would the High Command do with all these men? Where would they go, how would they be fed? There was hardly a man who did not wish the best for them, and fear the worst.

In the course of the night the battalion commander, Vilshofen, received the news that the regiment was being pulled out of the ring of encircling forces, and that the battalions had to rendezvous in the woods north-east of Yuchnov near the Moscow road. His own battalion was to lead the regiment in an attack.

Vilshofen read his orders by the light of a torch.

"To open up the axis of advance, take the bridges at Shumyatino and Terentyeva and if possible push on and seize Maloyaroslavetz." The light of the torch moved over a piece of the map. Maloyaroslavetz, Tarutino, Voronovo —historic battlefields of the year 1812. His orders took him almost right up to Moscow.

Next day there were conferences at Division and Regiment; then conferences between battalion commanders and their squadron commanders. It was four in the afternoon before the regiment was ready for the attack and the advance guard under Lieutenant-Colonel Vilshofen moved forward: twenty-two tanks, a platoon of sappers, plus infantry sitting in twos and threes on the backs of the tanks. Altogether it was two hundred men who set out.

They drove through the infantry's forward positions. In front of the armoured column, driving two abreast, lay a road which the Germans had not yet trod, on which so far there had been no fighting. The tanks drove fast —right through Russian troops forming up to attack. There were swarms of Red Army men on either side of the road, and from the ditches flew out hand grenades and incendiary flasks. The tank crews heard the tinkle of the bottles as they struck, while on the backs of the tanks the infantry sat exposed to a hail of fire.

The tanks fired as they moved, broke through the attackers and scattered them to right and left into the woods. They drove through a village, fired tracer into the houses without halting, left the burning village behind them and drove on into the falling darkness.

The first bridge came into sight. The gunners were still digging in—they threw away their spades and ran to their guns; but they were mown down before they could reach them. The tanks drove on across the bridge, firing to either side, and continued their advance.

Forty-five minutes after their starting time the bridge at Terentyeva lay before them. Wild firing broke out from mortars, small arms, tanks and anti-tank guns. More and more of the infantry were shot off the tanks which fired without pause and silenced the enemy strong points. The first objective lay before their eyes. They had only to drive on and form the bridgehead.

"A message from Division, sir—Halt at once. Withdraw at once."

They were to swing the tanks round under fire and make their way back, leaving a rearguard a thousand yards from their objective.

The order from Division was repeated.

"Advance guard will halt immediately and return to start line. Await further orders there." There was nothing for it—the commander passed the order on to his tanks: "Halt, all halt. Point troop will form a rearguard. All others withdraw."

In the seething darkness shots flashed once more. Wounded shrieked: "Take me with you!" A motor-cycle ran into a tank, another disappeared into a shell-hole. A recovery vehicle slid down a bank. Painfully the little formation turned about. Wounded were left lying—the rearguard would pick them up.

The battalion drove back and passed through the burning village. Once more hand grenades exploded and petrol flasks tinkled on the sides of the tanks. In pitch dark they reached their start line, stopped at the infantry regiment and brought it back its dead.

They ate in the open. Morale was low. Vilshofen said to himself: "All it needs now is for us to have to do the same thing all over again tomorrow." It was not long before a runner came to the table. "You have to report to Division at once, sir."

An hour later Vilshofen came back. The leaguer was in a wood overgrown with thick brush; the men had been too tired to put up their tents: they lay beside their tanks wrapped in their coats. They were exhausted, but could not sleep because of the drug which had been issued to them for the new effort. It was the same with Vilshofen. He lay down on the heap of dry leaves his wireless operator had made, wrapped himself in his greatcoat and shut his eyes, only to open them again and look up into the thick darkness.

It was just as he had feared. According to his orders they had to cover the same road again next day, and were to push on to Maloyaroslavetz into the bargain. They were to go through the town and if possible seize the bridge on the Protva. He had pointed out that since the element of surprise was lost they would have to reckon with stiffer resistance, with mined roads and blown bridges. The regimental commander was sorry about the withdrawal orders, but there had been nothing he could do about them. They were dealing with an operation on a divisional, indeed on a corps, scale, and obviously that evening Corps had been behind schedule.

Next day it caught up. Vilshofen was given command of a fully-motorised advance guard and his battalion was made operationally independent. Another rapid advance on Maloyaroslavetz—then he must push on through the town; it would be left to the regiments behind to capture it.

The new assignment led farther towards Moscow than that of the previous evening. Neither Division nor Corps could expect the Protva line to be reached in one bound. The thrust by Vilshofen's regiment, which had been strengthened by the inclusion of armoured divisional engineers, some infantry and a few Mark IIIs and Mark IVs, would be the first of a series of blows delivered in quick succession; everything would depend on whether Regiment, Division and Corps followed up quickly.

A chill descended from the sky and pierced the blanket of leaves. Vilshofen wrapped himself tighter in his coat. The leaguer was close to the enemy; the wild wood round about was primitive forest. Each sound in the undergrowth, even if only of a dry twig falling, broke into his sleep. He tried to pierce the darkness with his eyes. His nostrils were full of the smell of damp moss and of withered leaves which had mouldered in the night frosts. In these woods, perhaps, Napoleon's grenadiers, or the warriors of the Golden Horde, once had lain, and like them he was striving to reach the great walls of the town; for Moscow must be conquered before the great cold began, before the winter.

Reveille was at five. At five-fifteen, while the advance guard formed up, the squadron commanders had a conference with the CO. The regimental commander was there, too, and stayed on when Vilshofen collected the tank crews round him. The men had no longer the carefree spirit of the early days; each of the tank-crews gathered here had come to know the Russians and their tough fighting qualities. Vilshofen looked round him—there was scarcely a face left from the early battles; most of the regular officers had fallen or been sent back wounded. The war had become harder, and a new secret war had been added to it—the unseen danger from partisans. The men's nerves were stretched to the limit; the slight panic as the column turned about the night before made one think. It was time to reach Moscow and end the war.

In his address Vilshofen did not conceal the difficulty of the task before them and warned his men against underestimating the Russian resistance: "But, after all, we have put over a hundred miles behind us in the last few days—now we have the last lap ahead. Our battalion has been reinforced with engineers and lorried infantry. We have Mark IIIs and Mark IVs."

Most of his tanks were Czech tanks from the Skoda works and were hopelessly inferior to the Russian T34s. There was no point in saying anything about that; the men knew themselves that they were outgunned.

He praised the fire control of the crews.

"Excellent fire control, the element of surprise and the superior speed of our tanks are the advantages on our side. We must exploit them to the full. What we have lost since yesterday in the way of surprise must be made up for by maintaining speed."

Bullets whistled over the edge of the nearby wood.

Under the circumstances it was advisable to cut orders short and come quickly to a close. The regimental commander said he did not wish to say anything. Vilshofen merely added: "I shall wait on the road until the whole column is formed up—then we will go all out."

The road lay in bright sunshine. It had thawed the day before and frozen again slightly in the night; the puddles were covered with a thin layer of ice. The crews went to their tanks and clambered in. At a minute past seven the first tank under the command of Sergeant-Major Nauert moved off. Vilshofen's was the third in the line.

The column accelerated to twenty-five miles an hour right away, and then to thirty. As on the previous evening tommy-gun and rifle fire came from the woods; small calibre shells rattled on the armour; hand grenades exploded and petrol flasks broke with a tinkle. But this time the tanks carried no infantry. They went through the burnt-out village and came to the first bridge, driving on through anti-tank and mortar fire.

One troop with Mark IVs stayed behind to hold the bridge until the regiment moved up; the others drove on at the same speed. There were odd trucks dashing about in the open; a Russian appeared here and there on the edge of the woods. Not a breath of air stirred the leaves. Clumps of trees stood out in the golden light and were left behind; then thick wood closed in around the tanks.

Suddenly the road burst into flames. Flame-throwers had been put into position close together on either side of the road and all turned on at once. The leading tanks were already in the midst of it and could not turn back.

"Drive on—drive on."

If one tank stopped the whole column would be halted and burnt out. It got hot in the tanks. The drivers could no longer see. The engines began to choke. Their supply of air was being cut off.

"Change down to first and give full throttle." The engines needed less air in low gear. "We must get through —get on, Nauert. Watch the man in front and don't ram him."

Nauert was through; the second tank was through; Vilshofen, too, came into the open. He shoved open the top of his turret, looked back and counted—twelve, fourteen, sixteen. They were all through, had all passed through the fire. As they came past they had raked the flame-throwers with fire. That stretch of road was now clear for the regiment coming up behind.

Eight o'clock and a bright sunny morning.

In front of them lay the bridge and the village of Terentyeva, the first objective—the point where their advance had been halted on the previous evening. There were dead Germans lying by the side of the road; they had been stripped naked during the night. From either side of the bridge there came enemy fire from mortars and dual-purpose guns, but the tanks advanced at full speed, firing in all directions. Would it go up or not? Nauert, who had stayed behind with the rearguard the previous evening, had cut all the fuses, which obviously had not been replaced, for the bridge held. The column reached the farther bank and drove on, scattering Russian trucks and horsed transport, which went tearing off across country.

"Pirate, Pirate," came the call from the rear.

They went round a corner and in front of the point troop lay the town of Maloyaroslavetz on a bend of a river. They could see low wooden houses, a railway station, churches, a monastery. The October sun lay on the grey walls. Artillery shells and mortar bombs were falling in the fields to right and left.

"Pirate—halt. Stop where you are."

"Impossible—have achieved surprise—if we go on we take the town—am under mortar fire. Artillery ranging on us."

Fountains of earth from the fields close by rose into the air.

"Cannot remain in open—must advance or withdraw."

"Regiment orders you to halt where you are until Regiment comes up."

The column's recce plane came down over the column.

"What can you see?" asked Vilshofen.

"Nothing in the town—heavy traffic from the town in direction Protva crossing."

"And in this direction?"

"Several convoys."

"If we go on now. . ."

"Regiment orders you to halt until main body has come up."

"Cannot halt—am under fire. Having casualties. Request orders to attack."

Artillery shells burst between the tanks.

Regiment came on the air again: "You may attack. Advance and take Protva bridge. Form bridgehead."

They went on. At the entrance to the town there was a barrier of massive iron beams set up crosswise. The sapper sergeant-major came up with a detachment of divisional engineers. "Now then—get your sleeves rolled up and go to it. There's nothing else for it and we just can't stay here. If it's mined we'll see each other up there."

It was not mined.

A narrow passageway was cleared and the tanks drove through. An undamaged town—the first on their long road. All the shutters were closed, all the curtains drawn; the silence was uncanny. There was not a living creature to be seen, not a single human being, not one dog or cat. The town seemed to be dead. The tanks drove on slowly, two abreast, trying to find their way through the unfamiliar streets. They were wet with rain and the water was a foot deep in places, but radiant sunshine lay over it all and the ruined church was bathed in light; the red tiles gleamed through the crumbled plaster; the doorway was nailed up with boards.

They came to a square with empty market stalls and not a single human being; in the wide deserted space a Russian warrior in stone stood on a pedestal. A tablet recalled the 24th of October 1812. Here the French had found their road to Kaluga blocked. All the signboards had been pulled down and Vilshofen had to study a plan of the town to find the right road. At the edge of the town three staff cars came towards him. "Don't fire— let them come close." The men in the staff cars realised the situation too late: some jumped out, others sat where they were. Three or four shots and the cars were on fire; the column left them behind.

The point troop was now on the road to Moscow.

Vilshofen thought of the convoys which the recce plane had reported, of the Protva bridge and the bunkers on the other side. He looked at the air-photos in his hand.

The first convoy came in sight—a long column of horse-drawn wagons was coming towards the tanks. The drivers were sitting on the boxes, holding the reins loosely in their hands. Vilshofen, sitting in his open turret, could not hear for the rattle of the tracks that the first driver had struck up a song—perhaps the song of the wild pear-tree, or it might have been the song about Moscow, the Golden Capital.

The leading tanks opened fire. Wagons, horses and men became a knotted mass. As they passed by the tanks fired into the bloody clumps of wheels, animals and men. Horses went galloping over the open fields and bursts of machine-gun fire swept behind them.

"Increase speed—otherwise the bridge will go up before we get there."

Vilshofen took up the air-photos again—two strips of bridge running side by side, a railway bridge farther to the left, and bunkers all along the east bank of the Protva. He had kept the air-photos in his own tank and not shown them to his tank commanders. No tank unit likes to advance on to a prepared position. If the bunkers were not occupied then things would go all right, and there was no point in worrying the crews beforehand; if they were occupied and gunned there was nothing one could do about it anyway. The orders were to take the bridge.

Another convoy came towards them—a motorised one this time. The motor-cyclists at its head sounded their horns and the Russians—lorried infantry and tractors pulling light guns—pulled hard over to the right to make way for the approaching tanks which opened fire as they approached. In a second the trucks were in flames. Ammunition went up. Like spawn from a gutted fish Red Army men burst out of the mass of telescoped trucks, scattering blindly in panic.

"Get on—on to the bridge."

Suddenly they were among traffic as if it were the outskirts of a town.

"Don't halt—increase speed."

Ahead lay the line of bunkers.

"At the next corner we must see the bridge," said Vilshofen to his driver. And there it was, just as in the air photographs—two parallel wooden bridges with wooden railings, one for traffic towards Moscow, the other for traffic coming the other way.

There were the bridges, and something else as well: a huge herd of cattle and sheep and horses—livestock from the collective farms of a whole district—on their way east with herdsmen and drovers. The road was blocked —both bridges crammed with beasts.

"Halt"—was Vilshofen's automatic call to his driver. But the driver had not yet reacted to the shout, and meanwhile Sergeant-Major Nauert in the leading tank had sized up the situation more quickly than his battalion commander. A cow can't stop a tank. He changed down and opened his throttle, driving first into the cows, then on over cows, horses, wagons, herdsmen and drovers. The second and third tanks—all eighteen of them—did the same. They drove in a double column over the twin bridges which became one gory mass. Below the bridges, on the bank of the Protva, a squad of soldiers ran at full speed to the edge of the river—the demolition squad.

An immense explosion shattered the air. But it was the railway bridge farther to the left which with a roar collapsed in a cloud of smoke and dust. The two wooden bridges did not go up. Nor was there any firing from the bunkers, which obviously were not manned.

The advance guard drove on at full speed, up a rise in the road. A column of artillery, a whole battery, with four 150-mm guns and tractors straight from the works, was shot to pieces like the motorised infantry before it; the crews, taken by surprise, were killed or scattered.

Orders said: Form a bridgehead on the Protva.

The objective had been reached. At the top of the rise the battalion halted. Eighteen tanks had come through mud and fire, their hulls blackened, the paint flaked by the flames; hair, scraps of flesh and brains of men and animals in their tracks. Eighteen tanks and seventy-two men were deep in Russian territory, twenty-five miles from their regiment.

The commander of the advance guard reported back: "I have taken the bridge over the Protva."

"There must be some mistake. You cannot have taken the Protva bridge," came the reply.

The regimental commander himself came to the set.

"It's absolutely out of the question. I have the air photos here in front of me. You must have made a mistake, Vilshofen."

"I have taken the Protva bridge—am forming a bridgehead. Request Regiment to follow on."

"Well, if you're there stay where you are."

* * *

The Protva reached!

A little man with a scholar's spectacles, surrounded by telephones, map tables, adding machines. Mozhaisk has been taken, Maloyaroslavetz is in the hands of 19 Armoured Division. The Protva reached and crossed. The road to Moscow is open. Infantry, cavalry, dive-bombers to the front—above all infantry. Priority for the infantry this time. Forced marches, without regard to what lies on the flank, right on to the Nara first of all —there they can deploy from Tarutino through Kamenka to Naro-Fominsk. And supplies—ammunition, rations, petrol; everything to be got forward as quickly as possible. It is no longer a question of days but of hours. Each hour of rain makes each mile three times, ten times as long — quadruples the quantities of supplies needed, multiplies the number of stranded trucks.

The Protva reached!

The wire hums in a bunker. This is a town made up of bunkers, in an East Prussian wood, with code names like Quelle, Fritz and Wolf's Lair. The speedy advance of the German Army Groups on the eastern front has increased the already heavy burden of cares in the Chief of Staff's HQ. In the last few days the armies have advanced one hundred, and even more, miles a day. They are going forward at a speed which cannot be coped with by the supply services. The railway troops have been able to convert only three main stretches—to Leningrad, Rostov and Orel—and these have only two tracks. Forty-five to fifty trains are the maximum, but Army Group Centre needs up to one hundred and twenty trains a day to keep it supplied. Only the most urgent supplies of ammunition, petrol and rations can be moved. The lack of replacements is making itself felt all along the front. Hospital trains have to be cut out almost entirely. Is a further advance in winter to be recommended in these circumstances—with units which have been hit hard? That is the question which the C-in-C and the General Staff are faced with, and they consider it unavoidable to halt the armies and winter on the line they have now reached. But the front line troops which have been put into the offensive are still pushing on at express speed.

In the Wolf's Lair flags are pushed into maps, just as they are in the beer halls back in Germany where every success is taken for granted. According to intelligence reports eighty per cent. of the Russian Army is so badly cut up that it has no more offensive value; the Russian government is in flight; the revolution can be expected at any minute. The Rumanians have taken Odessa; 11 Army is attacking the Crimea; an armoured corps is before Rostov. In the north Leningrad is encircled and the spearhead of the attack is in front of Tikhvin; Guderian is marching on Tula. In the centre Mozhaisk is falling, Maloyaroslavetz is falling.

In the great bunker at the Fuehrer's Headquarters an immense map completely covers one wall: Russia from the White Sea to the Black Sea, and to the Urals in the east—and that is only a seventh of the country.

The same map on a smaller scale covers the table. The man behind it with spectacles on his nose has once more been confirmed in his views. The soldiers at the front understand his plans intuitively and carry them out. Only the Generals stand between him and the ordinary man—with their second thoughts and scruples and old formulae.

"The Protva has been reached—push on at once to the next river line."

* * *

When the regiment reached the Protva, the regimental commander came forward and brought the General with him.

"You did wonderfully, Vilshofen. I congratulate you on this success. But now we must exploit surprise and thrust on towards Moscow. You will have air support; dive-bombers have been put in and are bombing the roads."

Vilshofen looked east and saw the flak bursts; the whole sky was sprinkled with white puffy balls.

"We have exhausted our ammunition; we must replenish and fill up with petrol. Then there won't be much time left, sir, before nightfall."

"We must get on to the next river line—to the Nara and as close to Moscow as possible. It is an order from the Fuehrer. You will take over the point troop, Vilshofen."

The crews were tired and worn out with action, but it seemed as if the distance they had come acted as a stimulant which would carry them through.

"Today we will simply drive right through, sir."

"To Moscow."

"Right into the Red Square."

"Nothing can stop us."

"I don't like that sort of talk, boys. Rashness is a bad counsellor, and it is just as bad to underestimate the enemy. We have had a lucky trip so far, but there can still be tough going today. We need the utmost concentration. There is a long stretch of wood in front of us and you know what that can mean. We must get through the wood at full speed. That's all. Now mount."

A long stretch of wood can easily be a graveyard for a tank unit. The silence was uncanny; rifle fire, mortar or even anti-tank fire would have been a relief. Each bush seemed to be a gun. The pace of the column increased without any order having to be given. They had to drive round craters on the road and transport hit by the recent dive-bombing attack.

The talk on the intercomm. was just as optimistic as it had been back at the halt; it got on Vilshofen's nerves. He passed a hand over his brow; his hand was wet.

"MT seen on the left," reported the last tank.

A stupid report.

"Wireless silence," said Vilshofen. "No more messages except in emergency—switch over to reception."

He had seen the MT trucks long ago, and other MT, too—there were masses of it in the wood, brand new trucks belonging to supply units. Fresh tracks led from the road into the undergrowth. At the entry points sentries in steel helmets with slung rifles or machine-pistols stood and looked indifferently, or with amazement, at the fast-travelling tanks and at the officer standing in an open

266

turret with a field service cap on his head.

Vilshofen did not allow his tanks to open fire—all they had to do was drive on as fast as they could. He looked at the map, compared it with the mileometer and said:

"Three more miles."

"Two more miles."

"Watch out at the next corner."

The road began to climb.

"Watch out—slow down. Halt."

But Nauert, who was in the leading tank, and the one behind him were travelling at such a speed that they reached the top of the rise before they could stop. Vilshofen could just see over the crest and look down; the road fell away dead straight, eight hundred yards of it, down to the bridge. At the very moment when Nauert drew up flashes appeared below them, and the sharp, splitting bursts told Vilshofen that they came from 76-mm Russian anti-tank guns. There were flashes to the left, too. The shells passed close overhead, but the firing was irregular—and therein lay a chance. Something of the element of surprise remained.

"Drive on—full speed."

They went over the hill.

"Give them everything the engines have got."

As they drove downhill a murderous fire broke out. The two gun positions became six, and then nine; they grew in number until there were so many they could not be counted—the whole bank was a line of flashes. Vilshofen remembered the sky spattered with flak clouds as he had seen it during the conversation with the regimental commander. These were the gun positions— troop upon troop—of the outer ring of Moscow's ack-ack defence. No other town in the world—not even London —as he knew from the men who had flown over Moscow, had such a strong defence. And with a few turns of a handle these anti-aircraft guns could be converted to an anti-tank role.

"Keep going—keep firing."

They loaded and fired, loaded and fired again. It was no longer possible to distinguish between their own fire and the enemy's. But the fact that they were driving downhill was an advantage, for the tanks in the rear could fire over the heads of those in front.

"Keep going and keep firing. Give them everything you have—never mind if you hit anything or not." No one could aim on the move at this mad speed. "Keep on —keep on."

They were a fire-spitting dragon rushing down the hill. The shock began to have its effect on the anti-aircraft gunners. The wall of fire down below began to show gaps. Many guns fell silent, although all of them could not have been hit; the fire became thinner and began to stray off the road. Vilshofen did not dare to believe his eyes and ears. The bridge groaned under their weight as they tore over it, then it was left behind—all eighteen tanks had passed it. Now they went up-hill with the impetus of their charge. At the top there were four guns ready to receive what was expected to be the limping remnants of a tank battalion, but the sight of the tanks tearing towards them bore so little relation to what they had imagined that the gun teams abandoned their pieces. The tanks shot them up and the crew of a fifth gun hidden in the wood was dealt with as it trained its piece on the leading tank of the column.

"Halt."

It was the third time on their long road. They had crossed the Protva and now the Nara. A signal was sent back; there were congratulations on this latest success.

The squadron formed a bridgehead and put its tanks across the road. In front of Sergeant-Major Nauert's tank a twelve-yard-long swastika flag was laid out—the ground-air signal of the farthest-forward troops.

The woods were alive with Russians. They opened fire with rifles, machine-pistols and machine-guns. In the soft ground Vilshofen examined the traces of a tank with an enormously wide track—ahead he saw two of the monsters, 52-ton KV 52s, disappear round a curve.

"Pirate—Pirate. Push on to the next river line."

"Further advance impossible," Vilshofen wirelessed back.

In the rear there was a renewed noise of firing. The regiment was coming down the road on the other side of the river at full speed, but was not having the same luck as the leading squadron. The anti-aircraft gunners had recovered from their first shock—besides, the tommy guns of the commissars were closer now than the tank guns. The regiment suffered some hits as it came down hill; one tank toppled over and lay on its back; another, burning, slewed across the road. Next moment a thick knot had formed.

But the Russian guns were firing inaccurately, and before they had registered on the tangle of tanks it was already sorting itself out. The majority of the tanks began to move forward again and drove down to the bridge. A few minutes later they were across and coming up the hill.

The regimental commander came forward, driving in his tank into the midst of the semi-circle formed by the advance guard. He was standing in his open turret and Vilshofen went over to him.

"It is impossible, sir, to continue the attack until the infantry arrive."

"They won't get here very soon."

"The woods are full of Russians. A motor-cycle battalion has just arrived. We are under fire from infantry weapons of all calibres."

A burst of machine-gun fire swept the commander's tank. He pulled in his head, disappeared into the tank, then emerged again. Once more there was firing from the wood from rifles and tommy-guns. This time the commander stayed inside his tank, leaving his turret open. Vilshofen stood outside. It was difficult to conduct a conversation.

"We have lost two officers; some tanks have been left with their crews. But we must go on—the Fuehrer's HQ expects us to cross the next river line at least today, and if possible take Kamenka."

"Out of the question, sir. We have expended our ammunition and must fill up with petrol."

"We'll bring everything up for you."

"I must still refuse the assignment."

The whole wood was full of trucks, wagons, motorcycles and guns; the commander could see it for himself. He pulled in his head again under a new burst of machinegun fire and agreed that no further attack could be carried out so close to night-fall.

"But secure this position and hold it," he said, and drove back to the bridge.

Even that was almost impossible without the help of infantry. Vilshofen made the tanks come closer together and form a "hedgehog". A house on the edge of the wood had been set on fire. It would burn at least three hours; all that time the tanks would be brightly lit and no one could tell what was hidden in the wood—whether the infantry would attack and the 52-ton monsters appear again. The regiment lay on the other side of the river and the regimental commander eight hundred yards away on this side of the bridge. There was nothing in between except Russians moving unconcernedly back and forth across the road. If you sat in a tank they could come close up and blow the vehicle sky high; if you stuck your head out of the turret they opened fire with tommy-guns.

Vilshofen sat near his tank and smoked his first cigarette since they had started off. The burning house collapsed; there was a shower of sparks, then the night became pitch dark. But the darkness brought no relief; the night was full of watching eyes; cigarettes glowed; the Russians could be heard talking among themselves. Every now and again one of them came up close and emptied his tommy-gun or threw hand grenades.

Vilshofen remained inside the hedgehog, going from tank to tank and speaking to the men. They were all awake—no one dared to close his eyes. "If they come too near fire straight at them—clear a space," he said.

Time seemed to stand still. Vilshofen sat beside his tank again. He saw cows—horned heads of cows, horses' heads with their ears laid back; they reared up and sank down again, then rushed on like a roaring stream under a dark sky. There was a rushing sound. It was raining. The black sky had opened.

At five a wireless message came through:

"Lieutenant-Colonel Vilshofen to report at once to Regimental HQ."

But how was he to get there? In his tank? The wood was full of anti-tank guns. On foot? It was eight hundred yards, and in the ditches Death sat smoking mahorka. Sergeant-Major Nauert advised him to go in the tank. Nauert watched him and saw how the tracer followed close behind the vehicle; but Vilshofen reached regimental HQ. The spot had been well chosen—it was slightly defiladed and the fire passed overhead.

Vilshofen was greeted enthusiastically by everyone.

"Congratulations—congratulations—did you hear the announcement? There has just been an announcement on the wireless all about how you got here."

Vilshofen thought of the cows. His face was wet with sweat and rain; his feet were cold; he felt depressed. Eight hundred prisoners, fifty guns, tractors, trucks, wagons—it all made no impression on him. In the night he had met all the ghosts of the shot horses. His mind could not deal with the tangled pile of dead men.

"If only this night would end," he said.

Vilshofen was an odd chap. His comrades at HQ shook their heads. Was this what a man looked like who had been proposed for the Ritterkreuz? So depressed and abstracted?

Vilshofen found the regimental commander under the bridge.

"It has been decided," said the commander, "that all the available ammunition and petrol will be brought forward to you. The attack will be continued immediately after daybreak—in the direction of Moscow. This is the last spurt—every hour is precious."

"In my opinion," said Vilshofen, "it is hopeless to go on with such a small force. There are a few KV 52s somewhere up the road and the woods are full of Russians."

"It is an order from the Fuehrer's HQ, and you know how short we are of regular officers who could carry out such an attack. You must go on."

"I take note of your order, sir."

"I can't do anything else, Vilshofen. You pushed on so far yesterday that the Fuehrer thinks you can do it again."

"When does the infantry arrive?"

"They can't be here before afternoon."

Vilshofen drove forward again—once more the ditches spat fire from all calibres.

"When it is light we go on, boys."

"But the whole place is full of Russians."

"Orders are orders—we must go on."

271

"And the infantry?"

Vilshofen shrugged his shoulders. There was still a hope that the petrol tankers would not arrive in time. And so it turned out—they were shot up in flames on the way and the petrol never reached the forward troops. When it grew light Regiment sent a new order. The attack was postponed indefinitely; the squadron had to stay where it was and hold the position.

*   *   *

The road to the bridge was under artillery fire and a troop was sent into the wood to find the Russian guns; it silenced some guns, but not those which continued to bring fire to bear on the road as before. The troop was not yet back from the wood when some KV 52s appeared and spattered the road with their 150-mm shells. A pack of T 34s also approached—they counted eight of them—and immediately afterwards a Russian dive-bomber attack went in on the bridge and Vilshofen's position. Mortars opened up; Russian infantry advanced out of the wood. A co-ordinated attack of all arms—that was a surprise such as there had not been all the way from Poland.

These were the first indications of a change in the Russian direction of the war.

Marshal Timoshenko had been relieved of his command. Hampered from the very beginning by lack of military plans and impossible operational orders, always under the tutelage of the Defence Committee which watched over all military decisions down to the smallest details, he had been unable to prevent the inevitable catastrophe. The new Marshal, who was furnished with extraordinary powers, was also largely relieved of political control; overnight the whole machinery of commissars disappeared, the commanders under him received unheard-of freedom of initiative, and they dreamt of further rights to be earned in the struggle for their fatherland. As far as the military hierarchy was concerned, Stalin and his advisers had taken a step back in order to take two steps forward. Thus, on the road to Moscow, the German tank commander with the forward troops experienced for the first time a combined attack, one of the new Marshal's concentrated efforts. Yet, worn as the battalion was, after forty-eight hours of unbroken effort they warded it off.

At noon the infantry arrived and ammunition and petrol came up. This time the battalion commander was asked whether he wished to volunteer to lead the attack ordered by the Fuehrer's HQ. Vilshofen, feeling that he could not accept the responsibility of leading his crews into certain destruction, declined the assignment and another squadron was put in.

The squadron drove off, ran into strong armoured forces lying in wait on the other side of the wood, and was shot to pieces. The infantry—too small a force to face the heavy fire—did not advance. The attack was pinned by the enemy's fire. A second and third attempt also failed. After two more days it became obvious that there were to be no more big advances.

A troop of tanks came back, beaten.

The troop commander had been shot up, together with his crew. A burst of fire had gone through Sergeant-Major Nauert's breast as he stood in the turret of his tank. Another tank had gone into a shell hole and stuck there; it had had to be abandoned.

The remaining tanks returned to the line held by the infantry. One of them had its side torn open, so that one could see inside, where the driver lay wounded and a lieutenant was at the controls. At the infantry positions he drew up and asked to be directed to the road. A sergeant-major showed him the way.

"Where have you come from?" asked the lieutenant.

"We are the forward troops—the division is on the way and must be nearly here."

At the point where Vilshofen's squadron had spent the first night the tank got back on to the road and made contact with its troop again. The tanks drove on down to the bridge. In the opposite direction the columns of the infantry division came marching past. On the road, as far as you could see, down to the bridge and up the hill on the other side, grey columns were moving forward —foot and guns and wagons and horses. It was raining and the road had turned into a muddy watercourse. "Look at them—the poor devils," said the tank lieutenant.

Dirty, ragged and unshaven, they splashed by with grey faces. They looked completely finished. In the last few days they had marched twenty-five, twenty-seven, twenty-eight miles; at evening they had been billeted in the crowded villages. Now they had their goal before them—the front line and the road to Moscow.

The damaged tank drove slowly past the marching troops and on over the wooden bridge, passed the staff cars driving in the opposite direction, passed the divisional commander sitting in an open car. (Even now, under the grey autumn sky, he wore green sun-glasses.) The tank drove uphill and guns came towards it—a horsed troop with its heavy horses in mud up to their bellies. The gunners on the limbers and in the saddles dozed as they drove along, and at the sight of the tired men and steaming horses the lieutenant did not feel like making the usual mocking remarks. Even the sight of a mounted sergeant-major with a Great War beard did not wring a smile from him. It was these gunners and the infantry who had to do it now—carry on the attack along the Moscow road where the tanks had stuck.

The horses of one troop began to slip coming down the hill. The gun slid across the road on the steep muddy slope and ended up with one wheel in the ditch. There was a traffic jam. The gunners clambered down from their limbers and some infantry came to help, but it all went slowly, and even the troop commander when he came up did not hurry them.

"You always get there in the end," said one of them, and that seemed to be what the troop commander thought, too. Quite a time went by before the gun stood on the roadway again and the column could move slowly on.

The tanks retired to a village where two badly cut-up squadrons were to be formed into one. The infantry went on over the bridge and were deployed on the hill; one regiment went right forward and relieved the advance guard; the other two and the staff moved into villages on either side of the road.

The divisional commander, Lieutenant-General von Bomelbuerg, and his Chief of Staff sat in a peasant house with a map before them on the table. Lieutenant Hasse from the advance guard showed them on the map the sector he had occupied and gave them a situation report.

"The Russians are fighting hard," Hasse reported. "All

the crossings are in a bad state. Heavy trucks can scarcely get across. There are continual traffic blocks on the road up to the front, because the division on our flank is not keeping within its boundaries. But the maps are so inaccurate that they can only be used as approximate guides."

The Chief of Staff asked about billets.

"There is a whole armoured division scattered in the villages round about. It is a very tight squeeze, sir."

It was a very tight squeeze here, too. There was no stabling for the horses; they had to stand in the open at night. The fodder situation was bad; no real fodder had come forward for weeks, but here in the village they had found some unthreshed oats. The gunners had hit on the idea of holding bundles of oats between the spokes of revolving bicycle wheels so as to get a handful of grain for their animals. Supplies for the troops were almost as short as those for the horses. The second echelon was still far in the rear; winter clothing had not come forward—no gloves, not enough tents. The division had had an issue of boots but they were all worn out by now, and since August none of the men had had a proper change of clothes.

It was twenty-five miles to Podolsk and twelve more to Moscow. With proper equipment, if the supply system were functioning, and with dry roads, it looked like a task which could be carried out in a few days even against stiff enemy resistance. But as things were, in view of the absolutely incomprehensible slackness in the rear services —it really looked as if the supply services had broken down—it would at best be a difficult and hazardous undertaking. And the weather being what it was, there did not seem to be any further hope of support from the armour. Finally, the objectives were not clear; Podolsk was the farthest point of advance mentioned.

The plans aimed at a great encircling manœuvre as far as the rivers Moskva, Oka and Volga; and if the armour was not able to help it would mean more marching, more losses, more expenditure of material. There was no end to it.

In the operations room, the last conference on the attack which was to be mounted next day had just been held with the regimental commanders and liaison officers. Bomelbuerg had been in a rather unhappy frame of mind; he looked forward to coming events with a great deal of anxiety. Some extraordinary things had come to his ears.

The commander of one of the tank battalions here in the village had refused to carry out an order from the Fuehrer's HQ to attack because—as he had said—he did not wish to lead his troops to destruction.

That had actually happened. That sort of thing could happen. Bomelbuerg got up in a bad temper, and went out in front of the house where the regimental commanders and liaison officers reported to him to say goodbye. They were going to their quarters in the village, or forward to their troops, to carry on the attack next day. It occurred to Bomelbuerg that he could not let them go like that—that he must say a few words to them. Zecke and Schadow were there, the liaison officers and staff officers, Langhoff of the horsed troop, some runners and a few gunners and infantrymen from the advance guard quartered here in the village. He knew them all—they had been with him from the early days and he had come a long way with them. Admittedly a lot of faces had disappeared, but in what division was that not the case? All the formations which were gathering in front of Moscow in these days had been badly hit. And as far as he could make out no reinforcements had ever arrived.

"The last barrier before Moscow has been taken," Bomelbuerg began. "We have a long road behind us, a long victorious road—only a few miles still separate us from the Russian capital." Bomelbuerg looked up, looked uncertainly about him. So far what he had said had not been very different from the usual Corps or Army orders. That was not very satisfying—neither for him nor for his troops; they had a right to expect something else from him. Although the army was getting ready to strike the last blow, he was deeply depressed by all he had seen, all the things which were not quite right. If he must speak he also wanted to give vent to his feelings. He reviewed the campaign briefly and spoke about the tanks, recalling the first days of war.

"At Brest-Litovsk we cleared a bridge over the

Muchavetz for an armoured division. They did their job —but now they are finished. Their engines are worn out, they have transmission troubles—fifteen tanks set out and eight break down on the march. There are no spare parts and naturally the staff are in a filthy temper. Well, that is their business, and I'm telling you only to make it clear that we are all on our own. The armour is going off to rest in the area of Roslavl—for a general overhaul and to regroup their battalions. We infantry are relieving them. We have to thrust on to Moscow.

"The lungs of the infantry last longer than lungs of iron. That is something new we have learned. If it has been fully appreciated, and if the administrative services are using the knowledge to make urgent deliveries of rations and supplies to the infantry, then we can still go on. If not, then it is a grim outlook for us. For we know that war does not mean only rifles and guns and tanks: it means, first and foremost, soldiers—you people."

Evening was falling. A salvo of artillery fire fell in the village from the Russian troop which the tanks had still not been able to flush from the woods. The officers gathered closer round the General; they did not want to lose a word he said.

"Here we are," he went on, "and must go forward— there is no alternative. War has an ascent and a descent— here and now we are at its zenith. We are committed to war and cannot inquire now whether, when it began, it was just or unjust; we are committed to a war which carries with it a terrible threat. The question is not whether we take the village of Kamenka or the city of Moscow. It is our own cities and villages which are at stake—for on the day we marched away we left the frontiers open, and they have stayed open behind us. It may be a pity that it ever happened, but it has happened and that cannot be altered. On the ten or twenty miles which lie before us, at Tarutino where the fate of Europe was once before at stake, the decision will be made for whom these frontiers will stand open in future.

"Here we are—we must go forward and cannot lay down our arms, even if the wind and snow come and the Cossacks fall upon us as thick as snow-flakes. We have formed up in our ranks and must march forward."

There—he had said it—said what was in his heart. Tomorrow it might be too late, for no one knows what end awaits him.

The sky was black now over the forest of Tarutino. The Russian guns sent over another shell; a hut burst into flames. Bomelbuerg went back into his headquarters and the others scattered through the great empty countryside. In ones and twos they appeared for a moment in the red glare of the burning wooden hut and then disappeared into the night.

* * *

Mozhaisk had fallen, and in the north the Germans were marching on Kalinin. In the south-west they were crossing the Nara at Tarutino. From the south Guderian's tanks were approaching Moscow along the road from Orel to Tula. The capital was in the grip of panic. Not a single building was unaffected by it—the Government buildings, all the hundreds of offices, the committees for radio, art and films, the scientific and political institutes, the State publishing house, the Society of Authors, the Comintern itself were like overturned beehives. The railway stations for White Russia and Leningrad were empty—the main line had been torn up a few miles from the capital and was already in German hands. Women with shovels still gathered in the stations to go and dig tank traps on the branch lines. The Kasan station was the only one left open—the line running due east to the Tartar country. But for how long? It could only be a matter of days—perhaps only of one day. Perhaps the last train was on its way now. The grey station building seemed to float as lightly as a cork on the crest of a wave of humanity, and to be drifting away to the accompaniment of hundreds of anti-aircraft guns and the black smoke of bursting bombs from dive-bombers. But every time the smoke cleared away the old station still stood in its place. The wide square was filled to the last inch with refugees with suitcases and bundles who had been waiting for days to move on. All roads leading into the square poured in fresh masses—an endless stream of people and luggage. This was the evacuation of the bureaucracy, of the commissariats and institutes, of the heads of offices and their secretaries, of the writers, artists and savants, of the privileged who had up to now been clothed and fed by special shops allocated by the Government.

The people of Moscow stood aside and watched the process in silence.

On the Kasan station people left typewriters, trunks and suitcases, although the contents of these cases—the shoes, stockings and clothes—would be the only valid currency on the journey into the unknown. But the railway was not the only escape route. Offices and factories set their fleets of cars moving east. High officials drove off with furniture, with wives and children, heads of offices with their secretaries, the director of a shoe factory with a load of shoes. Refugees offered twenty and even thirty thousand roubles for a lift only to Gorki or Sverdlovsk. It was impossible to find a seat on the trains. The refugees arriving from the west were left behind; there were not enough coaches or locomotives.

Twenty trains stood side by side on the tracks. The people who had got as far as the train, after throwing away on the last lap any luggage which was too heavy to carry, and were now sitting in their places, had to undergo a further torture and wait hours for the train to leave. These people had days of anxiety and intrigue behind them. They had had to be put down on the list of "socially important elements". The completed list had then to be passed by the political branch of their office or organisation and almost anyone might be struck off it. Finally, the formation of special trains—and there were only special trains—depended on approval by the People's Commissar for Transport. All these difficulties had had to be overcome.

Anatoly Arkadyevitch had still to negotiate some, at least, of these obstacles. He was no longer young—his heart was not sound and the excitement of the last few days had been hard on him. He was, besides, no hero —he admitted it; he had too much imagination to be a hero.

On the last day before leaving he had got up early, had made his breakfast and eaten it standing. His wife, with his mother-in-law and the children, had been in a rest home at Plyess on the Volga since the middle of summer, and so far they had fared well. He had got

Pravda from the letter-box and read that Moscow was in great danger. Then he hurried off to be at the pay-desk in the State Publishing House before the cashier opened. He was not the only one there; everybody had come today—the queue reached out into the corridor and on to the steps. One rumour followed hard on another. "Mozhaisk has fallen." The messenger with the money from the bank had not arrived yet. According to another story, women had come back from digging anti-tank ditches at Kutchkovo because the Germans had already got as far as that. But whether it was Kutchkovo or Klin or Podolsk, there was no doubt that the Germans might arrive here in front of the State Publishing House at any minute.

And the messenger from the cashier's office still did not come. When at last he arrived he brought very little money with him. Only 600 roubles could be paid out to each person irrespective of how much he had on his account. With that they had to begin a journey of uncertain duration into the unknown; and for a single loaf on the black market you paid eighty roubles.

Anatoly Arkadyevitch went home. Being too excited to rest he telephoned his acquaintances one after another. So-and-so was gone, they said, and so was such-and-such a person. "And Ilya Ehrenburg with his dogs isn't to be seen any more."

"Oh, he has a special mission and left by plane."

In the evening Anatoly Arkadyevitch went to the club where the transport lists for the next day were being made up. There was no time to lose—everybody still had plenty to do with preparations for the move, yet the discussions, the scheming and the formation of groups went on endlessly. There were not enough places for everybody and so some people had to be taken off the list again. Everyone fought for his place, and not for his own place only—his wife and mother-in-law and his divorced wives and their mothers and children wanted to be taken, too.

An important member of the Society of Authors might be struck off because the mistress of a more important and more exalted functionary had to find a place on the list. In was a life and death lottery. When the list was finally settled the confusion began again over the question of destination. One transport went to Kasan, the other to Central Asia. Those who were detailed for Central Asia seemed at first to have been lucky in the draw, but when it became clear that only completely unimportant names were on the list of travellers to Tashkent and Alma Ata the bargaining and haggling began again. This time the aim was to be struck off one list and taken on to another, the one with all the prominent names on it; for in their company there was more chance of getting special rations.

Anatoly Arkadyevitch was not precisely one of the leading figures of Soviet literature. He collaborated on various periodicals, was essayist and critic, reader for some publishing departments and author of short plays for production in trade union clubs. In the debates and discussions on Socialist realism he had stood out against the formalists—and so he had got a flat which the formalist, Smirnov, who had been unmasked, had had to vacate. Even if he wasn't a Gladkov or a Fedin or a Fadeyev, he was still on the list of people going to Kasan. He had managed it and could go home satisfied.

He groped through the black-out. Faces loomed at him out of the dark. There was a clank of metal and the sound of tired feet trailing along the road. It was troops coming back from the suburbs, and they brought into the town with them a smell of sweat and bodily corruption. It seemed as if a door had opened in the night on to a damp world full of inexplicable death.

Before it was light he dragged his things down into the street. The lorry with the first group of people from the block had already driven off to the station and there was no sign of its coming back as had been arranged. More and more people gathered in the street from the nine-storey block of flats which the Society of Authors had built for its members, and in which there lived authors, editors and employees of the Society. They stood in the street with their belongings and stared into the damp mist. Some of them could wait no longer and dragged their things to the tram-stop. Soon they returned, for the passengers were ill-disposed to people travelling with luggage, and did not let them get on; they even threw things which had been placed on the platform back into the street. How was one to get away? There were no taxis, nor porters—none were to be had even for a thousand roubles. At last help came from Arkadyevitch's friend Mihail Mihailovitch, a major in the Moscow garrison, who sent a truck from his unit.

The square in front of the station was jammed with people, a seething mass of faces, and curses came from the vast crowd who had to stay behind. But at last Anatoly Arkadyevitch was sitting in a coach; he even had a window seat. At the entrance to the station he had discarded most of his luggage, but that didn't matter any more; from now on the rule was that one could only have as much as one could carry on one's own shoulders. Sweat ran down his back. He kept seeing familiar faces everywhere. On the next line stood a train with theatre people; farther off was the Comintern train, farther off still the train with the staff of the Frunze Military Academy.

He had arrived at eight in the morning. It wasn't until twelve o'clock that the trains began to move, and then they left at fifteen-minute intervals, so there would have been time to organise the departure with more care and less annoyance; but that could not have been foreseen. The main thing was that the train was moving at last and he had hopes of reaching Kazan. The only question was how his wife Natalya Timofyevna, his mother-in-law and children would get away from Plyess.

* * *

On the 10th of October the Defence Committee and Stalin's secretariat began to move out the most important documents and files; they were to be stored in a mine beyond the Urals. On the 11th of October the gold from the State Bank together with huge quantities of decorations and plates for printing notes were carried, under escort, through the streets of Moscow to the station and there loaded into an armoured train. It moved off towards the east.

On the 12th of October, when the front had practically ceased to exist, the ministries, including the Ministry for the Interior together with some of its huge police force, left the capital in great haste. In the offices there remained only people detailed to burn the documents which had been left behind. In the great NKVD block in the Lubyanka the chimneys smoked day and night.

The evacuation of the NKVD was the beginning of the end. Along all the exit routes to the east there now moved convoys of trucks loaded with furniture, carpets and household goods, with their owners following behind in saloon cars. The employees of the Central Commissariats, the actors, the authors, the professors and lecturers from Moscow University and the Scientific Institutes, the Germans, Spaniards and Frenchmen from the Comintern had all got away. But a lot of people had been left behind—people in offices, on administrative staffs and from co-operatives, people who had arrived too late and people who had not been considered important enough for organised evacuation. Then there were the masses of refugees from areas which the Germans had already occupied. They pulled everything which could move on rails out of the sheds—including cattle-trucks, coal-trucks and all the rolling stock from Moscow Underground and put it on the track which led to the east, along with locomotives and pilot engines from depots and repair yards. The trains drove on as long as the coal lasted; then they used wood from the forests. Many people went down to the harbour on the Moskva river and unmoored coal barges and freighters or got into boats and drifted down to the Oka. Others again went on foot, and with them all—the refugees on the railway, on the waterways and on the roads—the panic which gripped Moscow spread further and further across the land.

On the night of October 15th the last tram drove past the blacked-out houses and the dark gaping doors. The axles were worn and needed oil; the wheels rattled; overhead there were constant breaks in contact with the live wire when, for a second or two, the long rows of old grey houses, with their flaked plaster façades, were bathed in blue light.

The tram rattled on and drove into the depot. The driver went home. The conductress first settled her accounts. This evening they all had a lot left in their pockets after they had handed in their ticket money, for today the passengers had not been interested in the change of a rouble—it was as if money already had no more value. One of the tired women in felt boots with a tramwayman's cap on her head was called Turuchina, Praskova Turuchina, the wife of Quartermaster-Lieutenant Anatoly Turuchin. She had not—as he had feared—had to work in a munitions factory but had been employed as a conductress on the tramways. When she reached her house in Shabotovska Street a man was standing in the dark doorway. She was frightened and scarcely recognised her husband.

"Anatoly!"

"Keep quiet."

Turuchin had come back a deserter, in a terrible state of raggedness, without shoes, his face almost black. And he was, as he said right away, covered with lice from head to foot. He did not want to stay—merely to have a wash and a change of clothes. And he must have a pair of shoes. But everything must be done very quietly; no one must notice that he had visited her.

*   *   *

In a well-kept wooden house out in the Petrovsky Park two women were sitting opposite each other in old-fashioned armchairs; one was young and the other rather older. The latter had a book in her hand, but her mind was not absorbed by what she was reading, and she listened to every noise from outside. Several times she had thought she heard the garden gate open; each time she had been mistaken. The other made no attempt to occupy herself; when she was not busy in the little household she brooded; she hardly ever ate. For hours she stood in front of the almost empty shops to bring home a piece of bread, or a bottle of paraffin for the lamp, or whatever else there was to buy.

"Cheer up, Nina Mihailovna. You will get over it." Lena Fyodorovna knew what had destroyed the other's will to live. When Anna Pavlovna brought her she had explained what was wrong. To bear a child out of wedlock, even by the wrong man, wasn't the end of the world; but to lose the right man and everything with him— friends, one's house, permission to live in Moscow—that was a catastrophe which would have overtaken Narishkin's widow, Lena Fyodorovna, by now if the officials had been able to get through the mounting piles of documents. As it was she might as well have disappeared already, for no one dared to visit her any more. One exception was Mihail Mihailovitch, a major in the Moscow garrison, who had always been a great reader and was able to talk about books and foreign authors and old Russian writers with Lena Fyodorovna and her daughter, Anna Alexeyevna. It was a great good fortune for Anna to know Mihail, and some comfort for the girl who had so unexpectedly found herself in this new situation. She had looked about for a job and got one in a ministry, but that would only last until they had got through the documents and then. . .

All they could do was wait; perhaps everything would be different soon—the wildest rumours were going about the town. It was even said that Stalin had been arrested. All the high officials had fled; in Anna's office everyone was gone; only a handful had stayed behind to clear things up and destroy any papers which could not be dealt with. Anna had rung up and said that she would be late—she had a lot of things to do—but now it was time for her to be home.

Lena Fyodorovna laid down her book at last.

"Anna Alexeyevna is a long time."

"The trams are very irregular—but there won't be any more now," said Nina Mihailovna.

"She will have to come all the way on foot, and the streets are unsafe and full of all sorts of undesirable characters."

*   *   *

Moscow lay under a black sky, but the population was not sleeping. There were people in the streets again; the curfew no longer meant anything, for there were no patrols to see that orders were obeyed.

The Foreign Embassies, the Diplomatic Corps and the People's Commissariat for Foreign Affairs had gone to Kyubishev on the Volga, the town which had once been called Samara. The People's Commissariat for Internal Affairs—the NKVD—and the Central Committees were spread out between Sverdlovsk and Tshakalov on the borders of Asia. They had evacuated European Russia. The Soviet intelligentsia was on its way to Sverdlovsk, to

285

Tashkent and Alma Ata. The train carrying the Society of Authors was approaching Kazan. And at the Moscow airport some airliners and a picked squadron of fighters stood ready to take off with the highest rulers in the land, the members of the Politburo.

Red Square, the Kremlin wall with its crowning towers, the empty mausoleum in front of them, and the cathedral of Saint Basil at the far end of the wide expanse, lay in deep and silent darkness. None of the nocturnal wanderers ventured thus far, and the anti-aircraft fire of the inner defence ring was twenty miles away. Only the steps of the sentries echoed through the silence. From the top of a tower came twelve muffled strokes of a bell.

Behind the Kremlin walls, in the old palace of the Czars, in the wing where Catherine II had once lived and which now had been converted into a flat for Stalin's use, with committee rooms, offices, secret doors and staircases and subterranean passages, the members of the Politburo were gathering in a simple, panelled room.

The Politburo was assembled and awaited one man.

He arrived dressed in a simple blouse and long boots and took his place at the end of the table. Deliberations could now begin between these fifteen men with heavy hearts and grim faces. The first speaker was a mountainous man, Shcherbakov, the secretary of the Moscow Party Committee.

The question at this moment of deadly crisis was not that of drawing up a testament. No breath of the great traditions of the past, no cold wind of self-criticism, was felt at the conference table. The maintenance and extension of their power throughout the world—that was the only consideration of these men. The fifteen faces collected round the table were empty masks; the problem for one and all was how to hold on to power. The particular question of the moment was: Is Moscow to be held or must it be abandoned?

Some days before Stalin had said: "Moscow is lost unless a miracle happens."

Tonight he sat there, listening to what the others said and saying nothing himself.

* * *

In the communal dwelling in Shabatovska Street,

Anatoly Turuchin had been splashing liberally with soap and water—his wife had given him her only piece of real soap—and had wakened first of all his mother-in-law, who was sleeping in the same room, and then the other families living in the same flat. Varvara Nikolayevna was the first of these to wake up.

"Who is that with Praskovya?" she said going to the door of the next room to listen. "Anotoly Yemelyanovitch has come back," she reported.

The families who shared the flat collected in the communal kitchen, which was precisely what Anatoly Yemelyanovitch had hoped they would not do. Now he had to go out into the kitchen—for not to show himself at all would have been still more suspicious—and say hello. As he did so he looked distrustfully at them all in turn, but it did not occur to anyone to denounce him. There was, in fact, no one left now to receive denunciations, and the house superintendent had overnight become a modest, retiring person.

Anatoly Yemelyanovitch told how he had fought at Minsk, at Smolensk and Dorogobush and killed Germans by the dozen.

"And how was it in Berlin? I thought you were going to march into Berlin," asked Varvara Nikolayevna, who was always cheeky.

"If you have chewed up so many Germans—why are they at the gates of Moscow?" asked her husband, the fitter Vavilov.

"I can explain that to you—they have far fewer men, but they have machines and everyone is motorised. Trucks and troop carriers and assault guns and all sorts of things —their trucks are bigger than our tanks and the earth shakes as they come. And when we have beaten them at one place they drive off, and by the time we have run after them they have broken through on our flanks and surrounded us."

Anatoly Yemelyanovitch told his tale, but he kept glancing round to the door; he felt he was in a trap here.

At last Praskovya came to his aid.

"You are sure to be very tired," she said.

"Yes, I am—I'll go and have a sleep," he said, and was glad to get out of the kitchen.

"What does he think he looks like? He'll give lice to the whole block," said Varvara Nikolayevna once he had gone.

Anatoly Yemelyanovitch had no intention of sleeping. When he was back in his room he wished his mother-in-law goodnight, put out the lamp, lay down beside Praskovya and listened. When everything was quiet outside he got up again and slipped away as he had come.

*   *   *

Anna Alexeyevna had not only rung her mother, she had also rung their friend, Major Mihailovitch, and arranged with him that he would fetch her from the office, but not at the usual time—much later—for there were some things she still had to do. At one in the morning Mihail Mihailovitch stood at the door of the ministry. When neither Anna Alexeyevna nor anyone else appeared he went into the building. In the porter's lodge the porter looked up half asleep. What was that?—a smart uniform with stars on the collar. He let Mihail Mihailovitch go past without question. The latter wandered through the half-lit corridors, found a watchman at last and gave the name of a department and the head under whom Anna Alexeyevna worked.

"There's not a soul there," said the watchman.

"But that's impossible," replied Mihail Mihailovitch. He produced a packet of cigarettes, offered the man one and gave him a light. The watchman took a few draws and became a little more talkative.

"Yes, the boss was up there with some people from the office—there was some drinking going on," he said.

"I see—drinking? With the young secretaries?"

"Yes—and it wasn't only the young ones. It was a real do," said the man.

"Listen—this concerns my future wife. Where did the company go then?"

"I heard them ordering cars to go to the Savoy or the Metropol."

That was enough for Mihail Mihailovitch. He went to the Savoy. Things were in full swing there—all the tables were covered with bottles; there was a big crowd and a lot of noise and shouting. But he did not find Anna.

He went on to the Metropol. Even in the foyer the

noise from the main room came to meet him. A palm was lying overturned on the floor; the glass of the show-cases was broken, and the luxuries on sale for foreigners had been stolen. It was not without a certain reticence that Mihail Mihailovitch walked in, for to enter the Metropol was normally a risky undertaking for any Soviet citizen who did not come with a special mission. But tonight none of the rules held. In the big room he was met with a smell of sweat and perfume and a loud hum of voices; cigarette smoke hung over the tables. Several hundred well-dressed people were sitting there; the women in expensive dresses and jewellery; the men in uniform or evening dress. The cellars had been opened—vodka, Crimean wine, Caucasian champagne were flowing freely —and the band, forty strong, played jazz.

Mihail Mihailovitch looked among the tables, looked over the mirror-smooth dance floor and in the balconies, where he caught sight of half-naked girls. Everywhere he saw officers of the Red Army, colonels and even Generals; deserters sat side by side with high officials, prostitutes with the wives of officials. The girls from the Taganka bazaar went from table to table, stuffing themselves with whatever they could lay hands on and filling their pockets into the bargain. The blonde NKVD girls danced as they did every night; they looked as if they had come out of the window of a foreign dress shop with their waved hair, silk dresses and silk stockings. Beside them Anna Alexeyevna looked like Cinderella.

Suddenly someone shouted above the din: "German tanks in the outskirts."

Outside, sirens howled. The anti-aircraft guns opened up. Some dive-bombers had broken through and a bomb exploded near by. Death was falling from the skies and approaching along the roads into the city. The men clasped the women tighter to them, regardless of their surroundings.

The band played on, ever louder, far into the night.

* * *

The conference in the Kremlin had reached its climax.

The members of the Politburo had heard the military experts: Marshal Voronov for the artillery, Marshal Govorov for the air force, and finally the Chief of the

289

General Staff, Zapozhnikov.

The picture which emerged from the military information was shattering. No one had expected anything else, but it still left them speechless. The Red Army, which had so long stood between Moscow and the German Wehrmacht, had crumbled away. The newly-appointed Marshal, Zhukov, who had been confirmed in his post by this very meeting and given quite exceptional powers, would be a Field-Marshal without troops until the armies from the Far East arrived. Moscow was in the greatest danger; and not only Moscow but the whole land.

Vossnesensky, leading economist and head of all the planning commissions, closed the notes he had been making on Zapozhnikov's speech and exchanged a glance with Zhdanov, the most powerful man on the Politburo after Stalin. Molotov had spread out his expensive cases in front of him—cigarette case, pencil case, cases for every conceivable thing—and was smoking one cigarette after another. Now he was watching his rival Zhdanov from behind his glasses with an uncertain blinking of his eyes. He was wondering whether to adopt whatever attitude Zhdanov took up and give him his support. A sober view of the circumstances left him no other course.

But Zhdanov, the colossus, elected to say nothing. In his place a younger member of the Politburo began to speak. It was Alexander Sergevitch Shcherbakov. Since they were dealing with the fate of Moscow, and Shcherbakov was Party Secretary for Moscow, this was quite in order. Shcherbakov demanded that Moscow be defended. In spite of the strained military situation, and even if the situation seemed hopeless, everything possible must be done to save the city—the last man and the last woman mobilised and the last drop of blood hazarded in this sacred cause.

His appeal was a purely rhetorical one. In a mass meeting, his emotional approach and his savage determination not to yield a step in the face of adversity would have had some effect. But here such words had no power to convince.

A heavy silence followed.

Zhdanov, the man who controlled armaments, and Vossnesensky, the chief planner, again said nothing—

they were waiting to see what Molotov would propose. Molotov rearranged the cases which he had piled in front of him and stood up. He based his position on what the experts had said—Marshal Voronov, Marshal Govorov and the Chief of the General Staff, Zapozhnikov—and stated in conclusion that the military specialists had given little or no hope of a successful defence of Moscow. In addition, the Moscow workers were themselves an uncertain factor. According to reports which had come in, the shops were being plundered by the populace and the police were standing by and doing nothing. They had no longer control of the situation. And there were very unfavourable reports from the aircraft factories. Work had been stopped too soon and the workers sent home for an indefinite period; this had only produced confusion and disappointment. Special circumstances called for special measures. In the year 1812 Kutusov, who had been granted extraordinary powers, had stood behind these same Kremlin walls and said: "At this moment the fate of the country is in my hands. I order Moscow to be evacuated!" Once again one of the special measures which had to be taken was the immediate evacuation of Moscow. But there were other possibilities to be considered as well —among them were conversations, negotiations (Benes was the obvious go-between), even agreements, all of which would win a little time at the moment of supreme danger and could be abrogated later.

Zhdanov still sat silent in his place.

The fact that he did so was to be interpreted as a sign of agreement rather than otherwise. Vossnesensky, too, bided his time. It is true that Voroshilov opened his foolish blue eyes very wide, but he had come to the meeting a beaten man—he had lost the battle on the northern front and allowed the Germans to get within range of Leningrad—so he had even less than usual to say. Kaganovitch was in exactly the same situation. After his assurances that the Soviet railways were the most powerful in the world and Soviet transport the best organised, the breakdown of the transport system had been one of the main causes of the catastrophe—so the People's Commissar for Transport was not likely to make himself heard at this juncture.

The attack came from another direction. Mikoyan, the Petronius of the tyrant's court, spoke. Once he had been a poor boy who had the reputation, back there in Armenia, of being something of a gallant; now he was an ageing bachelor. He knew something about arts and books and could dress well—was, indeed, rather too elegant, too soigné; even at a time like this the trifling, play-acting side of his character did not desert him but was to be seen in the way he spoke, in his gestures and his choice of words.

"What sort of conversations are we speaking about? What sort of agreements are proposed, and what sort of negotiations is Benes to start?" he asked.

Molotov was dabbing at his brow with a silk handkerchief. A black cloud hung over the table. At any moment the thunder-bolt might fall and strike him.

Moscow would not settle things one way or the other, he said. Whether the capital was held or given up would not decide the outcome of the war. Had not Stalin said: "If the Far Eastern Armies come too late to keep the Germans out of Moscow they will still be in plenty of time to drive them out of the ruins?" And then one should not forget the colossal industrial potential of America and England. Very shortly they could expect large-scale aid and that could be utilised even if the line lay still farther back.

"But what sort of conversations do you mean?" he was asked again.

"What are you getting at, Comrade Molotov?" asked Mikoyan. "Do you want to treat with Hitler, by any chance?"

Zhdanov sat slumped in his chair and looked at his clenched fists, which lay before him on the table. At the far end of the table Stalin sat with a telephone at his ear. "Yes . . . yes . . . yes." The monotonous words fell like drops into the silence. He hung up the receiver again. Molotov tried to catch his eye. I have been with him for forty years, he thought, and people would laugh if they thought I didn't know what he was thinking. Then he threw down the sacrilegious proposal declaring that, in view of the facts of the situation, negotiations with Hitler must be begun without delay.

It was out now and could not be retracted. The cloud must be rent asunder. Everything depended now on Zhdanov and his attitude, but the colossus made no move. Stalin screwed up his eyes and looked at the faces round the table.

Then Vossnesensky, Malenkov and Beria spoke in turn. Voroshilov, too, sitting there wrinkling his brow, threw a word into the debate. Even Kaganovitch crept out of his retirement. There was some agreement but more disapproval and noisy opposition; harsh, even insulting, words were spoken.

Molotov and Zhdanov were the two pillars on whom the empire rested. The solution must be found in collaboration or compromise between the two.

One could negotiate, said Molotov, so long as one had something to negotiate about. They must believe him when he said that he made his proposals with a heavy heart, but that commonsense pointed to no other way out. As he defended his point of view, his yellowish face became red; he broke into a sweat and even fell into his old painful habit of stuttering.

It was a piece of black treachery to the Allies, cried Mikoyan. With these words he had gone as far as he could; all that remained to be said—but it would have required a sign of agreement from Stalin—was that Molotov was also a traitor to the Soviet Government.

At the other end of the table the tell-tale lamp glowed again and the receiver was unhooked. The deep, tired voice sounded through the room. "*Kak dyela . . . da . . . da . . . da.* Hold on, we will help."

Stalin took up his pencil and covered the paper before him with drawings. A huge question mark, then train wheels, always the same clumsy train wheels, took shape under his hand. He raised his eyes and looked at his Foreign Minister. He could see that this squat man with the broad face and the low bridge to his nose—this man who was really called Skryabin, and came from a patrician family which had produced a lot of scientists and artists —was going through a bad moment.

Events from beyond the Kremlin walls threw their shadow on the conference. Panic reports reached to the very ante-chamber. According to one of these reports, the Germans were already on the edge of the town, at Fili; according to another, German armour had taken the town of Maloyaroslavetz without a shot and had driven on and crossed the Protva. This second report turned out to be true. It was a terrifying thought that German armour had been able to break through the outer defence ring of Moscow, without meeting any resistance worth mentioning. Another day's work like that and the Germans would be in the southern outskirts of the city. For a time the ante-chamber and the telephone became more important than the argument between Molotov and Mikoyan. Stalin never took the receiver from his ear. His glance rested on the great question mark he had scribbled.

The great question mark was for the Germans.

What were their aims? Why did they not let their troops cross a certain invisible line? Moscow was theirs —it was incredible that they should not exploit their immense military superiority this very night and drop a couple of airborne divisions on the streets and squares of Moscow. What would the two or three detachments of worker volunteers that Shcherbakov was demanding do against them—detachments which had still to be mobilised by the house committees of the Party and then armed and trained?

The armies from the Far East, from Siberia and the Caucasus, were the only forces which could turn the course of events. Ten days before an order had been issued from the Kremlin:

The Far Eastern Army, all troops from Siberia, from the Caucasus, from the Republics of Central Asia, units from the training camps in Southern Russia, Kazakstan and Uzbekistan are to be despatched to Moscow, whatever their state of training, with the utmost speed, using all available locomotives, all available rolling stock and regardless of all safety measures on the railways.

By this step the frontiers with Afghanistan in the south, and with Japanese-occupied China in the east, were stripped and laid bare. But if the capital fell, the whole land, the Union of Republics, was threatened with collapse, and the possession of the city was as important to Stalin as to the Secretary of the Moscow District Committee or anyone else.

Stalin drew railway wheels.

For ten days the armies he had ordered to move had been on their way, and still they had a long way to come. When this troop movement had begun, Moscow was already no longer the centre of the communications network; all but one line had been cut and the bulk of the reinforcements had had to be sent round by it. There they had run into the chaotic movement of evacuees from Moscow going in the opposite direction—a movement which stretched out to the Urals.

Well, the line could and would be cleared. The reinforcements would get moving again. But more time would pass, and if experience was anything to go by the German armour would get to Moscow first.

The debate was drawing to its close. Mikoyan, Vossnesensky, Malenkov and the others supported Shcherbakov's plans. By a simple majority Molotov's proposal was rejected.

Shcherbakov gave more details of his plan. Immediate mobilisation of all the women in Moscow by the house committees; the building of earth-works on the outskirts to be speeded up; the erection of tank obstacles on all the roads leading into the town; the raising of four Worker's Divisions; preparations for the destruction of Moscow to be carried out by technical troops and sappers. The underground, all bridges, the government buildings, including the Kremlin buildings, the power stations, the gas and waterworks, all the important supply depots in the town were, in case of necessity, to be blown up as far as available explosives allowed.

The programme was not new; it differed only in the greater extent of the demolitions, and the larger number of probable victims, from the orders which had been given out in Minsk, Borissov, Smolensk and all the other towns which the Germans had taken—orders which still held for all future cases. The general principle was to destroy the means of existence of those who fell into German hands. Moscow was to be no exception.

* * *

That night there was an unusual change in the weather.

295

It began to rain. It was not just another local shower such as there had been in the last few days. It rained unceasingly in a steady downpour.

The guests who left the Metropol before dawn came out into the rain; they saw the great drops bursting on the black asphalt and turned back to carry on with the celebrations.

In the course of his wanderings Turuchin had been surprised by the rain in a long, monotonous street. He had taken refuge in a doorway and now stood there gazing at the curtain of water falling from the projecting wall of the house. Slowly he fell asleep with open eyes.

Anna Alexeyevna and Mihail Mihailovitch had left the Metropol before the rain began and reached his flat dryshod. From there Anna tried to telephone Lena Fyodorovna, but the telephone was not working and after a while she gave up the attempt. In any case, it would have been much too far to walk to the Petrovsky Park that night, even if it had not been raining.

In the wooden house near the Petrovsky Park a woman gazed through a window into the overcast sky. Lena Fyodorovna still waited for Anna Alexeyevna. The rain fell, the bare flower-beds in the little garden before the house crumbled, the water stood in gleaming puddles in the suburban road. Lena Fyodorovna felt as if her life were flowing away with the pouring rain.

At the same time another face was watching the rain through a window—a tired face with a prominent nose, with grey, dishevelled hair and eyes inflamed from many sleepless night.

"Those fools, those fools—there is the rain, there is Russia's old ally, General Bad Weather." The face at the window in Catherine's palace disappeared, and in the rooms beyond, in the long suite of lofty apartments, laughter echoed from the walls.

*　　*　　*

It rained.

It rained in Moscow and in Maloyaroslavetz. It rained from Moscow to Kazan, and from Moscow to Orel and Kursk. It rained from Lake Ladoga to the Sea of Azov. The rain fell on the forests and on the fields; it flowed down from the hills and all the plains turned into wastes of mud. Somewhere in a wood between Mozhaisk and Borodino Nikolai Uralov and the remnants of his battalion sat under dripping leaves.

Uralov had had time to think things over. He wouldn't go back to his own lines nor over to the Germans; that was the only decision he had taken so far. But they could not stay in the woods among the damp leaves in the cold and wet. The rain turned to snow, and for the first time the snow lay during the day.

Uralov had three men with him; Lieutenant Skryl, Ivan from Archangel and a soldier from the Kursk district. They had shot a hare and had followed its tracks and the drops of blood through the snow, brought it back to their bivouac and roasted it over an open fire.

That same evening they set out to find a village. Far on in the night they reached the edge of the wood and saw a little village lying in a hollow. The first houses rose black against the snow and dogs began to bark.

"We must wait for day," said Uralov. "It's no use arriving in the middle of the night; we will only frighten people and get nowhere." So they went back under the trees and gathered dried twigs, burned them and lay down on the hot ash—Uralov in the middle, Skryl, Ivan and the man from Kursk round about him. There they fell into a deep sleep.

"Hands up!" The tip of a boot touched Uralov and he awoke to see a German soldier standing over him. There was no time to draw his pistol and put a bullet through his own head as he had intended to do. He had not wanted to fall alive into German hands.

They had to hand over their weapons to the German patrol; their pockets were searched; some money Uralov had on him disappeared into the pocket of one of the German soldiers, together with a photograph of Nina Mihailovna. There were German troops billeted in the villages through which they were led. In the first village there was armour which had been parked on boards between the houses during the rainy season; now it had been towed out on to the frozen road and got ready for a move. In the village street stood a horsed troop of guns. Eight of the horses were harnessed to a field gun whose wheels had sunk deep into the soft ground and then frozen in. To the shouts of the gunners the horses strained on the harness, but the thick steel pin which held the shaft broke and the gun stayed where it was. The German soldiers were still wearing their summer uniform; some had Russian felt boots.

Uralov, Skryl and the man from Kursk were taken to Gzhatsk and shut up in a large cellar. It was in fact a vegetable dump, but now it had to serve as a PW collecting point; there was no room to sit or lie down, and more and more men kept being crammed in.

A day went past with nothing to eat. On the second and third days there was still nothing. On the fourth some rye was distributed—a tumbler full for each man; but it was rye which had been prepared for sowing. Many of the men took it in their hands, blew away the yellow dust and ate it. Others were afraid of poisoning themselves. Uralov was one of those who did not touch the rye; in the end he exchanged it for a handful of mahorka.

For these four days, and for the days that followed, the temperature remained below zero. The roads were hard; snow drifted over the countryside. Outside there was continual movement even at night; through the ventilation shafts they could hear the marching feet of columns on the move, and the cellar echoed the noise of heavy trucks and the rattling tracks of the armour. The Germans were going forward for a new offensive against Moscow.

* * *

Marshal Zhukov, Generals Rokossovsky, Belov and Konev were still commanders without troops; but it would not be for much longer. Next day each of them would have under his command a fully-equipped army used to winter conditions and armed to meet them.

The Kremlin had come to life again with an order to all officials "to ensure the defence of Moscow and to put an end to the destructive activity of spies, traitors and agents of German Fascism." NKVD patrols marched through Moscow once more; the prison van drove through the streets again and took those who were arrested to the Lyubianka; the execution squads got to work.

Shcherbakov's trucks and buses transported thousands of freshly-raised militiamen towards the front. Trucks carried the women the house committees had collected to the edge of the town to dig dugouts and trenches. The women were coatless and their shoes let in the wet; they wore the clothes they had on when they were conscripted. The militia had no training and almost no weapons—they had to take these from the cold hands of the dead out there in the snow. Each man had five rounds of ammunition in his pocket.

More and more convoys arrived from the Far East, from the Caucasus and the training camps of the south. The troops from the training camps in Central Asia, badly equipped and undertrained, were given a special issue of vodka and sent forward in waves to clear a path for the well-equipped and fully-armed troops from the Caucasus, Siberia and the Far East. These were élite formations with white tanks, white guns and white horses; the riders, the infantry and the ski-troops wore white cloaks; everything was camouflaged for operations on a snow-covered land.

Stalin counted the divisions as they arrived, and waited. At last he counted eighty divisions. The plans were ready; they were to cut off the twin prongs of the German pincer movement by a Russian advance towards Smolensk and the bend of the Dnieper at Orscha.

That day a German soldier at Kalinin wrote in his diary: "This is enough to drive you out of your mind. Our company is down to fifty men and they are all half dead." And an officer wrote: "We have orders to withdraw from the position tomorrow. We dug in with indescribable difficulty, literally scratching away the earth with our nails, and to do it we used up our last piece of wire, our last building materials. And now we are going to have to give it all up and hand over the territory we have won to the enemy. My God, what have we done that this should have to happen to us?"

The Russians came.

They crossed the Volga and the Oka in white-clad formations, bursting from the woods and clambering from the watercourses.

At Kalinin, near a village on the Volga, north of Moscow, the commander of a horsed troop stood in his OP at his bifocal telescope. The evening before he had celebrated the feast of St. Barbara, the patron saint of gunners, with his brother officers. A Russian nurse had come over the Volga on the ice to tell them about the preparations on the other side and had said: "They are going to attack tomorrow at midday."

The Russians advanced punctually at twelve noon. It was a cold, steely winter day; nothing moved in the yellow sky. On the other side of the Volga rose a stretch of open country; beyond was high forest. They began to come forward out of the wood in groups, running down towards the Volga, not in open order, but in tight-packed formations. The German artillery opened up and many of them fell, but the human stream did not cease to flow —it advanced over the open country, reached the Volga and came on over the ice.

The troop commander at the telescope saw the ranks falling and others climbing over them. He had to shorten the range and bring fire down on to the frozen Volga. The shells ricocheted and the white surface was sprinkled with bursts, but the fire was not heavy enough to cover the target and there was neither enough ammunition nor enough guns. The snow-covered surface of the stream became covered with black dots and flecks; but that had no effect on the advancing columns. Not a man lay down, not one turned back; the mass of men swept on and reached the near bank.

The noise of battle rose from the line of the Volga. The German infantry fell back from the village; soldiers without gloves or winter clothing retreated through the gun positions, but the artillery held on. Assault guns were moved up and that evening the village was retaken.

That night the heavens opened; the storm burst out of the dark stillness and blew black masses of snow over the land. The morning was grey with wind and snow. The thermometer showed thirty degrees below zero.

Once more a trickle of men began from the high forest, streamed down to the Volga and on over the ice. Once more the troop went into action; new patches appeared beside the old ones which were now grey and covered with snow. Ammunition began to run out. They fired their solid shot, left over from the French campaign, and it bored deep into the Volga ice, and as a final gesture of defiance they used up their smoke shells on the edge of the wood beyond. Then it was all over.

The guns of the forward troop were blown up. The others fell back with eight horses to each gun—back to the edge of the wood first of all and then on over the railway line. The initiative was with the Russians; the German infantry spent the night in the open while the Russians lay in the villages and kept warm, sleeping in peace, for the German artillery had no more ammunition to shell the villages. They rose at three in the morning and advanced in swarms on the clearing where the Germans lay behind the railway line. There was a little firing; a few hand grenades were thrown, and that was all. The MGs were useless because the oil was frozen; all the automatic weapons had stoppages. Some of the infantry did not react at all but lay in the snow like dying flies; those who still had sufficient energy ran away. When day broke the regiment no longer existed; five days later the whole division was gone. The flanking division and the flanking corps were affected. The front began to crumble. It was days before it hardened again.

West of Moscow the situation was much the same; here, too, there was a precipitate retreat, blocked roads and heavy losses in men and equipment. To the north the order was given to withdraw and save what could be saved. Guderian, in the south, found himself without supplies of ammunition and petrol and broke off the action, withdrawing to the upper Don.

The whole group of German armies round Moscow was overtaken by the catastrophe. After the first week of retreat they recovered from the initial shock sufficiently for certain definite movements to emerge from the confusion. The troops from the Kalinin front fell back towards Rzhev, the centre towards Vyasma and Yuchnov, and the southern front towards Orel.

* * *

Vilshofen received orders to relieve a unit which had been cut off. But he could no longer muster a battalion; there was so little ammunition and fuel left that only a troop of four tanks could be mobilised. With these he set out.

He drove into the drifting snow. The road was smooth and polished and one of the tanks slid down a bank and turned on to its side. In the next village infantry in ones and twos were retreating eastwards; their heads covered with rags; their boots wrapped in scraps of runners or carpets stolen from Russian houses and secured with telephone wires. Many had thrown away their weapons.

"Where are you going?"

"We are being overrun."

"The Siberians are there."

Two field guns with eight horses yoked to each tore along the road, the drivers belabouring the horses. Machine-gun fire swept along behind them. The broad track marks of a KV 52 led to the abandoned troop position beyond the village; the huge Russian tank had overrun two guns. There were broken limbers and dead horses; the gunners lay pressed flat, rolled out in the snow. The smoke of recent destruction hung over everything; it must have happened only a few minutes before. Vilshofen's three tanks moved on over open country towards the edge of a wood.

"Not very pleasant," Vilshofen called to the lieutenant in the next tank.

"It looks sticky."

"It looks as if there is nothing left to relieve."

The lieutenant's reply was never heard; the words were torn from his mouth as a tongue of flame shot up. The tank burned fiercely and no one climbed out of it. Vilshofen could hear the bark of anti-tank guns, but there was nothing to be seen in the drifting snow. The anti-tank guns must be at the edge of the wood.

"Full speed ahead to the edge of the wood."

As they went Vilshofen saw the flashes. The second tank, too, was hit and left behind.

"Twelve o'clock—anti-tank gun. Get on to it, get on."

The gun stood fifty yards away—it could be seen clearly now, and the two men serving it as well. The tank-driver made straight for them and overran both gun and crew. Inside the tank they felt a bump as the trail snapped. They overran a second gun from the flank. "Keep on, keep on—round the tree." There was a third gun there. They got their tracks on to it; but one of the wheels of the gun would not give and a track got caught. The tank ran up on to the breastwork round the gun and

302

overturned.

With an effort they succeeded in opening the turret. When Vilshofen, the driver, the wireless operator and the gunner had climbed out a burst of machine-gun fire swept across. All four fell. Only Vilshofen and the driver raised themselves again and stumbled off into the snow squalls.

* * *

The retreating infantry and the field guns which Vilshofen had met, tearing in panic down the village street, belonged to Bomelbuerg's division, which had got within artillery range of the Moscow suburb of Podolsk. When the order to withdraw came through, they had been in danger of being cut off and had had to disengage at once.

Before the march began there had been a dixie of rice soup. It had been their one and only warm meal. Day and night they had marched, with rearguard actions becoming more and more fierce, and the flanks and even the head of the column constantly having to fight off attacks. The division was marching in reverse order, with the B echelons and the divisional staff ahead and the fighting troops behind. The general situation was obscure; there was no more contact with the neighbouring divisions, and even contact between units within the division was often lost. Trucks were abandoned through lack of petrol, and horse-drawn transport often had to be left, too; the exhausted and starved animals fell dead or foundered in harness. The road was lined with broken and capsized vehicles, their loads scattered on the ground. At first the rearguard came upon occasional boxes of ammunition lying about, then they became great heaps. Vehicles, equipment, guns and valuable instruments were left lying in the snow.

The night that Lieutenant-Colonel Vilshofen was wandering blindly through the snow with his driver, the leading units of Bomelbuerg's division became entangled with several other retreating divisions at a cross-roads a few miles from the Protva bridge. In the darkness and confusion some of the vehicles the division had so carefully husbanded got into another convoy and were never seen again. At the next road junction the divisional staff itself stuck fast in a hopeless tangle of horsed transport. It

303

was impossible to move.

"You'll have to use your fists," shouted Lieutenant-Colonel Neudeck from the command vehicle and climbed out. The convoy commander and Sergeant Riederheim, who was at his side, were already laying into the drivers with fists and sticks, but the tangle of wagons, traces and foundering horses would not unravel itself. Butz, the liaison officer, got out too. Lieutenant-General Bomelbuerg was left alone, but presently, growing impatient of the delay, he, too, climbed out of his car.

To the right there was a thick wall of wood stretching to the Protva; to the left a clearing ran into the wood. Out of this clearing, which was barely half a mile wide, fate swooped down upon them.

Suddenly there were carbine shots and galloping horses with Asiatic riders swinging their swords. In a moment they were amongst the confusion of men and animals, severing heads from trunks and cutting the jugular veins of the horses. There was no organised attempt at resistance; the MGs were frozen and did not work. The only ones who really knew what to do were Riederheim, Gnotke, Feierfeil and the men from the old advance guard. Between them they managed to get a machine-gun into action, fired a few bursts and, when it was warm, oiled it. The riders made no attempt to approach the little troop behind its ring of wagons, dying men and plunging horses. When a second and third machine-gun had been got into action the attackers withdrew over the clearing and disappeared into the wood beyond. But some of them cut through the knot of vehicles and drove the troops, stumbling along in front of them in panic, down to the banks of the Protva.

After this attack it was only a sorry remnant of HQ Company which collected. Many were missing. Nor was the General to be found—either among the living or the dead.

Seven or eight miles away the HQ of Zecke's regiment found shelter for the night, along with another unit in a little village on a tributary of the Nara. There were not sufficient houses, and it was only by being completely ruthless that Captain Hasse was able to get a hut for headquarters. There were soldiers lying everywhere, even in the doorways, unshaven, dirty, clad in rags. Many of them had felt boots and quilted jackets which they had taken from dead Russians; as far as their dress went they were almost undistinguishable from Soviet troops. There were fights at the doors; many of the men tried to force their way in, even if it were only for a little while, to thaw their bread on the stove, for it was hard as stone.

Colonel Zecke established himself with his HQ in the hut which had been cleared for him. His regiment, too, had had to ward off a Russian cavalry attack on the march; the horsemen had attacked the baggage train and cut down the drivers. Now message after message was reaching the HQ about Russian penetrations; they were infiltrating into the houses at the edge of the village. Zecke sent the remains of HQ Company to clean up the eastern end of the place and seal it off. He kept Captain Hasse by him and Lieutenant Langhoff, whose troop HQ was in the same house.

The Russians were thrown out of the houses and the village was successfully sealed off. But that was not much help. To the south and west the village was surrounded by thick woods, through which the Russians were able to bypass the village and attack the rest of the battalion which was lying to the west. Zecke sat in the dim light of an oil lamp and listened to the runners reporting the end of his regiment.

His worst fears were coming true. He at least had gone into the catastrophe with his eyes open; he had expected nothing except disaster in the snow. Incredible, irreparable errors had been made in Russia. Now the war was being fought by the Russians not for Stalin but for the Fatherland; Hitler had mobilised not only the Communist Party and the bureaucracy but the whole land, a whole family of peoples against him. That was to say, against the Wehrmacht. The mighty reserves of a whole continent faced the German troops, and in the rear there was nothing for five hundred miles but snow. What was there one could do in these circumstances—what could be achieved? At best a Napoleonic retreat—the saving of ten men out of every hundred, so that some witnesses would be left to relate one day a bloody moral about ill-gotten gains.

Zecke took some photographs out of his pocket-book —his house in Potsdam, his wife, his two daughters who were themselves grown women and had children of their own. He put the photographs away again and listened. Planes were passing over the village and a moment later the first bombs began to drop. But Russian villages were not good targets for air bombardment; the log huts swayed like ships in a heavy sea; a direct hit killed thirty men in one hut, but the other huts remained standing. Under a rain of bombs like that, a village of stone houses would have been turned into a pile of rubble.

According to reports from the battalions the Russians were infiltrating towards the west, south of the road. A mounted orderly arrived from Divisional HQ and reported the cavalry attack at the cross-roads and the disappearance of Lieutenant-General Bomelbuerg. Lieutenant-Colonel Neudeck requested Colonel Zecke, as the senior officer, to take over the division at once.

The regiment was fighting its last battle in the woods. The campaign had been lost. Now came the news of Bomelbuerg's disappearance. Langhoff, who had seen how his commander's face fell, remembered that he still had in reserve a bottle of champagne from the feast of St. Barbara which he had celebrated with his gunners: he had meant to drink it on New Year's Eve. Now he brought the bottle and opened it.

"Drink some, sir."

At that moment there was a crash close at hand; a bomb had fallen in front of the hut and blasted a tree. As the windows blew in, Langhoff, the runners and the mounted orderly from Division threw themselves to the floor; the wind swept the snow into the room. Colonel Zecke lay groaning near the table. Captain Hasse, who was unhurt, fetched the MO, and by the flickering light of a candle which Langhoff held in his hand the doctor filed the neck of an ampoule, filled his syringe, and gave Colonel Zecke an injection.

"You must go back to Division at once, sir," said the MO when the colonel came round.

Langhoff and Hasse tried, too, to persuade him to be taken back to the rear on a horse-drawn sledge, but

Zecke refused.

"I cannot leave my regiment in this situation," he said. He sent the orderly back with a message suggesting that Lieutenant-Colonel Neudeck, the Chief-of-Staff, should take over the division himself.

*   *   *

The thermometer fell from thirty-four to forty, and then to forty-eight degrees below zero. The foam froze on the horses' mouths. The soldiers' breath formed a hard crust of ice on their coat collars and balaclavas. Crows, frozen to death, fell out of the sky.

A new day broke; the sky gleamed with flashing needles of ice. The next day brought a snowstorm, sweeping horizontally over the ground, drifting as high as the houses. Then came more storms with winds of hurricane force; there were no more fields, no woods, no roads, no deep-cut watercourses, no frozen streams—nothing but snow lying or drifting or blowing in violent gusts. Whether it was Rzhev or Mozhaisk or Yuchnov; whether it was December, January or February, it was all the same.

*   *   *

A muffled figure was wandering through an enchanted winter wood with hoar frost on every bush and tree; only the footsteps of the solitary wanderer crunching through the snow broke the silence. He had set out from his last billet with four tanks; one had skidded off the road and overturned, the second had gone up in flames, the third was burnt out and he had got away from the fourth with his driver. Now the driver was dead. Vilshofen came to the edge of the wood; before him stretched a wide snowfield, a scene of infinite silence, infinite distance, flooded with harsh sunlight. He must get on—foot by foot. At each step he sank into deep snow. Ahead in the bright sunshine there was a little mound in the snow, then another, and farther off another still. They were soldiers, two in one place, three in another; two more sat side by side with their heads resting together and a groundsheet draped round them on which the snow had drifted high. One was in a thin greatcoat; the other had no coat at all but wore the black jacket of the armoured troops.

"I will lead you back to your lines," said Vilshofen.

"Come with me, boys."

"Let us sit here. It's wonderful to be able to sit in peace. We are tired of being always on the move."

"I am the last who will come this way. After me there will be the Russians."

"We don't give a damn who comes—the Russians or the devil—we just want to sit here."

"But they won't even let you freeze. They'll kill you."

"We're done for, anyway. Whether it's today or six weeks from now—we don't mind."

"So long as we don't have to keep on the move for another six weeks."

"Give us a cigarette and leave us in peace."

"We won't see home again, in any case."

The wanderer walked on under the glittering ice-crystals hanging from the trees, made his trail across the great curved slope of the snow-covered field and disappeared into the woods again.

* * *

The next day brought a snow storm which filled the valley of the Protva with drifts, so that it was impossible to tell that it was a valley. Bomelbuerg, separated from his troops and accompanied by some drivers, without map or compass, had set out in what he believed to be the direction of Maloyaroslavetz, from which he hoped to reach his division. But there were no landmarks far or near under the howling, sulphurous sky; only drifts into which a man sank up to his belly, and often up to his head. The men trotted along in single file behind Bomelbuerg, not realising that the old General was nearly blind. If they could only have found the right direction it wouldn't have been far to Maloyaroslavetz, but the wading through the snow seemed never-ending. The men fell asleep as they walked and only noticed it when their heads sank forward. At last they caught sight of the blurred contours of roofs which swam on a sea of mist. Their weary hearts beat faster at the sight of those ghostly shapes. There was no smoke coming from the chimneys, which meant that they were approaching a village which was not occupied, either by Germans or Russians.

"A village, sir—a village, just ahead."

"Get on, then," said Bomelbuerg, who could not see

what was happening around him. The others were too tired to observe the shadows which sprang up out of the snow, piled up to the eaves of the shingled roofs. Not a shot was fired; blows rained down on to the men's heads; they were beaten to death, strangled, smothered in the snow.

Bomelbuerg tapped his way forward without looking to right or left. He had always believed that bullets could not harm him—and it was not a bullet that brought death now. He was seized by the partisans and dragged to the edge of the village, where, tied to a stake, he was drenched with water. Frozen to a pillar of ice he remained standing at the entrance to the village—a macabre sign-post for the fleeing Germans and the vanguard of the Russian offensive.

* * *

The wind blew thick snow-clouds over the land, swept great stretches bare and drove huge billows of snow before it. Horses and men sank deep into the powdered snow on roads, marked out by poles, which were often barely visible. The column of prisoners which had been formed at Gzhatsk had to reach Smolensk by side roads; the autobahn was crammed with armoured units, artillery and infantry marching side by side. The prisoners, who were even worse fed than the German troops, were exhausted and worn out before they even began their march west. There were twelve thousand of them, including women and children, and the column was nearly eight miles long. This huge multitude was driven by a hundred cavalry from an SS Brigade, reinforced by men from the guard company at Gzhatsk.

Uralov, Skryl and Ivan from Archangel marched in one file. The first day they covered nearly twenty miles through snow and wind; in this weather it was as much as the troops themselves could do in twelve hours to struggle six miles. They went on without halts and those who could not keep up were left lying by the roadside; many were left behind.

On the second day they approached a scene of recent battle where mounted units of the Red Army had broken through to Vyasma and beyond and had now been pushed back again. On either side of the road lay Russian and

German dead and abandoned, snow-covered equipment.

Whenever the column came to a dead German lying on the road they all had to halt. The SS sergeant-major rode along the column and drew up his horse here and there at one file or another, quite aimlessly. Uralov was not watching the face with the bright blue eyes and the blond stubble beard—although he saw these later in nightmares; at that moment he saw only the sergeant-major's outstretched finger, a plump finger playing the part of a blind god. The rider lingered beside Uralov's file. The finger came slowly nearer and pointed to Lieutenant Skryl. Why Skryl? Perhaps because he was so big, perhaps because he had such a strong face and such ice-grey eyes. Uralov only knew that it was his friend who was seized by the escorting soldiers and shot. For every dead German soldier who lay on the road, twenty-five men from the column of prisoners were shot.

In the following night, where the road passed through a wood, Uralov managed to escape. With a bound he was under the trees; shots cracked after him as he ran, but in the darkness he soon evaded his pursuers and presently the uproar behind him died down. Now he only wanted to sleep, but sleep in this terrible cold was a thing to be feared. Tired and hungry he plodded on into the dawn and reached a clearing in which stood a row of abandoned Russian trucks. He found nothing to eat but collected a rifle and some ammunition, and searching further found footprints in the snow. A little farther on a man hailed him, a big fellow, heavily armed, who took him into an earth bunker where a warm stove was standing. The man gave him food and drink and led him to the partisan HQ.

Here Uralov found himself in the company of a slim girl with a boyish figure whose name was Irina, of a former Red Army NCO, Sergeant Subkov, and of an old man with a white beard and long hair who was called Shulga.

*   *   *

Langhoff had one gun left; with it and two limbers and their skeleton horses he entered the little town of Yuchnov on the Ugra. The town was crammed with convoys and the remnants of units from many divisions. Here and there were groups of stragglers, all reduced to a terrible state of exhaustion and raggedness. The billets were over-heated and the air was heavy with the odour of steaming clothes, unwashed bodies and bursting sores. Hoar frost glittered on the walls of the houses, but there was plenty of fuel to hand. No one went into the woods for there was snow there—and Russians. Instead, the troops burnt the rafters and the floors, and when there was nothing left the men in one hut tore down their neighbours' roof and walls. The horses stood unfed in their stalls and rattled their chains, gnawing the wood of the mangers and the doors and twisting round to eat their own dung.

"Company, fall in," said Corporal Gnotke. The troops were drawn up in the courtyard under the stars; twenty-three steaming mouths and muffled heads—the remains of a company of men. On their feet they wore the felt boots of the country; over their balaclavas they had steel helmets; on top of their rags they wore belts, equipment and ammunition pouches. Compared with the ragged soldiery which roamed the town, this body of troops was almost a show piece.

Sergeant Riederheim, who commanded the battle-group to which the regiment was now reduced, said to Gnotke:

"Well, you know what the job is, August."

It was a special job. The remains of the regiment's motorised transport company was completely demoralised, and in spite of all orders would not leave their billets—a labyrinth of farm buildings on the banks of the Ugra. It was to be Gnotke's task to separate the sheep from the goats; those who refused to obey orders from those who did not. The former were to be put under arrest and later brought before a field court-martial; the latter were to be split up as reinforcements among other units.

"I understand the order but I cannot carry it out," said Gnotke. Riederheim was deeply shocked. These were bad times without doubt, but they must be very bad indeed if even Gnotke could lose his nerve. For a full minute the two men stared at each other.

"Corporal Gnotke, go to your quarters and do not leave them without orders from me," said Riederheim. But he added under his breath: "Lie down, August, have a good sleep." Then he added aloud: "Corporal Feierfeil will take over the company."

311

Gnotke went to his quarters and Feierfeil moved off with the twenty-three men. Within an hour he returned to report that he had not been able to carry out his orders.

That night in a hut made of rough wood, with the holes in the windows stuffed with straw, the three men sat at a table in the light of a dimly-burning oil lamp. Gnotke, a man who seldom uttered more than an occasional gruff monosyllable was speaking. The words came in a torrent.

"Lost their nerve? No, what they've lost are arms and legs," he exclaimed. "Our company—more than our company, the whole division—has lost nearly all its men, and those who got away with a bullet through the lungs and black frozen stumps of legs have lost more than their nerve. As for the ones in the farm there on the Ugra —the drivers and second line troops—maybe they haven't been under fire much but they've done their bit in this war. They've pulled their vehicles out of a hundred holes; first their engines failed and then their horses. They've been frozen and starved for weeks. Now they are finished themselves. They are lousy from head to foot. When you go in there it's like a plague house. One man is looking at his black swollen foot. Another one is draining away the pus where his ears used to be, and another has his shins covered with mattering ulcers. And they're all like that. They are through. And what about me? I have been filthy even longer and have even more lice. I have ulcers, too—not only on my shins but on my backside and on my belly, and it's bloody agony when my trousers stick to the bits that are mattering. And because I have even more ulcers and am even more wretched than they are, I am supposed to be just the man to sort them out and bring them before a court-martial. And what does a court-martial mean nowadays? Where will they send them? What will they do with them?"

Feierfeil made a motion with his finger as if he were firing a burst.

"You're a fool, Feierfeil. But I can't blame you for it —I'm just as big a one and you're a fool, too, Hans." Gnotke looked at his old friends with defiance in his eyes. "Yes, we were invincible as long at the enemy was smaller or couldn't hit back. But now we have done a sixty mile sprint in retreat—and we're supposed to be a superior race and the Russians an inferior one. We haven't even clothes for ourselves. We have to strip the Russians whether they are dead or alive—it's all the same. We are flayers of corpses and we skin the living, too—which is even worse. That's what Hitler has brought us to. We have seen our chaps lying there on the fields between here and Moscow—lying in the snow in heaps like frozen sparrows. And our lives are rated as cheaply as sparrows!"

"Yes, we have had a reverse," said Riederheim. "But we will get on our feet again and hit back. We will get a breathing space."

"Rot!" said Gnotke curtly.

"But why not, August, it is possible?" said Feierfeil.

"Because things can't go on like that—you can't simply trample on people. A better life—fine, but not built on the bones of others. We must begin at home—there's plenty of room there for improvements. I understand now."

"You understand too much, August."

"All right, and now you—you can bash me in the face. That's what we always did. The people we beat up were always in the wrong. The men who had done the beating up just washed their hands and felt fine and righteous. That's how we improved the race! But now we see that there's no point any more in beating people up and saying, 'Yes' and standing to attention. This is where Hitler has got us to—to Yuchnov. But this would never have come about without you, Hans, and you, Emil, and me. It all began when we joined the Party in '32. And Hitler is the man who caused it all."

That was too much.

"Corporal Feierfeil!"

"Yes, sergeant!"

"Call out the guard."

Gnotke was led off.

Next morning, before the charge against him was written, the Russian artillery opened up on the overcrowded huts on the Ugra, and the ragged, demoralised troops were driven once more into the snow-storm. It was a long time before they held a line again.

* * *

313

There was a storm over Asia; it blew over the Urals and on over the Volga; the skies burst and emptied their burden over the continent. The icy breath blew to the ends of Europe. Between the Moscow river and the Protva the thermometer fell to fifty-six degrees below zero. In the snow lay dead crows and dead men, German and Russian, frozen and contorted.

The great Russian plan had come to a halt in the snow and broken on the desperate resistance of the ill-fed, lousy, frozen German troops. The Russians had not managed to put Army Group Centre in a pocket, but on the other hand they had succeeded in breaking the German offensive and greatly weakening the enemy forces. The completely new strategy with which the German armour had been met—the infiltration of large bodies of men through the thinly-held enemy lines, supported by paratroops dropped in the enemy's rear—had split up the German forces. But since the various separate parts had retained some of their powers of resistance, the result had been an extraordinarily confused situation in which German-held territory contained Russian islands, and ground recovered by the Russians held German pockets.

Over all, winter held sway. The storm had died away and left a frozen world with dunes of white powdered snow.

The authors' train was still moving on, east of the Caspian Sea through the Hungry Steppes: the journey had lasted twenty-two days already. In Moscow there were still demolition charges under all the bridges and important buildings. Lena Fyodorovna was still waiting for the day when the authorities would go through her file and banish her from the capital. Nina Mihailovna knocked during the night at the door of the Pavlov hospital and brought a child into the world two months before its time.

Colonel Zecke had gone back to Germany a sick man, and Captain Hasse had taken over the regiment. As president of a field court-martial he sentenced Corporal Gnotke to two years' imprisonment for refusal to comply with an order; the sentence was commuted to two years' front-line service with a punishment battalion.

* * *

A man walked on through the snow. He was so thin that his nose projected from his face like a hook. His

314

head was wrapped in bits of cloth; rags hung down to his feet. The man was bringing up the rear of a retreat, along a road which had once been the main axis of advance, and along which white-clad horsemen had swept to the counter-attack.

We have, he said to himself, we have—we have nothing left; frozen earth beneath us, the crystal sky above and burnt-out hearts within our bodies.

The horsemen sweeping on, the motor-sledges dashing through the empty wastes like gleaming insects, raising a trail of smoke, the German troops left sitting in the snow, the great gleaming eyes of a dying horse—these were things he might have seen within the last hour, yesterday or six weeks ago. They lay behind him. Ahead was nothing but the snow.

There was a shot, and then another. The snow puffed up ahead and then at his side. He could not throw himself down—it would be too much trouble to stand up again. He must keep on towards the great stranded fish which he could see in the distance. But it wasn't the back of a fish nor the carcass of a prehistoric monster; the strange shape in the snow was the shingle roof of a hut which had been torn from its base by blast and hurled far across the countryside. Now it served the partisans, not as a shelter—for they had their bunkers in the wood behind—but as an observation post from which they could see far and wide.

The two shots had come from the fish's back. A third shot would have found its target but it did not come. "Better not—let him come up," someone had said in the observation post. But the man who had his rifle to his shoulder pressed the trigger and missed. "I'll give him another," he said, but when the snow had spurted up at the feet of the approaching figure he let his rifle sink. His face was even redder than wind and snow and nature had made it. He was angry with himself, and angry with the woman whom he blamed for his bad shooting; but she commanded here. Yet she was right—two bullets were too many for a German with as many lice on him as that.

Lieutenant-Colonel Vilshofen came nearer with slow, dragging steps. He had been fired on from the shelter, but that did not stop him from keeping on in the same direction. He came nearer and went in; there was no door. Fear lay as far behind him as the overturned tank on the Nara or the corpses in the snow. He raised his eyes to the wild figures. They had machine-pistols and hand grenades at their belts. Partisans, deserters, robbers —he could not tell which they were; he knew only one thing, that his life was spent and that they would take it from him. His dark blue eyes gleamed again; a weight fell from him; he smiled almost happily. It was rare to meet Death face to face and recognise him. Death had a pock-marked face of a wild red hue, and he seemed angry because he was unhappy—merely another tortured being. Then something extraordinary happened.

"Take your hands off him, Uralov," said a voice.

It was a fine voice but one of steel—and it belonged to a girl. Vilshofen recognised that face again—it was the girl from Minsk; yes, it was the same narrow head with parted dark hair and the same questioning look in the eyes. He had not had an answer to give them, and he still did not know one.

I stand here, he thought, in rags and face my fate. The girl from Minsk, the pock-marked man and another, an old man like the prophet Isaiah—these three hold my life in their hands.

Other partisans stood round without interfering, listening to the conversation between these three. It was indeed incomprehensible that there could still be conversation about him, thought Vilshofen—that words were still necessary.

He isn't worth a shot. Knock him on the head and have done. If you don't like that, let him go, and hunger and cold will finish him off. This was the meaning of the words as Vilshofen understood them.

But then a miracle happened.

It began with a great silence. They had all gone away and left him alone in the hole in the ground under the fish-back. There was a bed there with dry straw spread on it, and beside it a big piece of bread, a mug of water and an open tin of meat, loot from a German supply truck. There was no sentry at the doorway; he could get up and go if he wanted, but all he wanted was to sleep.

When he had taken a couple of bites and drunk a sip, he laid himself down on the bed and sank instantly into a deep sleep.

He awoke, ate, and slept again.

Later he awoke once more, from a sleep which had perhaps lasted for days. What was happening? Why was he lying here like a seed in the earth? He had visitors —sometimes one person, sometimes another. There were stammered questions, to which he replied as best he could in their language, advancing questions of his own. Perhaps, he thought, we each contribute something towards the truth. It is not the end of the road yet; many wrong turnings still lie ahead.

Once the old man with prophet's face came. "Men are given the earth from the hands of God, without frontiers," he said. "The whole earth belongs to all."

There came a day when Vilshofen felt strong enough to stand up again, and now he understood the position of his hosts. They were a desperate band living on what they could plunder from German or Russian supply trucks. They lived on the narrow crest between two worlds; they could expect only death from either side, and being themselves on the threshold of death they found satisfaction in snatching back a life that had been lost.

And so Vilshofen was released. The old man, the girl from Minsk and the man with the red face went with him through the woods, where the snow sparkled in the winter sunlight, until at length they stood at the edge of the forest line and looked down on a valley. Below them, surrounded by snow-walls and trenches, lay a village.

"Your people are down there—go to them," said the girl. She still had the question in her eyes, but now there seemed to be something else as well.

"The best thing would be for me to let him have a bullet in the back," said the red-faced man, as he watched the German officer stumble slowly down the white hillside, but he did not raise his rifle.

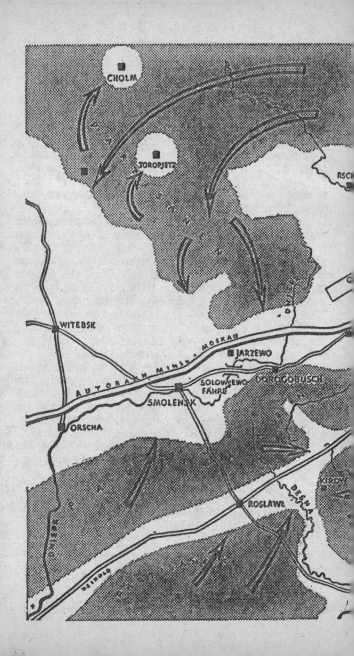

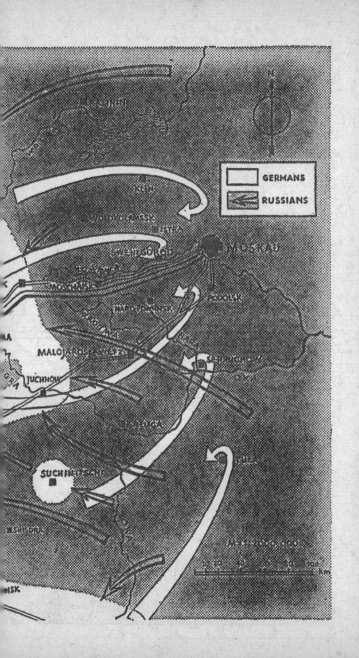